La Possession de S.

W9-BCY-705

Introduction to

COMPLEX

ANALYSIS

Introduction to

COMPLEX

ANALYSIS

Zeev Nehari

PROFESSOR OF MATHEMATICS

CARNEGIE INSTITUTE OF TECHNOLOGY

Boston   ALLYN AND BACON, INC.   *1961*

COLLEGE   MATHEMATICS   SERIES

Copyright © 1961 by Allyn and Bacon, Inc.

150 Tremont Street, Boston

All rights reserved. No part of this book may be reproduced in any form, by mimeograph or any other means, without permission in writing from the publishers.

Library of Congress Catalog Card Number: 61-11974

Printed in the United States of America

Preface

The usefulness of the theory of functions of a complex variable in many branches of science and engineering is generally recognized, and this recognition is reflected in the growing number of students in these fields who are taking an introductory course in function theory. The important role of complex variables in applied mathematics is partly due to such "dividends" of the theory as the use of residues in the evaluation of certain real integrals and the application of conformal mapping to problems in potential theory. However, of perhaps even greater importance to the scientist and engineer is the ability to use the basic techniques and methods of complex analysis. These techniques are of value in many applied areas, including some which may appear to have little if anything to do with complex variables. It is the aim of this text to provide an introduction to these techniques and to some of their applications.

The first four chapters treat the topics usually covered in an elementary complex variable course. The only significant departure is the introduction and occasional use of the "conjugate coordinates" z and $\bar{z}$ (especially in Chapter I, Section 4, and Chapter II, Section 3). The use of conjugate coordinates constitutes a very effective labor-saving device in many branches of mathematical analysis and applied mathematics. Although this technique has been successfully applied for over three decades, it does not seem to have found its way into introductory text books until now.

The discussion of conformal mapping in Chapter V contains, in addition to the basic theoretical material, a derivation of the Schwarz-Christoffel formula and a detailed consideration of a number of individual conformal mappings which are of importance in the applications.

Chapter VI gives an introduction to the application of conformal mapping to boundary value problems in electrostatics and two-dimensional fluid flow.

The subject matter of the first six chapters is suitable for a three-hour, one-semester course for seniors and first-year graduate students in mathematics, engineering, and the sciences. If it is desired to place less emphasis on the applications, Chapter VI —and, possibly, parts of Chapter V—may be replaced by the topics treated in Chapter VII.

Although, with very few exceptions, all theorems are proved, no attempt has been made to prove every proposition in its utmost generality. The overriding concern has been clarity of presentation.

The exercises, which will be found at the end of almost every section, are designed to help the reader acquire an active mastery of the subject.

Prerequisites for the study of the book are a good general knowledge of the calculus, plus a few topics—such as line integrals and the convergence of series—which are ordinarily covered in the first semester of an advanced calculus course.

Z. N.

Contents

Introduction to

COMPLEX

ANALYSIS

I

COMPLEX

VARIABLES

1 COMPLEX NUMBERS

The numbers used in elementary algebra and in the ordinary calculus are either positive, or negative, or zero. Such numbers—collectively called *real numbers*—can be represented by the points on a straight line, in the manner familiar from analytic geometry. There are, however, simple algebraic operations which cannot always be carried out in terms of real numbers. An example is the extraction of the square root of a given real number c, i.e., the problem of finding a number x such that $x^2 = c$. If c is positive, the problem has two solutions, denoted by $\sqrt{c}$ and $-\sqrt{c}$. If c is zero, the solution is $x = 0$. If c is negative, there clearly does not exist a real number x such that $x^2 = c$, since the square of a real number is either positive or zero, but never negative.

The same difficulty is encountered in an attempt to solve the general quadratic equation $x^2 + 2bx + c = 0$, where b and c are real numbers. Since the equation may be brought into the form $(x + b)^2 = b^2 - c$, it clearly cannot have a real solution x if $b^2 - c$ is negative. Accordingly, a quadratic equation with real coefficients may, or may not, have real solutions. This, however, does not exclude the possibility of the equation having solutions which belong to a more general class of numbers. To illustrate this situation by an elementary example, let us suppose that we have no conception of negative numbers and that we are called upon to solve the equation $x + a = b$, where a and b are positive numbers. We would then have to distinguish between two cases. If $b \geq a$, the equation has a solution, and if $b < a$ it has not. As we all know, this distinction is made unnecessary by the introduction of negative numbers, i.e., by postulating that the equation $x + 1 = 0$ has a solution and by denoting this solution by -1. This procedure may initially look rather arbitrary, but it is then justified by showing that the usual laws of arithmetic can safely be applied to negative numbers, provided a few simple rules—such as, for example, $(-a)(-b) = ab$—are observed.

The problem of finding a number whose square is a given negative number can be treated in a similar way. We *define* a number i by the equation

(1) $$i^2 = -1$$

and we then show that the introduction of this number and the use of numbers of the form

(2) $$\alpha = a + bi,$$

where a and b are real numbers, are compatible with the usual laws of arithmetic if certain elementary rules are observed.

At this point, one may object that all we have done is invent a new symbol, and that this does not constitute a proof that there exists a number i with the very unusual property (1). This objection was indeed raised at the time the number i was first introduced into algebra, and the ensuing long controversy on the subject is responsible for the number i being called an *imaginary* number. This term, with its unfortunate connotations of unreality and artificiality, is thus a survival from the days in which the role in mathematics of numbers of the form (2) was not properly understood.

The question as to the existence of these numbers and as to the legitimacy of their use in algebraic operations is, however, easily settled once it has been realized that operating with a number of the form (2) is the same as operating with the two real numbers a and b according to certain simple rules. It is entirely possible to discuss these numbers without ever mentioning the "imaginary" number i. The reason this is not done is one of convenience. As we shall see, the use of the symbol i makes it possible to condense all the laws of operation involving numbers of the form $a + bi$ into the following simple rule: Apply the usual rules of algebra and, whenever i^2 appears, replace it by -1. At the end of this section we shall, however, show how all these operations can be carried out in terms of real numbers.

First, a few definitions. A number α of the form (2) is called a *complex number*. The real number a is called the *real part* of the complex number α and is denoted by the symbol Re α, or Re(α); the real number b, denoted by Im α or Im(α), is called the *imaginary part* of α. If $a = 0$, we write $\alpha = ib$, and α is said to be *pure imaginary*. If $b = 0$, α reduces to the real number a.

The addition of two complex numbers, $\alpha = a + bi$ and $\beta = c + di$, is defined by

$$(3) \qquad \alpha + \beta = (a + bi) + (c + di) = a + c + (b + d)i,$$

and their multiplication by

$$(4) \qquad \alpha\beta = (a + bi)(c + di) = ac - bd + (ad + bc)i.$$

The reader will observe that the last result can be obtained by multiplying out the two parentheses and using (1). Another fact which is easily confirmed from (3) and (4) is that $\alpha + \beta = \beta + \alpha$ and $\alpha\beta = \beta\alpha$, i.e., both addition and multiplication are independent of the order in which they are carried out. It is equally obvious that, in the case of three complex numbers $\alpha, \beta, \gamma, \alpha + (\beta + \gamma)$ is identical with $(\alpha + \beta) + \gamma$. The parentheses are therefore not necessary and we write the result as $\alpha + \beta + \gamma$. A short computation will confirm that, similarly, $\alpha(\beta\gamma) = (\alpha\beta)\gamma$. This product may therefore be written $\alpha\beta\gamma$.

The operations of addition and multiplication are thus both commutative and associative. Since it is easily confirmed that $\alpha(\beta + \gamma) = \alpha\beta + \alpha\gamma$, multiplication is also distributive with respect to addition, or, to state it in less elegant language, expressions in parentheses may be handled according to the usual rules.

The number $\gamma = \alpha - \beta$ is defined by $\alpha = \beta + \gamma$; in view of (3), γ will thus be the complex number $a - c + i(b - d)$. In particular, $\alpha - \alpha$ is the number $0 + 0i$, i.e., the real number zero. A complex number is therefore zero only if both its real and its imaginary parts are zero. It is clear that $\alpha \cdot 0 = 0$ for any complex number α. Conversely, we can have $\alpha\beta = 0$ only if at least one of the numbers α, β is zero. Indeed, because of (4) the equation $\alpha\beta = 0$ implies that $ac - bd = 0$ and $ad + bc = 0$, and therefore

$$0 = (ac - bd)^2 + (ad + bc)^2 = (a^2 + b^2)(c^2 + d^2).$$

Since this is impossible if both $a^2 + b^2$ and $c^2 + d^2$ are different from zero, the result follows.

The quotient $\gamma = \alpha/\beta$ of two complex numbers α and β is defined by $\alpha = \beta\gamma$. If $\alpha = a + bi$, $\beta = c + di$, and $\gamma = e + fi$, we thus have to find two real numbers e and f such that

$$a + ib = (c + id)(e + if),$$

i.e., e and f have to be solutions of

$$a = ce - df, \qquad b = cf + de.$$

Since

$$ca + db = e(c^2 + d^2), \qquad cb - ad = f(c^2 + d^2),$$

we have

$$e = \frac{ca + db}{c^2 + d^2}, \qquad f = \frac{bc - ad}{c^2 + d^2},$$

provided $c^2 + d^2$ is not zero. Since $c^2 + d^2 = 0$ implies that $c = d = 0$, our result is that the quotient α/β is a uniquely determined complex number unless β is the complex number zero.

The preceding discussion may be summed up by saying that, except for the additional rule (1), the rules of arithmetic for complex numbers are the same as those for real numbers. Any computation involving complex numbers and the operations of addition, subtraction, multiplication, and division will again lead to a complex number. The only exception is the division by zero which, as in the case of real numbers, is not a meaningful operation.

We add here a definition which often simplifies computations involving complex numbers. If $\alpha = a + bi$ is a complex number, the complex number $a - bi$ is called the *conjugate*, or *complex conjugate*, of α and is usually denoted by the symbol $\bar{\alpha}$. Clearly, the conjugate of $\bar{\alpha} = a - bi$ is the complex number $a + bi$, i.e., α. If $\alpha = a + bi$ and $\beta = c + di$, we have $\overline{\alpha + \beta} = a + c - i(b + d) = a - ib + c - id = \bar{\alpha} + \bar{\beta}$. Similarly, $\overline{\alpha\beta} = \bar{\alpha}\bar{\beta}$, and a moment's reflection will make it evident that an equation between complex numbers involving the operations of arithmetic will remain true if all the complex numbers concerned are replaced by their conjugates.

Since

(5) $\alpha\bar{\alpha} = (a + bi)(a - bi) = a^2 + b^2,$

the product of a complex number α and its conjugate is a positive number unless $\alpha = 0$. To illustrate the use of this fact, we give an alternative derivation of the rule for finding the quotient of two complex numbers. If $\beta \neq 0$, we may multiply both numerator and denominator by $\bar{\beta}$. Hence,

$$\frac{\alpha}{\beta} = \frac{\alpha\bar{\beta}}{\beta\bar{\beta}} = \frac{\alpha\bar{\beta}}{c^2 + d^2} = \frac{ac + bd}{c^2 + d^2} + i\frac{bc - ad}{c^2 + d^2},$$

in accordance with our previous result.

We now give an alternative definition of complex numbers and their rules of operation, which uses only real numbers and avoids the use of the symbol i. A complex number is defined as an *ordered pair of real numbers* (a, b), the word "ordered" indicating that it is important which of these numbers comes first and which second. The addition of the complex numbers (a, b) and (c, d) is defined by

(3') $(a, b) + (c, d) = (a + c, b + d)$

and their multiplication by

(4') $(a, b)(c, d) = (ac - bd, ad + bc)$.

A comparison of (3') and (4') with (3) and (4) shows that these operations correspond formally to those defined by (3) and (4), and we are therefore relieved of the necessity of proving again that both addition and multiplication are commutative and associative, and that multiplication is distributive with respect to addition. The rules for inverting the operations of addition and subtraction must also be similar to those obtained before, and we have therefore

$$(a, b) - (c, d) = (a - c, b - d),$$

$$\frac{(a, b)}{(c, d)} = \left(\frac{ac + bd}{c^2 + d^2}, \frac{bc - ad}{c^2 + d^2}\right), \quad c^2 + d^2 \neq 0.$$

Although the operations (3') and (4') are called "addition" and "multiplication," they are certainly not identical with the addition and multiplication as we know them from the real number system. They become, however, indistinguishable from the latter in the case in which the two ordered pairs are of the form $(a, 0)$ and $(c, 0)$. Indeed, (3') and (4') show that $(a, 0) + (c, 0) = (a + c, 0)$ and $(a, 0)(c, 0) = (ac, 0)$. We may therefore identify the ordered pair $(a, 0)$ with the real number a. In particular, the pair $(0, 0)$ will thus be identified with the real number zero.

The ordered pair $(0, 1)$ is of particular interest. According to (4′), we have $(0, 1)(0, 1) = (-1, 0)$. Since $(-1, 0)$ is the real number -1, the complex number $(0, 1)$ has the square -1. If we agree to use the symbol i for the complex number $(0, 1)$, and we remember that $(a, 0)$ is the real number a, an application of (3′) and (4′) shows that

$$a + bi = (a, 0) + (b, 0)(0, 1) = (a, 0) + (0, b) = (a, b).$$

This provides the justification for replacing the symbol (a, b) by $a + bi$, where a and b are real numbers, and i − the ordered pair $(0, 1)$ − is such that $i^2 = -1$.

Exercises

1. If $\alpha = \cos t + i \sin t$, where $0 < t < 2\pi$, show that

$$\frac{1 + \alpha}{1 - \alpha} = i \cot \frac{t}{2}.$$

2. If $\alpha = a + bi$ and $b \neq 0$, $\alpha \neq \pm i$, show that the expression

$$\frac{\alpha}{1 + \alpha^2}$$

will be real only if $\alpha\bar{\alpha} = 1$.

3. Use (5) to prove that $\alpha\beta = 0$ is possible only if at least one of the number α, β is zero.

4. Show that

$$\mathrm{Re}(\alpha) = \frac{1}{2}(\alpha + \bar{\alpha}), \quad \mathrm{Im}(\alpha) = \frac{1}{2i}(\alpha - \bar{\alpha}).$$

5. If a and b are real numbers, verify that

$$(a^2 - iab - b^2)(a + ib) = a^3 - ib^3,$$

and show that this implies the real identity

$$[(a^2 - b^2)^2 + a^2b^2](a^2 + b^2) = a^6 + b^6.$$

2   THE COMPLEX PLANE

The complex number $\alpha = a + bi$ is completely characterized by the two real numbers a and b. As shown in analytic geometry, a point in a plane is also completely determined by two real numbers, its abscissa and its ordinate. It is therefore possible to establish a one-to-one correspondence between all complex numbers and all points of a plane. If we associate the complex number $a + bi$ with the point whose Cartesian coordinates are (a, b), it is clear that to any complex number there corresponds one point of the plane and, conversely, to every point of the plane there corresponds one complex number. The points corresponding to real numbers have the ordinate 0, and they will therefore lie on the horizontal axis. The latter is, for this reason, often referred to as the *real axis*. Conversely, all points on the real axis correspond to real numbers. Similarly, the vertical axis is the locus of all points corresponding to pure imaginary numbers, and it is therefore called the *imaginary axis*. The origin of the coordinate system corresponds to the complex number 0.

From what we have said so far it may appear that the association of complex numbers with the points of a plane is merely a kind of visual aid, making it possible to think of complex numbers in geometric terms. It is, however, much more than that. We shall see that the arithmetic operations described in the preceding section correspond to very simple geometric constructions in the plane and that, as a result, the use of geometric language provides not only a very vivid and suggestive terminology for the treatment of complex algebra and analysis, but indeed furnishes in many ways a more adequate expression of the nature of a complex number than the purely arithmetic definition.

The plane whose points represent the complex numbers is called the *complex plane*. Although there is, of course, a conceptual difference between the complex number $\alpha = a + bi$ and the point (a, b) of the complex plane, we shall often refer to them as though they were one and the same thing. It is convenient to do so, and no confusion can be caused by this practice. Accordingly, rather than refer to the point of the complex plane whose abscissa is $\text{Re}(\alpha)$ and whose ordinate is $\text{Im}(\alpha)$, we shall speak about "the point α."

If, instead of the rectangular coordinates a,b, we use polar coordinates r,θ in the complex plane, we obtain a different representation of the complex number $\alpha = a + bi$. Since

$$a = r \cos \theta, \qquad b = r \sin \theta,$$

we have

(6)
$$\alpha = r(\cos \theta + i \sin \theta),$$

where the positive number $r = \sqrt{a^2 + b^2}$ is the distance of the point α from the origin. This quantity is called the *absolute value*, or the *modulus*, of α and is denoted by the symbol $|\alpha|$. The angle θ is called the *argument* of α and is denoted by arg α or arg(α). As (5) shows, we have

$$|\alpha| = \sqrt{\alpha\bar{\alpha}}.$$

If α and β are two complex numbers, we have

$$|\alpha\beta|^2 = \alpha\beta\bar{\alpha}\bar{\beta} = \alpha\bar{\alpha}\beta\bar{\beta} = |\alpha|^2|\beta|^2,$$

and therefore

(7) $$|\alpha\beta| = |\alpha|\,|\beta|.$$

If, in (7), we replace α by $\dfrac{\alpha}{\beta}$ $(\beta \neq 0)$, we have $\left|\dfrac{\alpha}{\beta}\,\beta\right| = \left|\dfrac{\alpha}{\beta}\right||\beta|$, and thus

$$\left|\frac{\alpha}{\beta}\right| = \frac{|\alpha|}{|\beta|}.$$

By repeated application of (7), we can obtain a result for products of more than two factors. For instance, $|\alpha\beta\gamma| = |\alpha|\,|\beta\gamma| = |\alpha|\,|\beta|\,|\gamma|$, or, for n factors $\alpha_1, \alpha_2, \cdots, a_n$,

$$|\alpha_1\alpha_2 \cdots \alpha_n| = |\alpha_1|\,|\alpha_2| \cdots |\alpha_n|.$$

If, in particular, $\alpha_1 = \alpha_2 = \cdots = \alpha_n = \alpha$, we obtain

$$|\alpha^n| = |\alpha|^n.$$

As known from elementary geometry, the distance between the points $\alpha = a + bi$ and $\beta = c + di$ is $\sqrt{(a - c)^2 + (b - d)^2}$. Since this is also the absolute value of the complex number $\alpha - \beta$, it follows that *the distance between the points α and β is $|\alpha - \beta|$.* It is also known from elementary geometry that the sum of two sides of a triangle is larger than the third side, provided the three vertices of the triangle do not lie on a straight line. Applying this to the triangle $(0, \alpha, \beta)$ and noting that its sides are $|\alpha|$, $|\beta|$, $|\alpha - \beta|$, we find that $|\alpha - \beta| \leq |\alpha| + |\beta|$. If we replace β by $-\beta$ and observe that $|\beta| = |-\beta|$, we obtain the important inequality

(8) $$|\alpha + \beta| \leq |\alpha| + |\beta|.$$

The reader will easily verify that the sign of equality in (8) will occur if, and only if, arg α = arg β. If we replace α by $\alpha - \beta$, (8) takes the form $|\alpha| \leq |\alpha - \beta| + |\beta|$. If β is again replaced by $-\beta$, we thus have the inequality

(9) $$|\alpha + \beta| \geq |\alpha| - |\beta|,$$

which provides a lower bound for $|\alpha + \beta|$. The inequalities (8) and (9) can also be obtained by a direct computation. We have

$$|\alpha + \beta|^2 = (\alpha + \beta)(\bar{\alpha} + \bar{\beta}) = |\alpha|^2 + \alpha\bar{\beta} + \bar{\alpha}\beta + |\beta|^2$$
$$= |\alpha|^2 + 2\,\mathrm{Re}(\alpha\bar{\beta}) + |\beta|^2.$$

Since $a^2 \leq a^2 + b^2$, the real part of a complex number cannot be larger than its absolute value. Hence, $|\mathrm{Re}(\alpha\bar{\beta})| \leq |\alpha\bar{\beta}| = |\alpha|\,|\beta|$, and it follows that

$$|\alpha + \beta|^2 \leq |\alpha|^2 + 2|\alpha|\,|\beta| + |\beta^2| = (|\alpha| + |\beta|)^2,$$

which is equivalent to (8). Inequality (9) is obtained in a similar fashion if it is observed that $|\mathrm{Re}(\alpha\bar{\beta})| \geq -|\alpha|\,|\beta|$. It will be a useful exercise of the reader to determine, by the use of this method, the cases in which the sign of equality holds in (8) and (9).

An elementary geometric argument, combined with the definition (3) of the sum of two complex numbers, shows that the four points $0, \alpha, \beta, \alpha + \beta$ form a parallelogram in which 0 and $\alpha + \beta$ are opposite vertices. The addition of two complex numbers can therefore be carried out graphically by the parallelogram construction familiar from vector analysis.

EXERCISES

1. If $|\alpha| \leq 1$ and $|\beta| \leq 1$, show that

$$|\alpha + \beta| \leq |1 + \bar{\alpha}\beta|.$$

When does the sign of equality hold?

2. If $z = x + iy$, where x,y are rectangular coordinates, show that the general equation of a circle in the xy-plane is

$$|z|^2 + 2\,\mathrm{Re}(\alpha z) = c,$$

where α is an arbitrary complex number and $c > |\alpha|^2$.

3. Show that the curve determined by the condition $\mathrm{Re}(\alpha z^2) = c \neq 0$, where α is complex and c is real, is a hyperbola.

4. If a and c are real numbers, show that the equation $|z|^2 + a\,\mathrm{Re}(z^2) = c$ represents either an ellipse or a hyperbola, provided $a \neq \pm 1$.

5. If $\alpha_1, \alpha_2, \cdots, \alpha_n$ are complex numbers, show that

$$|\alpha_1 + \alpha_2 + \cdots + \alpha_n| \leq |\alpha_1| + |\alpha_2| + \cdots + \cdots |\alpha_n|,$$

where the sign of equality holds if, and only if, all the numbers $\alpha_1, \cdots, \alpha_n$ have the same argument.

6. If $\alpha_1, \alpha_2, \cdots, \alpha_n$ are complex numbers, show that

$$|\alpha_n - \alpha_1| \leq \sum_{k=1}^{n-1} |\alpha_{k+1} - \alpha_k|$$

and find the conditions under which the sign of equality holds.

7. If α, β, γ are complex numbers and α/β is not real, show that there always exists a uniquely determined pair of real numbers s, t such that $\gamma = s\alpha + t\beta$. If the points α, β, γ do not all lie on a straight line passing through the origin, show that the values of s and t are given by $\operatorname{Im}(\gamma\bar{\alpha}) = t \operatorname{Im}(\beta\bar{\alpha})$ and $\operatorname{Im}(\gamma\bar{\beta}) = s \operatorname{Im}(\alpha\bar{\beta})$.

3 ARGUMENTS AND ROOTS

In analytic geometry, polar coordinates have to be used with a certain amount of caution. This is due to the fact that the angle θ associated with a given point of the plane is determined only up to a multiple of 2π. In other words, adding $2\pi, 4\pi, -2\pi$, etc. to the angle does not affect the position of the point in the plane. If it is desired to make the polar coordinate system single-valued, that is, to make it such that to each point other than the origin there belongs exactly one angle θ, this can be achieved by restricting θ to an interval of length 2π. We may, for instance, decide that θ is always such that $0 \leq \theta < 2\pi$. Another possibility would be to decree that θ always satisfies $-\pi < \theta \leq \pi$. It should be noted, however, that the origin will always remain an exceptional point since, for $r = 0$, the value of θ becomes completely indeterminate.

On the other hand, there are situations in which it is *not* desirable to make the argument θ single-valued. The reader may recall from analytic geometry that the polar equation of the Archimedean spiral is $r = a\theta$, where θ is permitted to vary from 0 to ∞. The curve is winding around the origin an infinite number of times, increasing its distance from the origin all the while. If, say, $\theta = 4\pi + (\pi/4)$, we know not only that the corresponding point lies on a line making the angle $\pi/4$ with the positive axis, but also that this is the third time the curve intersects this line. If we were to restrict θ to the interval $0 \leq \theta < 2\pi$, we would not be able to describe the entire spiral by the single equation $r = a\theta$. It would then be necessary to say that the spiral consists of infinitely many pieces with the equations $r = a\theta$, $r = a(\theta + 2\pi)$, $r = a(\theta + 4\pi)$, and so forth. This would certainly be an unnecessary and artificial complication.

In complex analysis, both of these situations are encountered. Sometimes it is of advantage to use a single-valued polar coordinate system, i.e., to restrict the arguments of the complex numbers involved to an interval of length 2π. In other cases, things are simpler if the argument is left unrestricted. It should always be clearly understood which of these alternatives is used.

The representation (6) leads to a simple geometric interpretation of the multiplication of two complex numbers. If α and β have the representations

$$\alpha = r\,(\cos\theta + i\sin\theta), \qquad \beta = \rho(\cos\varphi + i\sin\varphi),$$

we have

$$\alpha\beta = r\rho[(\cos\theta\cos\varphi - \sin\theta\sin\varphi) + i(\sin\theta\cos\varphi + \cos\theta\sin\varphi)].$$

Since $\cos\theta\cos\varphi - \sin\theta\sin\varphi = \cos(\theta + \varphi)$ and $\sin\theta\cos\varphi + \cos\theta\sin\varphi = \sin(\theta + \varphi)$, it follows that

$$(10) \qquad \alpha\beta = r\rho[\cos(\theta + \varphi) + i\sin(\theta + \varphi)].$$

Comparing this with (6) we find that the complex number $\alpha\beta$ has the absolute value $|\alpha|\,|\beta|$—in agreement with (7)—and the argument $\theta + \varphi$, i.e.,

$$(11) \qquad \arg\alpha\beta = \arg\alpha + \arg\beta.$$

The point $\alpha\beta$ can thus be found by a simple geometric construction: Its argument is obtained by adding the arguments of α and β, and its absolute value by multiplying $|\alpha|$ and $|\beta|$.

Applying (10) to the case $\alpha = \beta$, we have

$$\alpha^2 = r^2\,(\cos 2\theta + i\sin 2\theta).$$

Applying (10) again, this time identifying the two numbers with α^2 and α, respectively, we obtain

$$\alpha^3 = r^3\,(\cos 3\theta + i\sin 3\theta).$$

Continuing in this fashion we arrive at the general formula

$$(12) \qquad \alpha^n = r^n\,(\cos n\theta + i\sin n\theta),$$

where n may be any positive integer. Since $\alpha = r\,(\cos\theta + i\sin\theta)$, this is equivalent to the identity

(13) $$(\cos\theta + i\sin\theta)^n = \cos n\theta + i\sin n\theta,$$

known as *De Moivre's formula*. This relation can be used to derive trigonometric identities with a minimum of labor. For instance, to obtain expressions for $\sin 3\theta$ and $\cos 3\theta$, we set $n = 3$. The right-hand side of (13) is, in this case, $\cos 3\theta + i\sin 3\theta$. If the left-hand side is expanded according to the binomial theorem, we obtain $\cos^3\theta + 3i\cos^2\theta\sin\theta - 3\cos\theta\sin^2\theta - i\sin^3\theta$. Since two complex numbers can be equal only if they agree in both their real and imaginary parts (their difference must be the complex number zero!), we find that

$$\cos 3\theta = \cos^3\theta - 3\cos\theta\sin^2\theta, \qquad \sin 3\theta = 3\cos^2\theta\sin\theta - \sin^3\theta.$$

If, as is customary in the case of real numbers, $\alpha^{-m}\,(m > 0)$ is defined as the reciprocal of α^m, it is easy to see that Formula (12) remains valid if n is a negative integer. Indeed,

$$\alpha^{-n} = \frac{1}{\alpha^n} = \frac{\bar{\alpha}^n}{\bar{\alpha}^n\alpha^n} = \frac{\bar{\alpha}^n}{|\alpha|^{2n}} = \frac{\overline{(\alpha^n)}}{|\alpha|^{2n}}.$$

Since $|\alpha| = r$ and, by (12), the conjugate of α^n is

$$r^n(\cos n\theta - i\sin n\theta),$$

we find that

$$\alpha^{-n} = r^{-n}(\cos n\theta - i\sin n\theta).$$

In view of the fact that $\cos(-\theta) = \cos\theta$ and $\sin(-\theta) = -\sin\theta$, this is exactly what we would have obtained from (12) by substituting $-n$ for n.

Our next application of Formula (12) is the extraction of the nth root of a given complex number $\alpha = r(\cos\theta + i\sin\theta)$, i.e., the problem of finding a complex number $\beta = \rho(\cos\varphi + i\sin\varphi)$ such that $\beta^n = \alpha$. According to (12), we have

$$r(\cos\theta + i\sin\theta) = \rho^n(\cos n\varphi + i\sin n\varphi),$$

which means that the relations $r = \rho^n$ and

(14) $$\cos\theta + i\sin\theta = \cos n\varphi + i\sin n\varphi$$

must be satisfied. Conversely, if these two relations hold, we have $\beta^n = \alpha$.

The first of these relations gives us nothing that is new; we knew before that $|\beta|^n = |\alpha|$. The relation (14), however, reveals the surprising fact that there are n different numbers β all of which satisfy the relation $\beta^n = \alpha$. To show that this is the case we first note that (14) is clearly satisfied if $\varphi = \theta/n$. But, since the functions $\cos \theta$ and $\sin \theta$ do not change their values if θ is replaced by $\theta + 2\pi$, $\theta + 4\pi$, $\theta + 6\pi$, etc., we have

$$\cos n \left(\varphi + \frac{2\pi k}{n} \right) = \cos (n\varphi + 2\pi k) = \cos n\varphi$$

and

$$\sin n \left(\varphi + \frac{2\pi k}{n} \right) = \sin (n\varphi + 2\pi k) = \sin n\varphi,$$

if k is any integer. This shows that (14) will hold if φ has the value

(15) $$\varphi = \varphi_k = \frac{\theta + 2\pi k}{n},$$

where k is an arbitrary integer. However, since the replacement of φ_k by $\varphi_k + 2\pi$ does not change the complex number $\rho(\cos \varphi_k + i \sin \varphi_k)$, and since $\varphi_{k+n} = \varphi_k + 2\pi$, there are only n values of φ_k which give rise to essentially different values of $\sqrt[n]{\alpha}$. These values are, for instance, obtained by setting k successively equal to $1, 2, \cdots, n$. We thus have the result that the different values of the nth root of

$$\alpha = r(\cos \theta + i \sin \theta)$$

are

(16) $$\sqrt[n]{\alpha} = r^{1/n} \left[\cos \frac{\theta + 2\pi k}{n} + i \sin \frac{\theta + 2\pi k}{n} \right], \quad k = 1, 2, \cdots, n.$$

The proof of the fact that the numbers (15) are the only values satisfying (14) and that, therefore, Formula (16) gives *all* the nth roots of α is left as an exercise to the reader. It may also be noted that a comparison of Formulas (12) and (16) provides the justification for writing $\alpha^{1/n}$ instead of $\sqrt[n]{\alpha}$. To put it differently, if $\sqrt[n]{\alpha}$ is denoted by $\alpha^{1/n}$, (16) shows that (12) remains true for exponents of the form $1/n$. The appearance of the terms $2\pi k$ in (16) is simply due to the fact that a complex number does not change if its argument θ is replaced by $\theta + 2\pi k$.

If (16) is applied to the complex number $\alpha = 1$, we obtain the so-called *roots of unity*

(17) $$\omega_k = \cos \frac{2\pi k}{n} + i \sin \frac{2\pi k}{n}, \quad k = 1, 2, \cdots, n,$$

i.e., numbers ω_k such that $\omega_k^n = 1$. They all have the absolute value 1 and their arguments are $2\pi/n$, $4\pi/n$, $6\pi/n$, $\cdots$, 2π, i.e., they form the vertices of a regular polygon of n sides, inscribed in the circle of radius 1 about the origin. One of the vertices coincides with the point 1.

The positive nth root of a positive number α is obtained from (16) for $k = n$. In elementary algebra, this positive root plays a distinguished role, and it is therefore customary to reserve the symbol $\sqrt[n]{a}(a > 0)$ for this particular root. For instance, the symbol $\sqrt{4}$ is assigned the value 2; if it is necessary to indicate both solutions of the equation $x^2 = a(a > 0)$, one writes $x = \pm\sqrt{a}$. In dealing with complex numbers, this convention clearly loses its meaning since, in general, none of the roots are positive. Accordingly, the symbol $\sqrt[n]{\alpha}$ stands for all the n numbers β such that $\beta^n = \alpha$, and none of these values get a special treatment. For instance, Formula (16) shows that $\sqrt{-1}$ has the two values, i and $-i$, and neither of these values can be regarded as a "positive square root" in any meaningful way.

The study of the power α^n of a complex number α will be taken up again in Section 6 of the following chapter. Using the results at our disposal then, we shall be able to assign to the symbol α^n a precise meaning if n is an arbitrary complex number.

EXERCISES

1. If $0 \le \arg \alpha - \arg \beta < \pi$, show that the area of the triangle whose vertices are 0, α, β is given by $\frac{1}{2} \operatorname{Im}(\bar{\alpha}\beta)$.

2. If $0 \le \arg \alpha_1 < \arg \alpha_2 < \cdots < \arg \alpha_n < 2\pi$, use the result of the preceding exercise to show that the area of the polygon whose vertices are at the points $\alpha_1, \cdots, \alpha_n$ is given by

$$A = \frac{1}{2} \operatorname{Im}\left\{ \sum_{\nu=1}^{n} \alpha_\nu \bar{\alpha}_{\nu-1} \right\}, \quad \alpha_0 = \alpha_n.$$

3. Show that the result of the preceding exercise may also be expressed in the form

$$A = \frac{1}{4} \sum_{\nu=1}^{n} (\alpha_\nu - \alpha_{\nu-1})(\bar{\alpha}_\nu + \bar{\alpha}_{\nu-1}).$$

4. Show that the exterior angles of the polygon of Exercise 2 are equal to

$$\arg \frac{\alpha_{\nu+1} - \alpha_\nu}{\alpha_\nu - \alpha_{\nu-1}}, \quad \nu = 1, 2, \cdots, n \ (\alpha_{-1} = \alpha_{n-1}),$$

and use this fact to prove that the sum of the exterior angles of the polygon is 2π.

5. If α and β are two fixed points, show that the locus of the points γ for which $\arg \dfrac{\gamma - \alpha}{\gamma - \beta}$ is constant is a circle passing through α and β.

6. If $c > 0$, show that the locus of the points α for which

$$\left| \frac{1 + \alpha}{1 - \alpha} \right| = c$$

is a circle if $c \neq 1$, and a straight line if $c = 1$.

7. Show that the roots of unity defined by Formula (17) may be written in the form $\omega, \omega^2, \omega^3, \cdots, \omega^n$, where $\omega = \omega_1$. Use this fact to prove that

$$\omega_1 + \omega_2 + \cdots + \omega_n = 0.$$

8. If m is a positive integer which does not contain the factor n, and $\omega = \omega_1$, show that

$$\omega^m + \omega^{2m} + \omega^{3\,m} + \cdots + \omega^{nm} = 0.$$

Hint: Multiply the left-hand side by $1 - \omega^m$.

9. If $\beta = \sqrt[n]{\alpha^m} = \alpha^{m/n}$ is defined by the equation $\beta^n = \alpha^m$, where m and n are non-zero integers and $\alpha = r(\cos \theta + i \sin \theta)$, show that β may take the n different values

$$r^{m/n} \left[\cos \frac{m}{n} (\theta + 2\pi k) + i \sin \frac{m}{n} (\theta + 2\pi k) \right], \quad k = 1, \cdots, n.$$

10. Show that if the real parameter t varies from 0 to 1, the point $\alpha + t(\beta - \alpha)$ describes the linear segment connecting the points α and β.

11. Let α, β, γ be three points which do not lie on one straight line, and let z be a point in the interior or on the boundary of the triangle whose vertices are at α, β, γ. Use the result of the preceding exercise to show that it is always possible to find non-negative numbers $\lambda_1, \lambda_2, \lambda_3$ such that

$$z = \alpha\lambda_1 + \beta\lambda_2 + \gamma\lambda_3, \quad \lambda_1 + \lambda_2 + \lambda_3 = 1.$$

Show that, conversely, all points z which are expressible in this way must be either in the interior or on the boundary of the triangle.

12. If, in the notation of the preceding exercise, $\lambda_1 = \lambda_2 = \lambda_3 = \frac{1}{3}$, show that z is the point of intersection of the medians of the triangle.

13. Let $\alpha_1, \alpha_2, \cdots, \alpha_n$ be the vertices of a *convex* polygon P, i.e., a polygon such that the linear segments connecting any two of its non-adjacent vertices are in the interior of P. If $\lambda_1, \cdots, \lambda_n$ are non-negative numbers such that $\lambda_1 + \lambda_2 + \cdots + \lambda_n = 1$, show that a point z can be written in the form

$$z = \sum_{\nu=1}^{n} \lambda_\nu \alpha_\nu$$

if, and only if, it is either in the interior or on the perimeter of P.

14. If n is a positive integer, show that $\cos n\theta = P_n(\cos \theta)$, where $P_n(x)$ is a polynomial of nth degree in x.

15. Show that the polynomial of the preceding exercise (known as the *Chebyshev polynomial*) has the representation

$$P_n(x) = \tfrac{1}{2}[(x + \sqrt{x^2 - 1})^n + (x - \sqrt{x^2 - 1})^n].$$

4 CONJUGATE COORDINATES

We begin this section by recalling a few definitions and results concerning real functions $g(x, y)$ of two real variables x,y. Such functions may be defined for all finite values of x and y, as, for instance, the function $g(x, y) = x^2 + xy + y^2$, but it may also happen that the range of the variables x and y must be subjected to certain restrictions. A simple example is the function $g(x, y) = \sqrt{R^2 - x^2 - y^2}$, which is evidently not defined unless x and y are such that $x^2 + y^2 \leq R^2$. If we interpret x and y as rectangular coordinates in the xy-plane, we may use geometric language and say that this function $g(x, y)$ is defined in the interior and on the circumference of the circle $x^2 + y^2 = R^2$. If we extend this geometric terminology to the case of a general function $g(x, y)$, we may say that such a function is defined either in a certain portion of the xy-plane, or in the entire xy-plane. In the next section it will be shown that, for practical purposes, the rather vague notion of "a certain portion of the xy-plane" has to be replaced by a more precise concept. For our present discussion it is sufficient to assume that the variables x,y are restricted to the interior of a circle in which the function $g(x, y)$ is defined.

The function $g(x, y)$ is said to be continuous at the point (x_0, y_0) if $\lim f(x, y,) = f(x_0, y_0)$ when x tends to x_0 and y to y_0. In terms of the ϵ,δ terminology used in advanced calculus, this may also be expressed in the following way: If ϵ is an arbitrarily small fixed positive number, it is always possible to find a positive number δ such that

$$|g(x, y) - g(x_0, y_0)| < \epsilon,$$

provided $\sqrt{(x - x_0)^2 + (y - y_0)^2} < \delta$.

The partial derivative $g_x(x, y)$ is defined by

$$(18) \qquad g_x(x, y) = \lim_{h \to 0} \frac{g(x + h, y) - g(x, y)}{h}$$

if this limit exists, and a similar definition holds for $g_y(x, y)$. There exists, however, a stronger concept of differentiability, which requires more than the mere existence of $g_x(x, y)$ and $g_y(x, y)$. If, for $\epsilon^2 = h^2 + k^2 \to 0$,

$$\lim \frac{1}{\epsilon} [g(x + h, y + k) - g(x, y) - hg_x(x, y) - kg_y(x, y)] = 0,$$

$g(x, y)$ is said to be totally differentiable, or to possess a *total differential*

$$(19) \qquad dg = g_x \, dx + g_y \, dy$$

at the point (x, y). This total differential exists if the partial derivatives g_x, g_y are continuous at the point in question. The latter condition is, however, not a necessary one.

If both x and y are differentiable functions of a parameter t, and if $g(x, y)$ has a total differential, the derivative of g with respect to t exists, and is given by the formula

$$(20) \qquad \frac{dg}{dt} = g_x \frac{dx}{dt} + g_y \frac{dy}{dt}.$$

If $x = t \cos \theta$, $y = t \sin \theta$, where θ is a fixed angle, this formula yields the *directional derivative*

$$(21) \qquad g_\theta = g_x \cos \theta + g_y \sin \theta.$$

Evidently, g_θ is the rate of change of the function $g(x, y)$ in the direction which makes the angle θ with the positive x-axis.

We finally remind the reader of the fact that, under a co-ordinate transformation $x,y \to u,v$ whose Jacobian $x_u y_v - x_v y_u$ is not zero, the total differential (19) transforms into

$$(22) \qquad\qquad dg = g_u\, du + g_v\, dv.$$

We are now going to do something which, at the first glance, may appear to cause unnecessary complications. We shall identify the xy-plane with the complex plane and replace the real variables x and y by the *complex variables*

$$(23) \qquad\qquad z = x + iy, \qquad \bar{z} = x - iy.$$

It may be objected that one of these variables is unnecessary, since the knowledge of the complex number z—or the complex number $\bar{z}$—already implies the knowledge of the two real numbers x and y. This is indeed true but, for formal reasons, it is nevertheless desirable to have two variables and not just one. In Chapter II it will be seen that the so-called *analytic functions* of a complex variable—whose study is the principal aim of complex analysis—are distinguished by the fact that they can be adequately treated in terms of the complex variable z alone.

Formula (23) may be regarded as a kind of coordinate transformation which replaces x and y by the complex coordinates z and $\bar{z}$; since the latter are complex conjugates of each other, we shall call them *conjugate coordinates*. This aspect of (23) should, of course, not be taken too literally. Since z can be obtained from $\bar{z}$ and vice versa, these two "coordinates" are not really independent of each other, as genuine coordinates should be. The rules for operating with z and $\bar{z}$ cannot, therefore, be deduced from the general laws governing coordinate transformations, but must be verified in each case.

The "coordinate transformation" inverse to (23) is, obviously,

$$(24) \qquad\qquad x = \frac{1}{2}(z + \bar{z}), \qquad y = \frac{1}{2i}(z - \bar{z}).$$

If $g(x, y)$ has continuous partial derivatives g_x, g_y, and we apply (24) and the formal rules of partial differentiation, we obtain

$$\frac{\partial g}{\partial z} = \frac{\partial g}{\partial x}\frac{\partial x}{\partial z} + \frac{\partial g}{\partial y}\frac{\partial y}{\partial z},$$

i.e.,

$$(25) \qquad\qquad \frac{\partial g}{\partial z} = \frac{1}{2}\left(\frac{\partial g}{\partial x} - i\frac{\partial g}{\partial y}\right).$$

Similarly,

$$\frac{\partial g}{\partial \bar{z}} = \frac{\partial g}{\partial x}\frac{\partial x}{\partial \bar{z}} + \frac{\partial g}{\partial y}\frac{\partial y}{\partial \bar{z}},$$

and thus

(26) $$\frac{\partial g}{\partial \bar{z}} = \frac{1}{2}\left(\frac{\partial g}{\partial x} + i\frac{\partial g}{\partial y}\right).$$

This procedure for obtaining the "derivatives" (25) and (26) is, of course, purely formal. Since, moreover, the expressions (25) and (26) cannot, in general, be defined by means of limits of the type of (18) (where the increment h is added to z and $\bar{z}$, respectively), one might indeed ask whether there is any reasonable way in which (25) and (26) may be regarded as "partial derivatives" of the function g with respect to z and $\bar{z}$.

The best way to meet these objections is to proceed in the opposite direction and to define two differential operators, denoted by $\partial/\partial z$ and $\partial/\partial \bar{z}$, by

(27) $$\frac{\partial}{\partial z} = \frac{1}{2}\left(\frac{\partial}{\partial x} - i\frac{\partial}{\partial y}\right), \quad \frac{\partial}{\partial \bar{z}} = \frac{1}{2}\left(\frac{\partial}{\partial x} + i\frac{\partial}{\partial y}\right).$$

This merely amounts to the introduction of two new symbols and requires no further justification. The operations (27) can be applied to any function $g(x, y)$ which has partial derivatives with respect to x and y.

We shall now show that, as far as the Formula (19) for the total differential is concerned, the expressions (25) and (26) behave like genuine partial derivatives. Since, by (25) and (26),

(28) $$\frac{\partial g}{\partial x} = \frac{\partial g}{\partial z} + \frac{\partial g}{\partial \bar{z}}, \quad \frac{\partial g}{\partial y} = i\left[\frac{\partial g}{\partial z} - \frac{\partial g}{\partial \bar{z}}\right],$$

(19) may be replaced by

$$dg = (g_z + g_{\bar{z}})\,dx + i(g_z - g_{\bar{z}})\,dy$$
$$= g_z(dx + i\,dy) + g_{\bar{z}}(dx - i\,dy),$$

where g_z and $g_{\bar{z}}$ are abbreviations for $\partial g/\partial z$ and $\partial g/\partial \bar{z}$, respectively. If we write $dx + i\,dy = d(x + iy) = dz$ and $dx - i\,dy = d(x - iy) = d\bar{z}$, this takes the form

(29) $$dg = \frac{\partial g}{\partial z}\,dz + \frac{\partial g}{\partial \bar{z}}\,d\bar{z}.$$

A comparison with (22) shows that this is exactly what we would have obtained if the replacing of x and y by z and $\bar{z}$ were a genuine coordinate transformation, and if g_z and $g_{\bar{z}}$ were the partial derivatives of the function g with respect to z and $\bar{z}$.

If $z(t) = x(t) + iy(t)$, where $x(t)$ and $y(t)$ are differentiable functions of a real parameter t, the same considerations show that the formula (20) can be replaced by

$$(30) \qquad \frac{dg}{dt} = \frac{\partial g}{\partial z} z'(t) + \frac{\partial g}{\partial \bar{z}} \overline{z'(t)}.$$

It will be seen later that, in many parts of complex analysis, the use of conjugate coordinates leads to a very considerable saving of computational labor, and also to a deeper insight into the nature of an analytic function of a complex variable. The usefulness of conjugate coordinates also extends to certain parts of real analysis. This is largely due to the easily confirmed identity

$$4 \frac{\partial^2 g}{\partial z\, \partial \bar{z}} = \frac{\partial^2 g}{\partial x^2} + \frac{\partial^2 g}{\partial y^2}.$$

The fact that the operator $\dfrac{\partial^2}{\partial x^2} + \dfrac{\partial^2}{\partial y^2}$—the *Laplace operator*—can be essentially replaced by the successive differentiations with respect to z and $\bar{z}$ provides a powerful computational tool in the many situations in pure and applied mathematics in which the Laplace operator plays an important role. Some examples for this application of conjugate coordinates will be met later.

Exercises

1. Let $x,y \to u,v$ be a real coordinate transformation and let $J = x_u y_v - x_v y_u$ be its Jacobian. If $z = x + iy$, $\bar{z} = x - iy$ and $w = u + iv$, $\bar{w} = u - iv$ are conjugate coordinates in the xy- and uv-planes, show that

$$J = |z_w|^2 - |z\bar{w}|^2.$$

2. If $z = x + iy$, $w = u + iv$, and

$$z = \frac{\alpha w + \beta \bar{w}}{\gamma w + \delta \bar{w}},$$

where α, β, γ, δ are complex constants, show that the Jacobian of the transformation $x,y \to u,v$ vanishes identically.

3. If r,θ are polar coordinates in the xy-plane and $g(x, y)$ has continuous partial derivatives with respect to x and y, show that

$$\frac{\partial g}{\partial z} = \frac{1}{2z}\left(r\frac{\partial g}{\partial r} - i\frac{\partial g}{\partial \theta}\right), \quad \frac{\partial g}{\partial \bar{z}} = \frac{1}{2\bar{z}}\left(r\frac{\partial g}{\partial r} + i\frac{\partial g}{\partial \theta}\right).$$

4. Show that the differential operators (27) obey the usual formal differentiation rules, such as $(f + g)_z = f_z + g_z$, $(f + g)_{\bar{z}} = f_{\bar{z}} + g_{\bar{z}}$, $(fg)_z = fg_z + gf_z$, $(fg)_{\bar{z}} = fg_{\bar{z}} + gf_{\bar{z}}$, and the chain rule.

5. Show that

$$\frac{\partial(z^n)}{\partial z} = nz^{n-1}, \quad \frac{\partial(z^n)}{\partial \bar{z}} = 0,$$

$$\frac{\partial(\bar{z}^n)}{\partial z} = 0, \quad \frac{\partial(\bar{z}^n)}{\partial \bar{z}} = n\bar{z}^{n-1}.$$

6. If $f(x, y) = g(x, y) + ih(x, y)$, where g and h are real functions, show that

$$\frac{\partial \bar{f}}{\partial \bar{z}} = \overline{\left(\frac{\partial f}{\partial z}\right)}.$$

7. If $P(z)$ is the polynomial

$$P(z) = \sum_{k=0}^{n} a_k z^k,$$

where the a_k are complex constants, show that

$$\Delta|P(z)|^2 = 4\left|\frac{\partial P}{\partial z}\right|^2.$$

5 SOME DEFINITIONS

Throughout this book we shall be concerned with sets of points in a plane. It is therefore necessary to be familiar with some elementary properties of such sets, and with some of the terminology used to describe them.

A *point* in the xy-plane is given by a pair of real numbers (a, b) which are to be interpreted as rectangular coordinates in this plane. A *neighborhood*—also called ϵ-neighborhood—of a point (a, b) is the set of points (x, y) such that $(x - a)^2 + (y - b)^2 < \epsilon^2$, where ϵ is a positive number. If we use the terminology of Section 2 of this chapter and identify the xy-plane with the complex plane, a point is given by a complex number $\alpha = a + bi$, and an

ϵ-neighborhood of α consists of those points $z = x + iy$ for which $|z - \alpha| < \epsilon$.

A point (a, b) is said to be a *limit point* of a set of points S if every neighborhood of (a, b) contains a point of S distinct from (a, b). This definition implies that every neighborhood of (a, b) contains an infinite number of points of S. Indeed, if there were a neighborhood which contains only a finite number of such points, we could draw a circle about (a, b) which passes through the point—or the points—nearest to (a, b). The points in the interior of this circle would then constitute a neighborhood of (a, b) which contains no points of S other than (a, b).

A limit point of S may, or may not, be a point of S. If every limit point of a set belongs to the set, we say that the set is *closed*. There are two distinct types of limit points of a set: *interior points* and *boundary points*. A limit point (a, b) is said to be an interior point of a set S if there exists a neighborhood of (a, b) which consists entirely of points of S. A limit point which is not an interior point of S, that is, a point (a, b) such that every neighborhood of (a, b) contains both points of S and points which do not belong to S, is called a *boundary point* of S. A set all of whose points are interior points is called an *open set*. A simple example of an open set is the unit disk, i.e., the set of points x,y for which $x^2 + y^2 < 1$. By adding to a set S all its limit points, we obtain the *closure* of S; for instance, the closure of the unit disk is the set of points x,y such that $x^2 + y^2 \leq 1$, that is, the unit disk plus the circumference $x^2 + y^2 = 1$. It is clear that the closure of any set is a closed set.

An open set S is said to be *connected* if any two of its points can be joined by a polygonal line—i.e., a continuous line made up of a finite number of linear segments—all of whose points belong to S. Intuitively speaking, a connected set is one which consists "of one piece." The set consisting of the points for which $(x - 2)^2 + y^2 < 1$ and those for which $(x + 2)^2 + y^2 < 1$ is not connected, since it is evidently impossible to connect a point in the first disk with a point in the second disk by means of a polygonal line which does not contain points not belonging to the set. For sets which are not open, connectedness has to be defined in a different way. For instance, a closed connected set is defined as a closed set which cannot be separated into two non-empty closed sets which have no point in common.

A set which is both open and connected is called a *domain*.

Domains are of basic importance in analysis, and it is easy to see why. If we want to define the continuity of a function on S at a point (x_0, y_0), we must be able to approach this point through points (x, y) which belong to the set S. The point (x_0, y_0) must therefore be a limit point of S. If we want to be able to approach (x_0, y_0) in an arbitrary manner, we must be sure that all points of a sufficiently small neighborhood of (x_0, y_0) belong to S, that is, (x_0, y_0) must be an interior point. For a convenient definition of continuity we shall therefore require that all points of S be interior points, i.e., that S be an open set. It is, of course, also possible to consider a more restricted type of continuity by imposing the condition lim $g(x, y) = g(x_0, y_0)$ only for a certain particular manner of approach to the point (x_0, y_0). For instance, we might restrict ourselves to the approach of (x, y) to (x_0, y_0) through points (x, y) such that $x > x_0$. For the unrestricted type of continuity, however, the function has to be defined on an open set. The reason for using connected sets is even more obvious. If a function is defined on a set consisting of a number of disconnected components, the values of the function on the different components have really nothing to do with each other, and it is more reasonable to consider the function on each component separately. Unless a statement to the contrary is made, the set of points on which a function of two real variables—or a function of a complex variable—is defined will always be a domain.

Some authors use the word *region* instead of "domain." The general custom, however, is to use the term "region" in a deliberately vague sense, somewhat like "a portion of the plane." We can thus speak of "the region of convergence" of a series without having to say whether this region is a domain, or a domain to which some of its boundary points are added, or the closure of a domain, or something more complicated.

If a set S is such that all the points (a, b) of S satisfy an inequality $a^2 + b^2 < R^2$ for some positive R, that is, if all points of S lie in some disk centered at the origin, S is called a *bounded* set. If this condition is not satisfied, the set is *unbounded*. In the same way, we speak of bounded and unbounded domains. The xy-plane, i.e., the set of all points (x, y) where x and y are real numbers, is an example of an unbounded domain.

The xy-plane—or, to use complex language, the z-plane—is not a closed set, since it contains subsets which do not have limit points within the z-plane. A simple example of such a subset is the set $z_n = n$, where $n = 1, 2, \cdots$. The z-plane can be closed by adding to it the point ∞, also called the *point at infinity*. Although the idea of assigning to the infinitely distant part of the plane the character of a point may at the first glance seem strange, it can be easily visualized by means of the following simple geometric model. A sphere of radius 1 is placed on the z-plane in such a way that its "south pole" rests on the point $z = 0$. To each point z in the plane, a point P on the surface of the sphere is made to correspond in the following manner: The "north pole" is connected with z by a straight line, and P is taken to be the point at which this line pierces the surface of the sphere. This procedure clearly establishes a one-to-one correspondence between all points of the z-plane and all points on the surface of the sphere other than the north pole. If the distance of the point z from the origin tends to infinity—i.e., if $|z| \to \infty$—the corresponding point P approaches the north pole. The fact that the latter is just one point on the sphere provides the justification for speaking of the "point at infinity" in the plane. The entire surface of the sphere (including the north pole) thus corresponds to a set consisting of the z-plane and the point ∞. This set is referred to as the *extended z-plane*.

II

ANALYTIC

FUNCTIONS

1 COMPLEX DIFFERENTIATION

If x and y are real numbers such that the point (x, y) may be identified with any point of a given domain D, we say that x and y are real variables in D. If we write $z = x + iy$, we may express the same idea by saying that z is a *complex variable* in D. Another possible way of combining x and y into a complex variable is to set $\bar{z} = x - iy$. Since the points $x + iy$ and $x - iy$ are symmetric with respect to the real axis, the domain of definition of the complex variable $\bar{z}$ is, so to speak, the mirror image $\bar{D}$ of D with respect to the real axis.

A function $f(z)$ of the complex variable z is defined by associating with each point z a given complex number $f(z)$. If this is done for all points z in D, we say that the function $f(z)$ is defined in D. The domain D is called the *domain of definition* of the function $f(z)$. There will arise occasions in which we shall have to consider functions which are capable of taking more than one value at a given point z, so-called *many-valued functions*. Most of our considerations, however, will refer to *single-valued* functions, that is, functions which take only one value at each point. Whenever we speak about a function $f(z)$ defined in a domain D, we tacitly assume that $f(z)$ is single-valued.

According to our definition, the function $f(z)$ is permitted to take complex values. Since we may write $f(z) = u(z) + iv(z)$, where $u(z)$ and $v(z)$ are, respectively, the real and imaginary parts of $f(z)$, this means that we are dealing with a pair of real functions of the real variables x and y. In the same way, a continuous function $f(z)$ of the complex variable z is equivalent to a pair of real continuous functions of x and y. Indeed, we define the continuity of $f(z)$ at the point z_0 by the requirement that $\lim f(z) = f(z_0)$ if $z \to z_0$, and this is clearly equivalent to the conditions that $\lim u(x, y) = u(x_0, y_0), \lim v(x, y) = v(x_0, y_0)$ if $z_0 = x_0 + iy_0, x \to x_0, y \to y_0$.

Something radically new, however, is obtained if we demand that our functions $f(z)$ be *differentiable* in the domain D. The definition of differentiability is formally exactly the same as the one used in the ordinary calculus. We define the derivative $f'(z)$ of the function $f(z)$ by

$$(1) \qquad f'(z) = \lim_{h \to 0} \frac{f(z + h) - f(z)}{h},$$

and we say that $f(z)$ is differentiable at the point z if this limit exists. There is, however, a fundamental difference between this derivative and the derivative of a function of a real variable. While in the latter case the value of the parameter h is either positive or negative, h may now be an arbitrary complex parameter which ultimately tends to zero. Geometrically speaking, the point $z + h$ may approach the point z along an arbitrary curve ending at z. By the statement that the limit (1) exists we mean that the limit exists, and is the same, regardless of the path along which z is approached. Just as in the real case, differentiability of a function $f(z)$ at a point z implies continuity of the function at this point. Clearly, the limit (1) would not exist if, for $h \to 0$, the expression $f(z + h) - f(z)$ had a limit other than zero.

The fact that the definition (1) is formally identical with the definition of the derivative of a function of a real variable permits us to draw the following important conclusion: *All the formal rules of differentiation are exactly the same as in the real case.* This relieves us of the necessity of proving all over again the familiar rules for the differentiation of sums, products, and quotients. These rules—as also the fact that the derivative of a constant c is zero, and that the derivative of $cf(z)$ is $cf'(z)$—are purely formal consequences of the definition (1). Another important application of the formal identity of the real and complex differentiation formulas can be made in the following situation. There are cases in which a differentiable function $f(z)$ is defined in a domain which contains a section L of the real axis, and in which $f(z)$ coincides at the points $z = x$ of L with a real function $f(x)$ familiar from the ordinary calculus. Since the derivative (1) may be computed by letting h tend to zero through real values, it follows that, for points z on L, $f'(z)$ will coincide with the real derivative $f'(x)$. Such functions will therefore retain their familiar differentiation formulas.

We now define some terms used in the discussion of differentiable functions. A complex function which is defined and differentiable at all points of a domain D is called an *analytic function*, or, more explicitly, an analytic function of the complex variable z. The reader should be warned that the term "analytic" is used in the literature on the subject in two different senses. The statement "$f(z)$ is analytic in D" means that $f(z)$ is defined and differentiable at all points of D. When it is said, however, that "$f(z)$ is an analytic function" without reference to a specific domain D, all that is implied is that $f(z)$ is defined and differentiable in *some* domain D. This ambiguity can be avoided by using the expression "$f(z)$ is *regular* in D" instead of "$f(z)$ is analytic in D." (In some books, the term *holomorphic* is used in the place of "regular.") An analytic function is said to be *regular at a point* z_0 if it is regular in a neighborhood $|z - z_0| < \epsilon$ of z_0. A point z_0 is called a *singular point* of $f(z)$ if $f(z)$ is not differentiable at z_0, but if every neighborhood $|z - z_0| < \epsilon$ contains points at which $f(z)$ is differentiable.

As an example of an analytic function, we consider the function

$$f(z) = z^n = (x + iy)^n,$$

where n is a positive integer. By (1), we have

$$f'(z) = \lim_{h \to 0} \frac{f(z + h) - f(z)}{h} = \lim_{h \to 0} \frac{(z + h)^n - z^n}{h},$$

provided the limit exists and is independent of the manner in which h approaches zero. According to the binomial theorem—which is a purely algebraic identity and therefore holds for complex as well as for real numbers—we have

$$f'(z) = \lim_{h \to 0} \left[nz^{n-1} + \frac{h}{2} n(n - 1)z^{n-2} + \cdots + h^{n-1} \right],$$

where, except for the first term, all terms on the right-hand side contain positive powers of h. If z is a fixed complex number, all these terms will therefore tend to zero if h tends to zero. Hence, $f'(z)$ exists for all finite values of z, and it is given by the familiar formula $f'(z) = nz^{n-1}$. The function z^n has thus been proved to be an analytic function of z which is regular at all finite points of the complex plane. The fact that the differentiation formula is the same as that of the real function x^n is of course not surprising, since for real values of z (i.e., for $z = x$) z^n coincides with the real function x^n.

It was pointed out above that the formal differentiation rules for sums, products, quotients, etc., are the same as in the real case. For instance, if the functions $f(z)$ and $g(z)$ have derivatives at a point, the same is true for the function $af(z) + bg(z)$, where a and b are constants, and the value of the derivative is $af'(z) + bg'(z)$. Hence, if $f(z)$ and $g(z)$ are analytic, the same is true of $af(z) + bg(z)$. It similarly follows that the product and the quotient of two analytic functions are analytic. In the latter case we must, however, except the points at which the denominator is zero and at which the division ceases to be defined. Applying these principles to the functions $z, z^2, z^3, \cdots$, we find that a polynomial

$$f(z) = a_0 + a_1 z + a_2 z^2 + \cdots + a_n z^n$$

is an analytic function of z, regular at all finite points of the complex plane. More generally, a *rational function*

$$f(z) = \frac{a_0 + a_1 z + a_2 z^2 + \cdots + a_n z^n}{b_0 + b_1 z + b_2 z^2 + \cdots + b_m z^m}$$

is an analytic function of z which is regular at all finite points of the complex plane at which the denominator is not zero.

We finally show that the chain rule for computing the derivative of a function of the form $f(z) = F[g(z)]$ remains valid for analytic functions of a complex variable, provided the proper precautions are taken. We suppose that $g(z)$ is analytic in a domain D and that the values which $g(z)$ takes in D are situated in a domain D'. If $F(z)$ is an analytic function which is regular in D', the expression $f(z)$ is defined for all values z in D. If z is a point of D for which $g'(z)$ is not zero, (1) shows that there exists a positive constant c such that

$$\left| \frac{g(z) - g(z_1)}{z - z_1} \right| > c > 0$$

provided z_1 is a point of D close enough to z. Hence, $g(z) - g(z_1) \neq 0$ for $z \neq z_1$, and we have

$$\frac{f(z) - f(z_1)}{z - z_1} = \frac{F[g(z)] - F[g(z_1)]}{g(z) - g(z_1)} \cdot \frac{g(z) - g(z_1)}{z - z_1}.$$

Passing to the limit, we obtain

$$f'(z) = F'[g(z)]g'(z).$$

The proof of this formula in the case in which $g'(z) = 0$ is left as an exercise to the reader.

Since $F[g(z)]$ is differentiable if the functions F and g are differentiable, we have shown that *an analytic function of an analytic function is again an analytic function.*

EXERCISES

1. If the function $F(z)$ is analytic in a domain D, show that the function $\text{Re}[F(z)]$ has a derivative only at those points of D at which $F'(z) = 0$.

2. Let $F(z)$ be regular at a point z_0. If h approaches zero along a linear segment making the angle θ with the positive axis, show that

$$\lim_{h \to 0} \frac{|F(z + h)|^2 - |F(z)|^2}{h} = F'(z)\overline{F(z)}$$
$$+ (\cos 2\theta - i \sin 2\theta)F(z)\overline{F'(z)}.$$

3. Show that the function $x^2 + axy + by^2$ is analytic only if $a = 2i, b = -1$.

4. If $u(x, y)$ and $v(x, y)$ are real differentiable functions of x and y, show that, unless the four partial derivatives u_x, u_y, v_x, v_y vanish simultaneously, $u(x, y) + iv(x, y)$ and $u(x, y) - iv(x, y)$ cannot both be differentiable at the same point.

2 THE CAUCHY-RIEMANN EQUATIONS

Up to this point we have stressed the similarities between the complex derivative (1) and the ordinary derivative $f'(x)$ of a real function $f(x)$; accordingly, our results were formally identical with the corresponding familiar results for real derivatives. In order to obtain something that is genuinely new, we must pay closer attention to a feature of the definition (1) which we have not utilized until now: The fact that the value of $f'(z)$ is independent of the manner in which h tends to zero. To see the implications of this fact, we suppose that h tends to zero in such a way that $\theta = \arg h$ remains constant; geometrically, this amounts to letting the point $z + h$ approach the point z along a straight line making the angle θ with the real axis. We first consider the two simplest cases, corresponding to $\theta = 0$ and $\theta = \pi/2$. In the first case, h tends to zero through positive values. If we write

$$f(z) = u(x, y) + iv(x, y),$$

where $u = u(x, y)$ and $v = v(x, y)$ are, respectively, the real and imaginary parts of $f(z)$, we have $z + h = x + h + iy$ and it follows that

$$\frac{f(z + h) - f(z)}{h} = \frac{u(x + h, y) - u(x, y)}{h} + i\frac{v(x + h, y) - v(x, y)}{h}.$$

Passing to the limit, we have the result

$$(2) \qquad f'(z) = u_x(x, y) + iv_x(x, y).$$

In the second case we set $h = ik$, where k is positive. Since we now have $z + h = x + i(y + k)$, we obtain

$$\frac{f(z + h) - f(z)}{h} = \frac{u(x, y + k) - u(x, y)}{ik} + \frac{v(x, y + k) - v(x, y)}{k}$$

and a passage to the limit leads to

$$(3) \qquad f'(z) = v_y(x, y) - iu_y(x, y),$$

if it is noted that $i^{-1} = -i$. Since the limits (2) and (3) must exist, it is seen that the assumption that $f(z)$ be differentiable at a point implies that the partial derivatives u_x, u_y, v_x, v_y of its real and imaginary parts must exist there. In view of the definition of differentiability, (2) and (3) must be equal, i.e., we must have $u_x + iv_x = v_y - iu_y$. Since two complex numbers can be equal only if both their real and their imaginary parts are equal, this proves the following result.

If $u = u(x, y)$ and $v = v(x, y)$ are, respectively, the real and the imaginary part of an analytic function $f(z) = u(x, y) + iv(x, y)$, then

$$(4) \qquad \frac{\partial u}{\partial x} = \frac{\partial v}{\partial y}, \quad \frac{\partial u}{\partial y} = -\frac{\partial v}{\partial x}.$$

These relations, which must be satisfied at every point at which the function $f(z)$ is regular, are known as the *Cauchy-Riemann equations*.

So far, we have let $z + h$ tend to z along a horizontal and a vertical line. In order to see what happens if the point $z + h$ approaches z along a line which makes the angle θ with the horizontal axis, we would have to set $h = r(\cos \theta + i \sin \theta)$, i.e., $z + h = x + r \cos \theta + i(y + r \sin \theta)$, and to compute the limit (1) for $r \to 0$. It is, however, just as easy to treat the more general case in which $z + h$ approaches z along an arbitrary differentiable curve. If $z = z(t)$—i.e., $x = x(t)$ and $y = y(t)$—is the equation of this curve and if, in order to avoid confusion, we denote the point at which f' is computed by z_0, we have

$$f'(z_0) = \lim_{z \to z_0} \frac{f(z) - f(z_0)}{z - z_0} = \lim_{z \to z_0} \frac{\dfrac{f(z) - (z_0)}{t - t_0}}{\dfrac{z - z_0}{t - t_0}},$$

where t_0 is such that $z(t_0) = z_0$. Hence,

$$f'(z_0) = \frac{\dfrac{df}{dt}}{z'(t)},$$

and this shows that the existence of $f'(z_0)$ implies the existence of df/dt. If we replace x and y by the conjugate coordinates z and $\bar{z}$ introduced in Chapter I, Section 4, this expression can be computed by Formula (30) of Chapter I. We thus obtain

$$(5) \qquad f'(z_0) = \frac{\partial f}{\partial z} + \frac{\partial f}{\partial \bar{z}} \frac{\overline{z'(t_0)}}{z'(t_0)}.$$

The dependence of the limit on the curve along which z_0 is approached is expressed by the value of $z'(t_0)$. For instance, if $z(t)$ is the straight line $z(t) = \alpha t$ where α is an arbitrary complex number, (5) shows that

$$f'(z_0) = \frac{\partial f}{\partial z} + \frac{\partial f}{\partial \bar{z}} \frac{\bar{\alpha}}{\alpha}.$$

If we choose α in such a way that $|\alpha| = 1$, we have $1 = |\alpha|^2 = \alpha \bar{\alpha}$, and the last formula may be written

$$f'(z_0) = \frac{\partial f}{\partial z} + \bar{\alpha}^2 \frac{\partial f}{\partial \bar{z}}.$$

Since the argument of α is arbitrary, this makes it clear that the value of $f'(z_0)$ can be independent of the manner of approach to the point z_0 only if

(6) $$\frac{\partial f}{\partial \bar{z}} = 0.$$

It is easy to see that this condition is equivalent to the Cauchy-Riemann equations (4). Indeed, if we observe that $f = u + iv$ and that the differential operator $\partial/\partial\bar{z}$ is defined by Formula (27) of Chapter I, we conclude from (6) that

$$\frac{\partial}{\partial x}(u + iv) + i\frac{\partial}{\partial y}(u + iv) = 0,$$

i.e.,

$$u_x - v_y + i(v_x + u_y) = 0.$$

Since a complex number is zero only if both its real and its imaginary parts are zero, this is identical with the conditions (4). Equation (6) is therefore referred to as *the complex form of the Cauchy-Riemann equations*.

These equations are, however, not only necessary for the existence of $f'(z_0)$; if $f(z)$ is a function which possesses a total differential (a condition which is always fulfilled if $f(z)$ has continuous partial derivatives with respect to x and y), they are also sufficient. Indeed, according to Section 4 of Chapter I, the derivative df/dt of such a function can be computed by Formula (30), and (5) shows that the conditions (6) imply

(7) $$f'(z) = \frac{\partial f}{\partial z}$$

(where z_0 has again been replaced by z). Since the value of f_z does not depend on the curve $z(t)$, it follows that the limit (1) is independent of the manner in which h tends to zero. We thus have the following result:

The derivative (1) *of a function $f(z)$ exists if, and only if, $f(z)$ possesses a total differential and satisfies the Cauchy-Riemann equations.*

As pointed out in Section 4 of Chapter I, $f(z)$ certainly has a total differential at a point at which the partial derivatives u_x, u_y, v_x, v_y exist and are continuous. The latter conditions, together with the Cauchy-Riemann equations, are thus sufficient to guarantee the existence of $f'(z)$.

We close this section with the remark that a function $f(z)$ whose derivative $f'(z)$ vanishes at all points of a domain must be a constant. Indeed, (2) and (4) show that $f'(z) = 0$ implies $u_x = u_y = v_x = v_y = 0$. The functions u and v depend therefore neither on x nor on y and thus reduce to constants.

EXERCISES

1. If $u(x, y) = x^3 - 3xy^2$, use the Cauchy-Riemann equations (4) to show that $v(x, y) = 3x^2y - y^3 + c$, where c is a constant.

2. If r, θ are polar coordinates in the xy-plane and w is a function of x and y, show that

$$\frac{\partial w}{\partial z} = \frac{1}{2z}\left(r\frac{\partial w}{\partial r} - i\frac{\partial w}{\partial \theta}\right), \quad \frac{\partial w}{\partial \bar{z}} = \frac{1}{2\bar{z}}\left(r\frac{\partial w}{\partial r} + i\frac{\partial w}{\partial \theta}\right).$$

3. Use the result of the preceding exercise to show that in polar coordinates the Cauchy-Riemann equations take the form

$$ru_r = v_\theta, \quad rv_r = -u_\theta,$$

where $u + iv = f(z)$.

4. Denote by $\partial/\partial n$ and $\partial/\partial s$ the directional derivatives in two directions which are perpendicular to each other. If a positive rotation of 90 degrees leads from the n-direction to the s-direction, and if $f(z) = u + iv$ is an analytic function, show that

$$\frac{\partial u}{\partial n} = \frac{\partial v}{\partial s}, \quad \frac{\partial u}{\partial s} = -\frac{\partial v}{\partial n},$$

and that

$$\frac{\partial f}{\partial s} = i\frac{\partial f}{\partial n}.$$

3   SOME APPLICATIONS

In Section 4 of Chapter I it was shown that a function of the real variables x and y may be considered to be a function of the conjugate complex variables z and $\bar{z}$. We also saw that z and $\bar{z}$ can be treated formally as independent variables, provided the "partial derivatives" with respect to z and $\bar{z}$ are defined by (27). In the light of these facts, the Cauchy-Riemann equations (6) take on a very simple meaning. Since, among all functions of z and $\bar{z}$, the analytic functions f are distinguished by the condition $f_{\bar{z}} = 0$, we may say that analytic functions are functions of the complex variable z only: They depend on z but not on $\bar{z}$. Another way of interpreting (6) is that *in the differentiation process $\partial/\partial\bar{z}$ the analytic functions $f(z)$ play the role of constants.* Equation (7) shows that the application of the operation $\partial/\partial z$ to an analytic function $f(z)$ produces its derivative $f'(z)$. These two remarks, combined with the fact that, in view of their definitions (27), the differentiation processes $\partial/\partial z$ and $\partial/\partial\bar{z}$ obey the usual formal rules for the differentiation of sums, products, quotients, etc., make it very easy to compute $\partial/\partial z$ and $\partial/\partial\bar{z}$ if an expression involving z and $\bar{z}$ is given.

Before we show some applications of these rules we remark that there are, of course, also functions which depend only on $\bar{z}$ but not on z, i.e., functions F such that $F_z = 0$. It is not difficult to see that such a function must be of the form $F = \overline{f(z)}$, where $f(z)$ is an analytic function. Indeed, if $F = p + iq$ where p and q are real functions of x and y, we have

$$2\frac{\partial F}{\partial z} = \frac{\partial}{\partial x}(p + iq) - i\frac{\partial}{\partial y}(p + iq) = p_x + q_y + i(q_x - p_y).$$

The condition $F_z = 0$ is therefore equivalent to the equations $p_x + q_y = 0$ and $q_x - p_y = 0$. If we set $p = u$, $q = -v$, the latter take the form $u_x = v_y$ and $v_x = -u_y$, and these are precisely the Cauchy-Riemann equations (4). By the results of the preceding section, the function $u + iv$ is an analytic function of z, say $f(z)$. Since $F = p + iq = u - iv$ we have $F = \overline{f(z)}$, and our assertion is proved. The same proof also shows that, conversely, every function F of the form $\overline{f(z)}$ satisfies $\partial F/\partial z = 0$. The conjugates $\overline{f(z)}$ of analytic functions $f(z)$ will therefore play the role of constants in the $\partial/\partial z$-differentiation. If the operator $\partial/\partial\bar{z}$ is applied to $\overline{f(z)}$, the result is obviously $\overline{f'(z)}$.

We now consider a number of applications of the preceding results. We begin by showing that neither the real part nor the absolute value of an analytic function $f(z)$ can be constant in a domain unless $f(z)$ itself reduces to a constant. If $f(z) = u + iv$, we have $f(z) + \overline{f(z)} = 2u = \text{const}$. Differentiating this with respect to z and noting that $[\overline{f(z)}]_z = 0$, we obtain $f'(z) = 0$ and this shows that $f(z)$ is indeed constant. (The corresponding result for the imaginary part follows in a similar manner, or else by noting that v is the real part of the analytic function $-if(z)$.) If $|f| = c$, we have $|f|^2 = f\bar{f} = c^2$ and thus

$$f(z) = \frac{c^2}{\overline{f(z)}}.$$

Since the right-hand side is the conjugate of an analytic function, its z-derivative is zero. Hence $f'(z) = 0$ and $f(z)$ is shown to be a constant. Another way of obtaining this result is to differentiate the identity $f(z)\overline{f(z)} = c^2$ successively with respect to z and to $\bar{z}$. This leads to $|f'(z)|^2 = 0$ and therefore to $f'(z) = 0$.

These results, of course, can also be obtained without the use of conjugate complex variables. For instance, to show that $u^2 + v^2 = |f(z)|^2$ can be constant only if $f(z)$ is constant, we differentiate the relation $u^2 + v^2 = c^2$ with respect to x and y and obtain the two equations $uu_x + vv_x = 0$ and $uu_y + vv_y = 0$. Since (except in the trivial case $c = 0$) $u^2 + v^2 = c^2 > 0$, u and v cannot both be zero, and the last two equations are therefore compatible only if the determinant $D = u_x v_y - u_y v_x$ is zero. In view of (4), we have $D = u_x^2 + u_y^2 = v_x^2 + v_y^2$. This shows that $D = 0$ implies that u_x, u_y, v_x, v_y must all be zero, and the result follows.

A comparison of the proof using conjugate complex variables and the "real" proof shows that, even in this simple case, the computation is easier if the complex formalism is used. In more complicated cases, the saving of computational labor made possible by the use of conjugate variables can be very considerable. As an illustration let us prove the following proposition, which contains the preceding results as a special case: If u is the real and v the imaginary part of an analytic function $f(z)$, and if the relation $a_1 u^2 + a_2 uv + a_3 v^2 + a_4 u + a_5 v = $ const. (where the a_k are constants) holds throughout a domain, $f(z)$ must reduce to a constant. Since

$$u = \frac{f(z) + \overline{f(z)}}{2}, \quad v = \frac{f(z) - \overline{f(z)}}{2i},$$

the given relation can be restated in the form

$$A_1 f^2 + A_2 f\bar{f} + A_3 \bar{f}^2 + A_4 f + A_5 \bar{f} = \text{const.},$$

where the A_k are different constants. If we denote the expression on the left-hand side by Q, we find that $Q_z = (2A_1 f + A_2 \bar{f} + A_4) f' = 0$. In any neighborhood in which $f' \neq 0$ we must therefore have $2A_1 f + A_2 \bar{f} + A_4 = 0$. Differentiating this with respect to

z and $\bar{z}$ we obtain $2A_1f' = 0$ and $A_2f' = 0$, respectively. Since $f' \neq 0$, we must have $A_1 = A_2 = 0$. Computing $Q_{\bar{z}}$, we show similarly that $A_3 = 0$. Hence, Q must be of the form $Q = A_4f + A_5\bar{f}$. But $A_4f' = Q_z = 0$ and $A_5\bar{f}' = Q_{\bar{z}} = 0$ and we find that the assumption that $f'(z) \neq 0$ in a neighborhood has led to a contradiction. Hence, $f'(z) = 0$ throughout the domain, and the proof is complete. The proof of this result by "real" methods is recommended to the reader as an exercise.

If $F(x, y)$ is twice continuously differentiable with respect to x and y, it follows from the definition of the operations $\partial/\partial z$ and $\partial/\partial \bar{z}$ that

$$(8) \qquad \frac{\partial^2 F}{\partial z \partial \bar{z}} = \frac{1}{4}\left(\frac{\partial^2 F}{\partial x^2} + \frac{\partial^2 F}{\partial y^2}\right) = \frac{1}{4}\,\Delta F.$$

This identity provides a powerful computational tool in the many areas of pure and applied analysis in which the Laplace operator Δ plays an important role. Before we illustrate the use of this device, we remark that a z-differentiation of the Cauchy-Riemann equation (6) yields $f_{z\bar{z}} = 0$, where $f(z)$ is an analytic function which possesses the required second derivatives (in Section 1, Chapter IV it will be shown that these derivatives always exist). By (8), this is equivalent to $\Delta f = 0$, or, if $u = \mathrm{Re}(f)$, $v = \mathrm{Im}(f)$, $\Delta u + i\,\Delta v = 0$. Since both Δu and Δv are real, this shows that *both the real and the imaginary part of an analytic function $f(z)$ are solutions of the Laplace equation $\Delta \phi = 0$*. This result may also be obtained from (4), as the reader will easily verify. Functions $\phi(x, y)$ which are solutions of the Laplace equation $\Delta \phi = 0$ are of basic importance in many branches of applied mathematics. Such functions are known as *harmonic functions*, or *potential functions*. This last name is derived from the fact that electrostatic potential, the velocity potential of an incompressible fluid, as well as other potentials considered in mathematical physics, are solutions of $\Delta \phi = 0$. Some of these potentials, and their treatment by means of the tools of complex analysis, will be considered in Chapter VI.

The knowledge of an analytic function of the complex variable z thus automatically provides us with the knowledge of two harmonic functions: Its real and its imaginary part. For instance, since z^3 is an analytic function and since $z^3 = (x + iy)^3 = x^3 - 3xy^2 + i(3x^2y - y^3)$, we can conclude that the functions $u = x^3 - 3xy^2$ and $v = 3x^2y - y^3$ must be harmonic. The connection between analytic functions and harmonic functions is, however, even closer than indicated by the facts proved so far. It is also true that *every harmonic function is the real part of some analytic function.* In other words, if we are given a real harmonic function $u(x, y)$ we can always find another real harmonic function $v(x, y)$ so that $u(x, y) + iv(x, y)$ is an analytic function $f(z)$ of the complex variable z. The harmonic function $v(x, y)$ is called the *harmonic conjugate* of $u(x, y)$. The existence of the conjugate can be shown very simply if we use the fact, known from the real calculus, that the relation $M_x(x, y) = N_y(x, y)$ (where both sides are continuous) implies the existence of a function $Q(x, y)$ such that $Q_x = N$, $Q_y = M$ (for a discussion of the single-valuedness of this function, see Section 4, Chapter VII). Since a harmonic function $u(x, y)$ is defined as a solution (with continuous first and second derivatives) of the equation $u_{xx} + u_{yy} = 0$, we may thus conclude from $(u_x)_x = (-u_y)_y$ that there exists a function v such that $v_y = u_x$, $v_x = -u_y$. But these are the Cauchy-Riemann equations (4), and we have shown above that two functions u,v which have continuous partial derivatives and satisfy (4) are the real and imaginary part of an analytic function.

We give yet another proof of this result, based on the use of conjugate variables. If $\Delta\phi = 0$, where ϕ may be a complex function, (8) shows that $\phi_{z\bar{z}} = 0$, i.e., $(\phi_z)_{\bar{z}} = 0$. ϕ_z is thus a solution of the Cauchy-Riemann equations (6), and it must therefore be an analytic function, say $F(z)$. Hence, $\phi_z = F(z)$. It will be shown later that every analytic function which is regular in a neighborhood is the derivative of some other analytic function, and we may therefore replace $\phi_z = F(z)$ by $\phi_z = f'(z)$. In view of (7), this may be written $(\phi - f)_z = 0$. As pointed out earlier in this section, any solution of the differential equation $(\ )_z = 0$ is the conjugate $\overline{g(z)}$ of an analytic function $g(z)$. Therefore, $\phi - f = \bar{g}$, i.e., the general solution of the equation $\Delta\phi = 0$ is of the form

$$\phi = f(z) + \overline{g(z)},$$

where $f(z)$ and $g(z)$ are analytic functions. The proof of the fact that ϕ will be real in a domain only if $f(z) = g(z) + c$, where c is a real constant, is left as an exercise to the reader.

Our next illustration of the use of conjugate complex variables concerns the partial differential equation $\Delta\phi = P(x, y)$, where $P(x, y)$ is a polynomial in x and y, i.e., $P(x, y) = \sum_{\nu=0}^{n} \sum_{\mu=0}^{m} a_{\nu\mu} x^\nu y^\mu$. Replacing x and y by conjugate variables $z, \bar{z}$, we have

$$\Delta\phi = \sum_{\nu=0}^{n} \sum_{\mu=0}^{m} a_{\nu\mu} \left(\frac{z+\bar{z}}{2}\right)^{\nu} \left(\frac{z-\bar{z}}{2i}\right)^{\mu}$$

or, in view of (8),

(9) $$4\phi_{z\bar{z}} = \sum_{\nu=0}^{n+m} \sum_{\mu=0}^{n+m} b_{\nu\mu} z^{\nu} \bar{z}^{\mu},$$

where the coefficients $b_{\nu\mu}$ are obtained from the $a_{\nu\mu}$ by a simple computation. It is sufficient to find one particular solution ϕ_1 of this equation, since its general solution will then be of the form $\phi = \phi_1 + u$, where u is a harmonic function (proof ?). The functions z^{ν} are analytic and the operation $\partial/\partial z$ produces, therefore, the same effect on these functions as ordinary differentiation; the functions $\bar{z}^{\mu}$, on the other hand, behave like constants. Hence, (9) may be "integrated with respect to z," and we obtain

$$4\phi_{\bar{z}} = \sum_{\nu=0}^{n+m} \sum_{\mu=0}^{n+m} \frac{b_{\nu\mu}}{\nu+1} z^{\nu+1}\bar{z}^{\mu} + \overline{f(z)},$$

where $\overline{f(z)}$—the conjugate of an arbitrary analytic function—plays the role of an "integration constant." Since we are interested only in one particular solution, we choose $f(z) \equiv 0$. Integrating again with respect to $\bar{z}$ and omitting the "integration constant" $g(z)$, we obtain

$$4\phi = \sum_{\nu=0}^{n+m} \sum_{\mu=0}^{n+m} \frac{b_{\nu\mu}}{(\nu+1)(\mu+1)} z^{\nu+1}\bar{z}^{\mu+1}.$$

If z and $\bar{z}$ are now replaced by $x + iy$ and $x - iy$, respectively, we arrive at the desired solution. For instance, to find a solution of $\Delta\phi = xy$, we have to integrate the equation

$$4\phi_{z\bar{z}} = xy = \left(\frac{z+\bar{z}}{2}\right)\left(\frac{z-\bar{z}}{2i}\right) = \frac{1}{4i}(z^2 - \bar{z}^2)$$

with respect to z and $\bar{z}$. The first integration yields

$$4\phi_{\bar{z}} = \frac{1}{4i}\left(\frac{z^3}{3} - z\bar{z}^2\right)$$

and the second,

$$4\phi = \frac{1}{4i}\left(\frac{\bar{z}z^3}{3} - \frac{z\bar{z}^3}{3}\right)$$

$$= \frac{z\bar{z}}{3}\left(\frac{z+\bar{z}}{2}\right)\left(\frac{z-\bar{z}}{2i}\right) = \frac{xy}{3}(x^2 + y^2).$$

This method of obtaining a solution of $\Delta\phi = P(x, y)$ is not restricted to the case in which $P(x, y)$ is a polynomial (and in which it is not too troublesome to find a polynomial solution by the method of indeterminate coefficients). It works just as well in all those cases in which the substitution of $z, \bar{z}$ for x, y transforms $P(x, y)$ into a function $Q(z, \bar{z})$ which is analytic in both z and $\bar{z}$ (and in which the required integrations can be carried out in terms of known functions).

We next apply conjugate variables to the problem of finding the general solution of the fourth-order partial differential equation $\Delta\Delta\phi = 0$ (written in full: $\phi_{xxxx} + 2\phi_{xxyy} + \phi_{yyyy} = 0$), which is of fundamental importance in the theory of elasticity. Because of (8), the equation may be replaced by

$$\phi_{z\bar{z}z\bar{z}} = 0,$$

and this shows that it may be solved by four integrations, two with respect to z and two with respect to $\bar{z}$. We may, however, shorten the computation by using the general solution $f(z) + \overline{g(z)}$ of the Laplace equation obtained previously. The equation $\Delta(\Delta\phi) = 0$ thus reduces to

$$\phi_{z\bar{z}} = F'(z) + \overline{G'(z)},$$

where $F(z)$ and $G(z)$ are analytic functions, and we have made use of the fact, alluded to before, that every analytic function is the derivative of some other analytic function. Integrating the last equation with respect to z, we obtain

$$\phi_{\bar{z}} = F(z) + z\overline{G'(z)} + \overline{h'(z)},$$

where $h(z)$ is another analytic function. Finally, an integration with respect to $\bar{z}$ yields

$$\phi = \bar{z}F(z) + z\overline{G(z)} + \overline{h(z)} + k(z),$$

where $k(z)$ is yet another analytic function. The factors z and $\bar{z}$ are, of course, produced by the fact that $\overline{G(z)}$ and $F(z)$ behave like constants in the relevant integrations. Since $\Delta\Delta$ is a real operator, both the real and the imaginary part of ϕ are solutions of $\Delta\Delta u = 0$. The most general real solution of $\Delta\Delta u = 0$ is therefore

$$u = \mathrm{Re}[\phi] = \mathrm{Re}[\bar{z}F + z\overline{G} + \overline{h} + k] = \mathrm{Re}[\bar{z}F + \bar{z}G + h + k].$$

Writing $F(z) + G(z) = \sigma(z)$, $h(z) + k(z) = g(z)$, we thus obtain

$$u = \mathrm{Re}[\bar{z}\sigma(z) + g(z)]$$

as the general solution of the equation of elasticity. If it is desired to remove all traces of the variables z and $\bar{z}$, this can be done by taking $\sigma(z) = zf(z)$. This substitution leads to

$$u = \mathrm{Re}[|z|^2 f(z) + g(z)] = |z|^2 \mathrm{Re}[f(z)] + \mathrm{Re}[g(z)].$$

Since, as shown above, any harmonic function is the real part of some analytic function, we finally obtain the solution

$$u = (x^2 + y^2)u_1(x, y) + u_2(x, y),$$

where u_1 and u_2 are arbitrary harmonic functions.

EXERCISES

1. Show that $\log |f(z)|$ is harmonic in a domain in which the analytic function $f(z)$ is regular and does not vanish.

2. If $f(z)$ is an analytic function, show that $\Delta(|f(z)|^2) = 4|f'(z)|^2$.

3. If, in a given domain, $f(z)$ is an analytic function such that $f'(z) \neq 0$, $|f(z)| < 1$, show that the function

$$w = \log \frac{|f'(z)|}{1 - |f(z)|^2}$$

satisfies the partial differential equation $\Delta w = 4e^{2w}$.

4. If $w = |f(z)|^2$, where $f(z)$ is an analytic function, show that w satisfies the partial differential equation

$$w\Delta w = w_x^2 + w_y^2.$$

5. If $f_1(z), f_2(z), \cdots, f_n(z)$ are analytic functions such that

$$|f_1(z)|^2 + |f_2(z)|^2 + \cdots + |f_n(z)|^2 = \text{const.}$$

at all points of a domain, show that all functions must reduce to constants.

6. If the condition of the preceding exercise is replaced by

$$|f_1(z)|^2 + \cdots + |f_n(z)|^2 = \sum_{\nu=1}^{p} \sum_{\mu=1}^{q} a_{\nu\mu} x^\nu y^\mu,$$

show that all functions $f_k(z)$ must be polynomials of degree not exceeding $p + q$.

7. If $f_1(z), \cdots, f_n(z)$ are analytic in a domain, show that the expression

$$|f_1(z)|^2 + \cdots + |f_n(z)|^2$$

cannot be harmonic unless all the functions $f_k(z)$ reduce to constants.

8. Let $g(t)$ be a twice differentiable function of the real variable t for $-\infty < t < \infty$, and let $u(x, y)$ be a twice differentiable function of the real variables x,y in a domain. If $w = g(u)$, show that

$$\Delta w = g''(u)(u_x^2 + u_y^2) + g'(u)\Delta u.$$

9. If $f(z)$ and $g(z)$ are non-constant analytic functions, show that the relation $f(z) = \overline{g(z)}$ cannot hold in a domain in which both $f(z)$ and $g(z)$ are regular.

10. If $u(x, y)$, $v(x, y)$ and $w(x, y)$ are real and harmonic in a domain, show that the relation $u(x, y)v(x, y) = w(x, y)$ can hold only if $v(x, y)$ is a constant multiple of the harmonic conjugate of $u(x, y)$.

11. If $v(x, y)$ is the harmonic conjugate of $u(x, y)$, show that the harmonic conjugate of $v(x, y)$ is not $u(x, y)$ but $-u(x, y)$. How do you explain this apparent lack of symmetry?

12. If $v = v(x, y)$ is the harmonic conjugate of $u = u(x, y)$, show that the functions $U(x, y) = e^u \cos v$ and $V(x, y) = e^u \sin v$ are harmonic and that $V(x, y)$ is the harmonic conjugate of $U(x, y)$.

13. If $f(z)$ is an analytic function which satisfies the ordinary differential equation $f'(z) = p(z)f(z)$, show that $w = |f(z)|^2$ is a solution of the partial differential equation $\Delta w = 4|p(z)|^2 w$.

14. If $y = f(z)$ is an analytic function which satisfies the ordinary differential equation $y'' + p(z)y = 0$, show that $w = |f(z)|^2$ is a solution of the partial differential equation $\Delta\Delta w = 16|p(z)|^2 w$.

15. Obtain a solution of the partial differential equation $\Delta u = (x + y)^{-1}$.

16. If $f(z)$ is an analytic function and α, β, γ are arbitrary complex constants, show that both the real and the imaginary part of the expression

$$[\alpha - \gamma f(z)]^{-1/2}[\beta - \gamma^{-1}\overline{f(z)}]^{-1/2}$$

are solutions of the partial differential equation $\Delta u = |f'(z)|^2 u^3$.

17. If the analytic function $f(z)$ satisfies the ordinary differential equation $f''(z) + af'(z) + bf(z) = 0$, where a and b are real constants, show that $u = |f(z)|^2$ is a solution of the partial differential equation $\Delta\Delta u = 4a^2\Delta u + 16b^2 u + 16ab u_x$.

4 THE EXPONENTIAL AND TRIGONOMETRIC FUNCTIONS

We saw in Section 1 that the rational functions $R(x)$ known from the ordinary calculus become analytic functions $R(z)$ if the real variable x is formally replaced by the complex variable z. As we shall see in the present section, this is by no means an isolated phenomenon. In fact, all the elementary functions studied in the calculus—such as the exponential function, the logarithm, the trigonometric functions—give rise to analytic functions of a complex variable z if their definitions are suitably extended from real values of the variable to complex values. In the case of the rational functions this "analytic extension" to complex values presented no difficulties at all, since a rational function can be built up from z and a finite number of constants by means of the operations of arithmetic, and this makes it clear what is meant by the symbol $R(z)$. If we try to extend the real function e^x to complex values of the argument, the situation is less obvious. It is easy to write down the symbol e^z, but nothing much is gained by doing this unless we can explain what we mean by a complex exponent. Since it is precisely the complex exponential function which gives meaning to the notion of a complex exponent, we must resort to a different procedure.

Our aim is to find an analytic function $f(z)$ of the complex variable z which, for real values of z (i.e., for $z = x$), coincides with the real exponential function e^x. It will be shown later (Chap. IV, Sec. 2) that there can exist only one analytic function which, for real values of the argument, coincides with a given real function. This uniqueness of the analytic extension of a real function provides the justification for calling this analytic function of the complex variable z by the same name as the real function of x. Since there is only one analytic function $f(z)$ for which $f(x) = e^x$, no confusion can arise if we give this function the name e^z (for reasons of typographical convenience, the symbol e^z is occasionally replaced by exp z, or exp (z)).

Since the real exponential function $f(x) = e^x$ is determined by the relations $f'(x) = f(x)$ and $f(0) = 1$, we may try to obtain its analytic extension $f(z)$ by constructing a solution of the differential equation $f'(z) = f(z)$ for which $f(0) = 1$. If there exists such a function $f(z)$, it will necessarily coincide with the real function e^x for $z = x$. Indeed, if z is real and we use the expression (2) for $f'(z)$, the equation becomes

$$u_x(x, 0) + iv_x(x, 0) = u(x, 0) + iv(x, 0),$$

and this is equivalent to the two real differential equations $u_x = u$ and $v_x = v$. Both u and v must therefore be of the form ce^x, where c is a real constant: Since $f(0) = u(0, 0) + iv(0, 0) = 1$, we have $u(0, 0) = 1$, $v(0, 0) = 0$, and this shows that $v(x, 0)$ vanishes identically, and that $u(x, 0) = e^x$. Hence $f(x) = e^x$ for any real x.

We now have to solve the equation $f'(z) = f(z)$ for complex z. Using (2) again, we find that the real part $u(x, y)$ and the imaginary part $v(x, y)$ of $f(z)$ must satisfy the equation

$$u_x(x, y) + iv_x(x, y) = u(x, y) + iv(x, y),$$

i.e., we must have

$$u_x(x, y) = u(x, y), \quad v_x(x, y) = v(x, y).$$

The integration of these equations again leads to exponential functions in x, but the integration constants may now depend on y. Hence

$$u(x, y) = p(y)e^x, \quad v(x, y) = q(y)e^x,$$

where, because of $f(0) = u(0, 0) + iv(0, 0) = 1$, we must have $p(0) = 1$, $q(0) = 0$. To find the functions $p(y)$ and $q(y)$, we apply the Cauchy-Riemann equations (4) to these expressions for u and v. This shows that $p(y) = q'(y)$ and $q(y) = -p'(y)$. Hence $q''(y) = p'(y) = -q(y)$ and $p''(y) = -q'(y) = -p(y)$, i.e., both $p(y)$ and $q(y)$ must be solutions of the differential equation $\phi''(y) + \phi(y) = 0$. It is known from elementary analysis that all solutions of this equation are of the form $A \cos y + B \sin y$, where A and B are constants. Since $q'(0) = p(0) = 1$ and $p'(0) = q(0) = 0$, we must have $p(y) = \cos y$ and $q(y) = \sin y$. Hence $u(x, y) = e^x \cos y$, $v(x, y) = e^x \sin x$, and the function $f(z) = u(x, y) + iv(x, y)$ is found to be of the form $f(z) = e^x(\cos y + i \sin y)$. For $y = 0$ we indeed have $f(x) = e^x$, and $f(z)$ is an analytic function, since by its construction it automatically satisfies the Cauchy-Riemann equations. (The reader may also note that the equation $f'(z) = f(z)$ implies the existence of the derivative.) The exponential function e^z is thus defined by

$$(10) \qquad e^z = e^x(\cos y + i \sin y), \quad z = x + iy.$$

This function is defined, and differentiable, for all finite values of z.

The exponential function is therefore regular at all finite points of the z-plane. Functions with this property are known as *entire functions*. The class of entire functions also includes the polynomials $P(z)$ discussed in Section 1, which are entire functions of a particularly simple type. An entire function which is *not* a polynomial is called a *transcendental* entire function.

One of the principal properties of the real exponential function e^x is its *addition theorem*, that is, the fact that $e^{x+t} = e^x e^t$ if x and t are real numbers. To show that the addition theorem is also valid for the analytic function e^z, we consider the expression $F(z) = e^z e^{a-z}$, where a is a complex constant. Differentiating $F(z)$, we obtain $F'(z) = e^z e^{a-z} - e^z e^{a-z} = 0$. Hence $F(z)$ reduces to a constant whose value can be found by setting $z = 0$. But $F(0) = e^0 e^a = e^a$, and this shows that $e^z e^{a-z} = e^a$. If we denote the complex number $a - z$ by w, we have thus proved that

$$(11) \qquad\qquad e^z e^w = e^{z+w},$$

where z and w may be any two complex numbers.

The addition theorem (11) shows, incidentally, that the exponential function cannot take the value zero at any point of the complex plane. Indeed, it would follow from $e^w = 0$ and (11) that $e^{z+w} = 0$ for all values of z, i.e., the exponential function would vanish identically.

If we apply Formula (10) to a pure imaginary number $z = it$, we have the identity

$$(12) \qquad\qquad e^{it} = \cos t + i \sin t,$$

which, although derived only for real values of t, will presently be given a proper meaning also in the case in which t is a complex number. Before we do so we note that (12) makes it possible to express the polar representation

$$z = r(\cos \theta + i \sin \theta)$$

of a complex number z of absolute value r and of argument θ in the more compact form

$$(13) \qquad\qquad z = re^{i\theta},$$

a fact which will be used frequently. We also note that, by (11), $e^{2z} = e^{z+z} = e^z e^z = (e^z)^2$, $e^{3z} = e^{2z+z} = e^{2z}e^z = (e^z)^2 e^z = (e^z)^3$. Continuing in this manner, we obtain $(e^z)^n = e^{nz}$. Applying this to $z = it$ and using (12), we obtain

$$(\cos t + i \sin t)^n = \cos nt + i \sin nt,$$

i.e., De Moivre's Formula (13) of Chapter I. This formula is thus seen not to be just a lucky accident, but a consequence of the addition theorem of the exponential function.

Formula (12) enables us to define two analytic functions which, for real values, coincide with the trigonometric functions $\sin x$ and $\cos x$. As already mentioned, whenever such an extension of a real function to an analytic function is possible, it can be done in only one way. We may therefore retain the symbols $\sin z$ and $\cos z$ for these analytic functions, but it should be clearly understood that the trigonometric associations of these functions are completely lost once z is a complex number. If we nevertheless call them *trigonometric functions*, this is merely a convenient way of referring to them.

To obtain their formal definitions, we supplement (12) by the companion formula

$$(14) \qquad e^{-it} = \cos t - i \sin t,$$

which is obtained from (12) by substituting $-t$ for t, and observing that $\cos(-t) = \cos t$ and $\sin(-t) = -\sin t$. Adding (12) and (14), and writing z for t, we obtain

$$(15) \qquad \cos z = \frac{e^{iz} + e^{-iz}}{2}.$$

Subtracting these two formulas from each other, we have

$$(16) \qquad \sin z = \frac{e^{iz} - e^{-iz}}{2i}.$$

As shown, (15) and (16) coincide with the real functions $\cos x$ and $\sin x$ for $z = x$. If z is a complex number, we use these formulas to *define* the analytic functions $\cos z$ and $\sin z$. Since the exponential function is regular for all finite values of its argument, these definitions show that this is also true of the functions $\cos z$ and $\sin z$. Both $\sin z$ and $\cos z$ are therefore entire functions of z.

As far as trigonometric identities are concerned, the functions defined by (15) and (16) behave very much like the real functions $\sin x$ and $\cos x$. It will be an instructive exercise for the reader to obtain some of these identities—for example, the fact that $\sin(z + w) = \sin z \cos w + \cos z \sin w$—by means of the definitions (15), (16) and the addition theorem (11) of the exponential function. The addition formula of the sine will thus remain true for complex values of the argument, and the same statement holds for all the other trigonometric identities with which the reader is familiar. In particular, the differentiation formulas

$$\frac{d}{dz} \sin z = \cos z, \quad \frac{d}{dz} \cos z = -\sin z$$

remain valid for complex z, as a glance at (15) and (16) shows.

Setting $t = 2\pi$ in (12), we have the curious looking formula

$$e^{2\pi i} = 1.$$

If we apply (11) to the special case $w = 2\pi i$, we therefore obtain the identity

(17) $$e^{z+2\pi i} = e^z,$$

which shows that the exponential function remains unchanged if its argument z is replaced by $z + 2\pi i$. This fact is also expressed by saying that *the exponential function has the period $2\pi i$*. By repeated application of this result it is easy to see that, more generally, the function e^z has the periods $2\pi i n$, where n is an arbitrary positive or negative integer. These are, however, *all* the periods the function has. Indeed, (11) shows that the identity $e^{z+p} = e^z$ implies $e^p = 1$. If we set $p = s + it$, it follows from (10) that $e^s \cos t = 1, e^s \sin t = 0$. Using the fact that, for real t, $\sin t$ is zero only for $t = n\pi$ and that $\cos n\pi = (-1)^n$, we obtain $e^s(-1)^n = 1$. Since e^s cannot be negative we conclude that n must be an even number and that $s = 0$. Hence, $p = 2\pi i n$.

If (17) is applied to the definitions (15) and (16), it is found that $\sin (z + 2\pi) = \sin z$ and $\cos (z + 2\pi) = \cos z$. These functions have therefore the real period 2π.

EXERCISES

1. Using only the fact that a function $f(z)$ is differentiable for $z = 0$ and that, for any complex z and w, $f(z + w) = f(z)f(w)$, show that $f(z)$ must be analytic for all finite values of z, and that it must satisfy the differential equation $f'(z) = f(z)$ as well as the condition $f(0) = 1$. *Hint:* Consider the expression

$$\frac{f(z + h) - f(z)}{h}.$$

2. Use (15) and (16) to prove the trigonometric identities:

(a) $$\frac{1}{2} + \cos \theta + \cos 2\theta + \cdots + \cos n\theta = \frac{\sin (n + \frac{1}{2})\theta}{2 \sin \frac{1}{2}\theta},$$

(b) $\cos \theta + \cos 3\theta + \cdots + \cos (2n - 1)\theta = \dfrac{\sin 2n\theta}{2 \sin \theta}$,

(c) $\sin \theta + \sin 2\theta + \cdots + \sin n\theta = \dfrac{\sin \frac{1}{2}n\theta \sin \frac{1}{2}(n + 1)\theta}{\sin \frac{1}{2}\theta}$.

3. Assuming that a solution of the differential equation $f''(z) + f(z) = 0$ is completely determined by the values of $f(0)$ and $f'(0)$, prove the identity $e^{iz} = \cos z + i \sin z$ and the addition theorem $\sin (z + a) = \sin z \cos a + \cos z \sin a$.

4. Show that $|e^z| < 1$ for $\mathrm{Re}(z) < 0$ and $|e^z| > 1$ for $\mathrm{Re}(z) > 0$.

5. The hyperbolic functions $\cosh z$ and $\sinh z$ are defined by $\cosh z = \cos iz$ and $i \sinh z = \sin iz$. Show that these functions are real for real values of z, and use your result to decompose $\sin z$ and $\cos z$ into their real and imaginary parts.

6. If $z = x + iy$, show that $|\sin z|^2 = \sin^2 x + \sinh^2 y$.

7. Show that the function $\sin z$ will take the value zero only if $z = 0, \pm\pi, \pm 2\pi, \cdots$.

8. If t is a real parameter, growing from $-\infty$ to ∞, and if a,b are real constants, show that the points $z = \cos (a + it)$ and $z = \cos (t + ib)$ describe, respectively, hyperbolas and ellipses whose foci are at $z = \pm 1$.

9. If z is a point on the perimeter of the square whose corners are $\pi n(1 - i)$, $\pi n(1 + i)$, $\pi n(-1 + i)$, $\pi n(-1 - i)$, where n is a positive integer, show that $|\tan z| < M$, where M is a constant which does not depend on n, and $\tan z = \sin z/\cos z$.

10. Using (15) and (16), show that the analytic function $f(z) = \tan z$ has the addition theorem

$$f(z + w) = \frac{f(z) + f(w)}{1 - f(z)f(w)}.$$

11. Show that an analytic function $f(z)$ which has the addition theorem of the preceding exercise and for which $f(0) = 0, f'(0) = 1$, must be a solution of the differential equation

$$f'(z) = 1 + f^2(z).$$

12. If α is a complex number such that $-\dfrac{\pi}{4} \leq \mathrm{Re}(\alpha) \leq \dfrac{\pi}{4}$, show that $|\tan \alpha| \leq 1$.

5 THE LOGARITHM

Our next task is to construct an analytic function $f(z)$ which, for positive values of z, reduces to $f(x) = \log x$. According to a remark made earlier, there can exist only one analytic function with this property. We shall denote this function by the symbol $\log z$. Since the derivative of the real function $\log x$ is x^{-1}, we shall try to construct $\log z$ from the relation

(18) $$\frac{d}{dz}\,[\log z] = \frac{1}{z}.$$

Writing $f(z) = u(x, y) + iv(x, y)$ and using (2), we can replace (18) by

$$u_x + iv_x = \frac{1}{z} = \frac{\bar{z}}{|z|^2} = \frac{x - iy}{r^2}, \quad r^2 = x^2 + y^2.$$

This shows that $r^2 u_x = x$, $r^2 v_x = -y$ and, because of the Cauchy-Riemann equations (4), $r^2 v_y = x$, $r^2 u_y = y$. We now introduce polar coordinates r, θ in the xy-plane. Since $x = r\cos\theta$ and $y = r\sin\theta$, we have $x_r = r^{-1}x$, $y_r = r^{-1}y$, $x_\theta = -y$, $y_\theta = x$. In view of $u_r = u_x x_r + u_y y_r$, $u_\theta = u_x x_\theta + u_y y_\theta$ and the corresponding formulas for v_r and v_θ, we obtain

$$u_r = \frac{1}{r},\, u_\theta = 0; \quad v_r = 0,\, v_\theta = 1.$$

Accordingly, both u and v depend only on one of the variables r, θ: u is a function of r, and v is a function of θ. Since $u_r = r^{-1}$ and $v_r = 1$, we must therefore have

$$\log z = \log r + c + i(\theta - \gamma),$$

where c and γ are integration constants.

These constants are determined by the requirement that $\log z$ should coincide with the function $\log x$ if z takes the positive value x. If, in particular, we are to have $\log 1 = 0$, we find that c and γ must satisfy the relation $c + i(\theta_0 - \gamma) = 0$, where θ_0 is the argument of the number 1. Hence, $c = 0$ and $\gamma = \theta_0$. Since, as pointed out in Section 3 of Chapter I, any of the numbers 0, $\pm 2\pi$, $\pm 4\pi$, $\cdots$ may be regarded as the argument of a positive number, we thus obtain

(19) $\quad \log z = \log r + i(\theta + 2\pi n), \quad n = 0, \pm 1, \pm 2, \cdots .$

The reader will easily confirm that the real and imaginary parts of this expression satisfy the Cauchy-Riemann equations, and thus that the right-hand side of (19) is indeed an analytic function of z. The differentiation formula (18) can then be obtained by means of (2).

Formula (18) shows that the derivative of $\log z$ is not defined for $z = 0$. The origin is therefore a singular point of the function.

Formula (19) seems to suggest that there exists an infinity of different logarithmic functions, belonging to different values of n. This, however, is not the case. As we shall see, all these are—to use a term which will be explained presently—*branches* of one and the same function, and the appearance of the indeterminate integer n in (19) expresses the fact that this function is *many-valued*.

For a proper understanding of the nature of a many-valued function it is essential to make full use of the fact that an analytic function is necessarily continuous at all points at which it is regular. This continuity may also be expressed in the following, geometrically suggestive, manner: *If the point z moves along a continuous curve which does not pass through a singular point, the value of the function changes continuously.* If the curve is closed and we return to our point of departure z_0 after having traversed the curve, there are two possibilities: Either we arrive again at the same value of the function with which we started, or we do not. In the second case, we are dealing with a many-valued function, and the symbol $f(z_0)$ will have at least two different meanings.

We now apply these considerations to the study of the function $\log z$. We specialize the definition (19) by choosing $n = 0$—or, what amounts to the same thing, by setting $\log 1 = 0$—and we let the point z move in the positive direction along the circle $|z| = r$, starting from the point $(r, 0)$. Since $\log z = \log r + i\theta$, $\operatorname{Re}[\log z]$ will remain constant, and $\theta = \operatorname{Im}[\log z]$ will grow continuously. If the point z finally returns to its original position, the function $\log z$ will therefore *not* return to its original value $\log r$; evidently, its value is now $\log r + 2\pi i$. If, starting from this value, we again describe the complete circumference $|z| = r$, we similarly obtain the value $\log z = \log r + 4\pi i$. Continuing in this fashion, it becomes clear that we can reach any value $\log r + 2\pi i n$ in a continuous manner, simply by describing this circle often enough; positive values of n are obtained by letting the angle θ vary counterclockwise, and negative values by letting it vary in the opposite direction.

This shows that the different values of log z which are associated with different values of n in Formula (19) all belong to the same analytic function.   Starting from any of these values, we can obtain any other by letting the point z describe a suitable closed curve.   The latter, incidentally, does not have to be a circle. Since the possible values of the argument of a complex number differ by a multiple of 2π, it is clear that describing any closed curve, even if the latter intersects itself an arbitrary number of times, will have the effect of changing θ by the amount $2\pi n$, where n is an integer.   The only restriction on the curve is that it must not pass through the origin.   The origin is a singular point of the function log z, and log z ceases to be continuous there.   There is therefore no possibility of "continuing" the function log z along a curve passing through the point $z = 0$.

The infinitely many-valued function log z can be easily decomposed into "branches" all of which are single-valued.   All we have to do is restrict the value of θ to an interval of length 2π.   For instance, if we impose the condition $-\pi < \theta \leq \pi$ we obtain a branch which is known as *the principal value* of log z.   Geometrically, the condition $-\pi < \theta \leq \pi$ is equivalent to a prohibition of crossing the negative axis.   Another way of describing this situation is by saying that we are *cutting* the z-plane along the negative axis.   In the cut plane, the principal value of log z is single-valued. The other branches of the function log z may then be defined by the conditions $(2n - 1)\pi < \theta \leq (2n + 1)\pi$.   All of them are single-valued in the plane which is cut along the negative axis.   Crossing the cut will have the effect of passing from one branch of log z to an adjacent one.   It should be noted that the choice of the negative axis as the site of the cut is due only to reasons of convenient formulation.   Any other continuous non-selfintersecting curve which starts at the origin and goes to infinity could be used equally well for the definition of a branch of log z, provided one of the "edges" of the cut is considered as belonging to the cut plane, and the other as not belonging to it.

It is known from the calculus that the real function log x has the addition theorem log $(ab) = \log a + \log b$.   To show that, with certain precautions, this identity can be extended to complex values, we use the representation (13) for two given complex numbers z and w.   Writing $z = re^{i\theta}$, $w = Re^{i\phi}$, we have

$$\log (zw) = \log (rRe^{i\theta}e^{i\phi}) = \log (rRe^{i(\theta+\phi)}).$$

It follows therefore from (19) that

$$\log (zw) = \log (rR) + i(\theta + \phi + 2\pi n).$$

Since the logarithm of a positive number is known to have the property $\log (rR) = \log r + \log R$, this yields

$$\log (zw) = \log r + i\theta + \log R + i\phi + 2\pi in,$$

or, again by (19),

$$\log (zw) = \log z + \log w + 2\pi im,$$

where m is some integer. Since $\log (zw) + 2\pi im$ is one of the possible values of $\log (zw)$, the formula

$$\log (zw) = \log z + \log w$$

will hold, provided it is interpreted in the following manner: The sum of one of the possible values of $\log z$ and one of the possible values of $\log w$ is equal to one of the possible values of $\log (zw)$.

We finally show that, just as in the case of the corresponding real functions, the exponential function and the logarithm are inverses of each other. By this we mean that the equations

(20) $w = \log z$

and

(21) $z = e^w$

are equivalent to each other. To prove this statement we consider the analytic function $F(w) = \log (e^w)$ which, since e^w never takes the value zero, is defined for all finite values of w. By the chain rule, we have

$$F'(w) = \frac{e^w}{e^w} = 1,$$

and it follows that $F(w) = w + c$, where $c = F(0) = \log 1 = 2\pi in$, and n may be an arbitrary integer. Hence, if we set $z = e^w$, we have $w + 2\pi in = \log (e^w) = \log z$. In other words, if z and w are related by (21), they also satisfy the identity $w = \log z - 2\pi in$. Since $\log z - 2\pi in$ is one of the possible values of $\log z$, this is equivalent to (20).

It may be noted that the many-valuedness of the logarithm and the periodicity of the exponential function are related to each other. Combining (20) and (21), we have the identity

$$e^{\log z} = z.$$

If, in the manner described before, log z is continuously changed into log $z + 2\pi i$ while the point z returns to its original position, we obtain

$$e^{\log z + 2\pi i} = z = e^{\log z},$$

and thus $e^{w+2\pi i} = e^w$.

Exercises

1. If the analytic function $w = \arcsin z$ is defined by the relation $z = \sin w$, show that

$$\arcsin z = -i \log [\sqrt{1 - z^2} + iz].$$

2. If $w = \arctan z$ is defined by the relation $z = \tan w$, show that

$$\arctan z = \frac{1}{2i} \log \frac{1 + iz}{1 - iz}.$$

3. Using the formula just obtained, show that

$$\arctan \left(\frac{z + w}{1 - zw} \right) = \arctan z + \arctan w,$$

provided the values of the many-valued function arctan are properly taken.

4. Use the results of Exercises 1 and 2 to obtain the differentiation formulas

$$\frac{d}{dz} \arcsin z = \frac{1}{\sqrt{1 - z^2}}, \quad \frac{d}{dz} \arctan z = \frac{1}{1 + z^2}.$$

Where are the singular points of these functions located?

5. If $|z| = 1$ (but $z \neq \pm i$), show that the possible values of Re $[\arctan z]$ are $\pi(n \pm \frac{1}{4})$, where n is an integer.

6. If $f(z)$ is an analytic function for which $f(z) \neq 0$, show that

$$\frac{\partial}{\partial z} [\log |f(z)|] = \frac{1}{2} \frac{f'(z)}{f(z)}.$$

7. If z and w are complex numbers whose real parts are positive, show that the identity log $(zw) = \log z + \log w$ will be valid if in all cases the principal parts of the logarithms are taken.

8. Show that, for real θ,

$$\arg \left(1 - e^{i\theta}\right) = \frac{\theta}{2} + \pi\left(2n - \frac{1}{2}\right),$$

where n is an integer. Show also that

$$\left|1 - e^{i\theta}\right| = 2\left|\sin\frac{\theta}{2}\right|.$$

6   THE FUNCTION z^α

We can use the results of the two preceding sections to give a definition of the function z^α in the case in which α is an arbitrary complex number. This function will be defined by

$$(22) \qquad\qquad z^\alpha = e^{\alpha \log z}.$$

In view of (20) and (21), this is equivalent to

$$(23) \qquad\qquad \log\left(z^\alpha\right) = \alpha \log z.$$

Since, for real α and positive z, (23) reduces to the familiar formula for the logarithm of a power, the definition (22) is thus compatible with the elementary properties of powers and logarithms.

Because of the many-valuedness of the logarithm, the function z^α will in general also be many-valued. Nonetheless, the familiar rules $z^\alpha z^\beta = z^{\alpha+\beta}$ and $(z^\alpha)^\beta = z^{\alpha\beta}$ remain true, provided that in each case suitable branches of the function (22) are taken. The first of these identities follows from

$$z^\alpha z^\beta = e^{\alpha \log z}e^{\beta \log z} = e^{(\alpha+\beta)\log z} = z^{\alpha+\beta},$$

and the second from

$$\left(z^\alpha\right)^\beta = e^{\beta \log\left(z^\alpha\right)} = e^{\beta(\alpha \log z)} = e^{\alpha\beta \log z} = z^{\alpha\beta}.$$

In order to get a clear idea of the many-valuedness of the function (22), we denote the principal value of the logarithm by Log z and write $\log z = \text{Log } z + 2\pi i n$, where n may be an arbitrary integer. Substituting this in (22), we obtain

$$z^\alpha = e^{\alpha \text{ Log } z}e^{2\pi i n\alpha} = P[z^\alpha]e^{2\pi i n\alpha},$$

where we use the symbol $P[z^\alpha]$ to denote the principal value of the function z^α.   The different values of z^α can therefore be obtained from the principal value by multiplication with the factor $e^{2\pi i n \alpha}(n = \pm1, \pm2, \cdots)$, and this shows that in general the function z^α will have an infinity of different values.

There are, however, cases in which only a finite number of these values are actually different from each other.   Evidently, these correspond to the cases in which only a finite number of the values $e^{2\pi i n \alpha}$, $n = 0, \pm1, \pm2, \cdots$, are different from each other. If this occurs, there must exist two different integers n and n' such that $e^{2\pi i n} = e^{2\pi i n'}$, or, in view of the addition theorem of the exponential function, $e^{2\pi i \alpha (n - n')} = 1$.   Since e^z takes the value 1 only if $z = 2\pi i m$, where m is an integer, this implies that $\alpha(n - n') = m$. Hence, α must be a rational number.   Conversely, if α is a rational number of the form m/n (where m and n have no common factor and $n \geq 1$), the set

$$e^{2\pi i (m/n) k}, \quad k = 0, \pm1, \pm2, \cdots$$

clearly contains only n different numbers.   The latter may be obtained, for instance, by choosing the values $k = 0, 1, \cdots, n - 1$. Our result is, therefore, that the function z^α is n-valued if, and only if, α is a rational number of the form m/n, where m and n have no common factors.   If α is not a rational number, z^α has an infinity of different values.

It is instructive to observe the change of the value of z^α as the point z describes a circle about the origin; just as in the case of the function $\log z$, this will make it clear how the various branches of the function z^α are connected with each other.   As described in detail in the preceding section, a given value $\log z$ will continuously change into $\log z + 2\pi i$ if z returns to its former position after describing a complete circle about the origin in the positive direction.   As (22) shows, a given value z^α will at the same time change into $z^\alpha e^{2\pi i \alpha}$.   Repeating this procedure, we obtain the value $z^\alpha e^{4\pi i \alpha}$, $z^\alpha e^{6\pi i \alpha}$, etc., and it is easy to see that we can reach any particular value of the function z^α from any other value by letting z move over a closed curve which surrounds the origin in a suitable way. As in the case of the logarithm, such a curve must not pass through the origin since—except if α is a non-negative integer—the origin is a singular point of the function z^α.   Indeed, the definition of a regular point contains the assumption that the function be single-valued in a neighborhood of this point and, as the preceding discussion shows, z^α cannot be single-valued in a neighborhood of $z = 0$

if α is not an integer.   If α is a negative integer, the function z^α is not continuous at $z = 0$ and therefore also not regular.

Exercises

1. Show that the derivative of the function z^α, defined by (22), is $\alpha z^{\alpha-1}$.

2. Use (22) to obtain De Moivre's formula of Section 3, Chapter I.

3. Generalize De Moivre's formula to the case in which n is an arbitrary complex number.

4. Use (22) to prove Formula (16) of Section 3, Chapter I.

5. The curves with the polar equation $r = ae^{b\theta}$ (a,b real) are called logarithmic spirals.   Show that the curves determined by

$$|z^\alpha| = \text{const.}$$

and by

$$\arg (z^\alpha) = \text{const.},$$

where α is an arbitrary complex number, are logarithmic spirals.

7 RIEMANN SURFACES

In the study of the functions $\log z$ and z^α we used two different devices in order to achieve a better understanding of the nature of a many-valued function.   The first of these was the idea of the cut—often also called *branch-cut*—which, if suitably applied to the z-plane, makes it possible to single out a single-valued branch of the function.   The second was the idea of observing the manner in which the value of $f(z)$ changes if z returns to its point of departure after continuously describing certain closed curves. This procedure provided information as to how the various branches of the function are connected with each other.

The best method for visualizing the behavior of a many-valued function $f(z)$ is provided by the *Riemann surface* of $f(z)$, a geometric construction which combines the advantages of both the devices just mentioned.   To illustrate this construction in a simple case, let us consider the function $f(z) = z^{1/n}$ which, as shown in the preceding section, has n different values for any given z (except, of course, for $z = 0$). Accordingly, $f(z)$ has n branches. Each of these branches is single-valued if z is restricted to the region obtained by cutting the z-plane along the negative axis. The idea leading to the construction of the Riemann surface of $f(z)$ is now the following: To each of the n branches of $f(z)$ we assign a replica of the cut plane, in which it is single-valued. These cut planes can be ordered according to the value of $z^{1/n}$ at a given point z, by associating the value $e^{2\pi im/n}P[z^{1/n}]$—where $P[z^{1/n}]$ is the principal value of $z^{1/n}$—with the plane of index m. There will thus be cut planes corresponding to the numbers $m = 1, 2, \cdots, n$. We now stack all these cut planes upon each other in such a fashion that the $(m + 1)$st plane lies immediately on top of the mth plane, and the corresponding points z in each plane have exactly the same position.

If we let the point z move along a closed curve which surrounds the origin in the positive direction, we pass from the given—say the mth—branch of the function to the $(m + 1)$st branch. Geometrically, we may describe this situation by saying that the upper edge of the cut in the mth plane is connected with the lower edge of the cut in the $(m + 1)$st plane. The two planes will accordingly be regarded as "glued" together at these edges along the entire negative axis. If we connect in this manner all pairs of neighboring planes, we obtain a connected surface which consists of n sheets and which has only two boundaries: The lower edge of the first sheet and the upper edge of the nth sheet. In order to see how to treat these boundaries, we observe that n complete circuits about the origin will return us to the original value of the function. To get a complete description of the behavior of the function it is therefore necessary to connect the upper edge of the cut in the nth sheet and the lower edge of the cut in the first sheet. If this is done, no free edges remain: The surface is closed. It should be noted that, in a physical model of such a surface, this last connection would have to cross all the previous connections. It is therefore impossible to build a paper model of a Riemann surface. This, of course, in no way affects the validity of our construction; all we are concerned with is, so to speak, a set of "traffic regulations" which tell us how to proceed whenever we reach one of the edges of the various cuts.

The closed surface which we have constructed is *the Riemann surface of the function* $z^{1/n}$. On this surface, the function $z^{1/n}$ is single-valued since, evidently, to each point on the surface belongs precisely one value of the function. This many-sheeted surface— and not the z-plane—is to be regarded as the true domain of definition of the function $z^{1/n}$.

The origin plays a special role in the Riemann surface just described. Unlike the other points, each of which lies on only one sheet, the origin belongs to *all* the sheets of the surface. Such a point, which belongs to more than one sheet of a Riemann surface, is called a *branch-point* of the surface. If it belongs to k sheets $(k > 1)$, we speak of a branch-point of order $k - 1$. In our particular case, the origin is thus a branch-point of order $n - 1$. A moment's reflection will make it clear to the reader that the two end-points of a branch-cut necessarily are branch-points of the surface. Since, in our case, all branch-cuts extend from $z = 0$ to $z = \infty$, the point at infinity is therefore also a branch-point and its order is likewise $n - 1$.

Next to the z-plane itself, the simplest of all Riemann surfaces is the surface of the function $\sqrt{z}$. It consists of two replicas of the z-plane which are crosswise connected along the negative axis. If, at a point z on one of the sheets, the function has the value z, its value at the corresponding point of the other sheet is $-z$. A slightly different, but basically similar surface is that belonging to the function $f(z) = \sqrt{z^2 - 1}$. To localize the branch-points of this surface, we write $f(z) = \sqrt{z + 1}\sqrt{z - 1}$. Since the only possible branch-points of the square root are the points at which the expression under the radical is either 0 or ∞, only the points $z = \pm 1$ and $z = \infty$ need be considered. The latter, however, can be immediately ruled out. We may write $f(z) = z\sqrt{1 - z^{-2}}$ and, since for large $|z|$ the value of $|z|^{-2}$ is small, the expression under the radical is different from either 0 or ∞ if z approaches ∞. We thus have two branch-points of first order—or, as we also say, *simple branch-points*—at the points $z = \pm 1$. The Riemann surface of the function $\sqrt{z^2 - 1}$ is therefore to be constructed in the following manner: We take two replicas of the *extended* plane and cut them along the linear segment $-1 \leq z \leq 1$; along this segment, we connect the upper edge of the cut in each of the planes with the lower edge of the cut in the other plane.

So far, we have considered functions which, for a given value of z, can take only a finite number of values. Accordingly, the behavior of the functions was adequately described with the help of Riemann surfaces which possess a finite number of sheets. For a function, such as $\log z$, which is capable of taking an infinity of different values for the same value of z, a Riemann surface with infinitely many sheets is needed. The construction of the surface of $\log z$ proceeds basically in the same way as in the case of $z^{1/n}$. The only difference is that we now have infinitely many sheets—associated with the numbers $\cdots, -2, -1, 0, 1, 2, \cdots$—and that each sheet has now two neighbors and is connected with them in the manner described above. It is interesting to note that this surface has only two boundary points, the points $z = 0$ and $z = \infty$. All other possible boundary points would have to lie on the ray $-\infty < z < 0$. But, since each sheet of the Riemann surface is connected with its two neighbors along the two edges of the cut along the negative axis, these points are—in all sheets—in the interior of the surface.

The points $z = 0$ and $z = \infty$—the end-points of the branch-cuts in all sheets—show a highly singular behavior. They are known as *logarithmic branch-points*. The branch-points considered earlier, which belong only to a finite number of sheets, are often referred to as *algebraic branch-points*.

EXERCISES

1. Let $R(s, t)$ be a rational function of the variables s and t (i.e., $R(s, t) = P(s, t)/Q(s, t)$, where P and Q are polynomials). If the function $f(z)$ is single-valued on a Riemann surface R, show that the same is true of the function $R[z, f(z)]$.

2. If $R(s, t)$ is a rational function of s and t, show that the function $R[z, \sqrt{z^2 - 1}]$ can be brought into the form $R_1(z) + \sqrt{z^2 - 1}\, R_2(z)$, where $R(z)$ and $R_2(z)$ are rational functions of z.

3. Show that the values at $z = \infty$ of the function $f(z) = z + \sqrt{z^2 - 1}$ are $f(\infty) = \infty$ in one sheet of the Riemann surface of the function, and $f(\infty) = 0$ in the other sheet.

4. If the positive integer n is an integral multiple of the positive integer m, show that the function $z^{1/m}$ is single-valued on the Riemann surface of the function $z^{1/n}$.

5. If the numbers a_1, a_2, a_3, a_4 are all distinct, show that the function $\sqrt{(z - a_1)(z - a_2)(z - a_3)(z - a_4)}$ is made single-valued by cutting the z-plane along two arcs, having no points in common, which connect a_1 with a_2 and a_3 with a_4, respectively. Use this fact to construct a two-sheeted Riemann surface for the function.

6. Show that the Riemann surface of the function $\sqrt{(z - a_1)(z - a_2)(z - a_3)}$ is of the same general character as the surface obtained in the preceding exercise, the only difference being that the role of the point $z = a_4$ is now played by the point $z = \infty$.

7. Show that the function $\log[(z - a)/(z - b)]$ is single-valued in a region obtained by cutting the z-plane along an arc connecting the points $z = a$ and $z = b$. Use this fact to construct an infinitely many-sheeted Riemann surface for the function.

8. The point $z = 0$ is a singular point of the function $f(z) = z(1 + \sqrt{z})$, although $f'(0)$ seems to exist. How do you account for this phenomenon?

8 CONVERGENCE OF COMPLEX SERIES

The analytic functions considered so far were all obtained by extending some of the real functions known from elementary analysis to complex values of the variable. Since the class of functions obtainable in this way is quite narrow, we need more general procedures for generating analytic functions of the complex variable z. As we shall show in the following section, a *power series* of the form

$$(24) \qquad a_0 + a_1 z + a_2 z^2 + \cdots + a_n z^n + \cdots,$$

or slightly more generally,

$$(25) \quad a_0 + a_1(z - a) + a_2(z - a)^2 + \cdots + a_n(z - a)^n + \cdots,$$

where $a_0, a_1, \cdots$ are complex constants, represents an analytic function in a neighborhood in which it converges. Power series provide therefore a convenient means for the construction of new analytic functions.

Before we can begin the study of power series, we have to define what we mean by the convergence of an infinite series $\alpha_1 + \alpha_2 + \cdots$ whose terms α_n are complex numbers. In doing so, we shall assume that the reader is familiar with the basic facts concerning the convergence of series of real numbers.

If $\alpha_n = b_n + ic_n$, where b_n and c_n are real numbers, the series $\Sigma \alpha_n$ is said to converge if, and only if, the two real series Σb_n and Σc_n converge. If the two real series have the sums B and C, respectively, the sum of the complex series is defined to be $B + iC$. The reader will recall that the formal definition of the convergence of the real series Σb_n runs as follows: The series $b_1 + b_2 + \cdots$, whose partial sums $b_1 + b_2 + \cdots + b_n$ are denoted by B_n, is said to converge to the sum B if, and only if, for any given positive number ϵ it is always possible to find a positive integer N such that $|B - B_n| < \epsilon$ provided $n > N$. It is easy to obtain a similar convergence criterion for series of complex terms. If we set $c_1 + c_2 + \cdots + c_n = C_n$ and $\alpha_1 + \alpha_2 + \cdots + \alpha_n = A_n$, the definition of convergence given above can be shown to be equivalent to the following criterion.

The complex series $\alpha_1 + \alpha_2 + \cdots$, *whose partial sums are denoted by* A_n, *converges to a complex number* A *if, and only if, for any given positive number* ϵ *it is always possible to find a positive integer* N *such that* $|A - A_n| < \epsilon$ *provided that* $n > N$.

Indeed, if the two real series converge we have $|B - B_n| < \epsilon$ and $|C - C_n| < \epsilon$ for $n > N$, and thus

$$|A - A_n| = |B - B_n + i(C - C_n)| \leq |B - B_n| + |C - C_n| < 2\epsilon.$$

Conversely, if $|A - A_n| < \epsilon$ it follows from

$$(B - B_n)^2 + (C - C_n)^2 = |A - A_n|^2$$

that $|B - B_n| < \epsilon$ and $|C - C_n| < \epsilon$. This proves the criterion.

The reader will also recall that the convergence of a real series may be defined without explicit reference to its sum. This is done by replacing the condition $|B - B_n| < \epsilon$ by the requirement that $|B_n - B_m| < \epsilon$ if both n and m are larger than N. With the help of the preceding argument, this can be translated into the following convergence criterion for complex series.

If A_n *denotes the nth partial sum of the complex series* $\alpha_1 + \alpha_2 + \cdots$, *the series will converge to a complex number if, and only if, for any given positive* ϵ *it is always possible to find a positive integer* N *such that* $|A_n - A_m| < \epsilon$ *provided* $n > N$ *and* $m > N$.

Since $\alpha_n = A_n - A_{n-1}$ it follows, in particular, that for a converging series $\Sigma \alpha_n$ we must have $\lim |\alpha_n| = 0$ for $n \to \infty$.

The series $\alpha_1 + \alpha_2 + \cdots$ is said to converge absolutely, or to be *absolutely convergent*, if the sum of the absolute values $|\alpha_1| + |\alpha_2| + \cdots$ converges. This is a stronger requirement than mere convergence. Indeed, if we set $D_n = |\alpha_1| + |\alpha_2| + \cdots + |\alpha_n|$, we have (for $n > m$)

$$|A_n - A_m| = |\alpha_{m+1} + \alpha_{m+2} + \cdots + \alpha_n|$$
$$\leq |\alpha_{m+1}| + |\alpha_{m+2}| + \cdots + |\alpha_n| = D_n - D_m,$$

and the preceding criterion shows that absolute convergence implies ordinary convergence.

If the terms of the series under discussion are not constants, but functions of a complex variable z—such as, for instance, the series (24) and (25)—the concept of *uniform convergence* becomes important. The definition of uniform convergence in the complex case is formally identical with that given in the real case.

If the functions $f_1(z), f_2(z), \cdots$ are defined in a region D, the series $f_1(z) + f_2(z) + \cdots$ is said to converge in D uniformly to the function $f(z)$ if, for any given positive ϵ, we can find a positive integer N such that $|f(z) - f_n(z)| < \epsilon$ for $n > N$ and any point z in D.

More informally, we may say that the convergence is uniform if, for a given ϵ, the same N will serve for all points z of D. In analogy to what happens in the case of real functions, the assumption of uniform convergence has the following important consequence.

If the functions $f_1(z), f_2(z), \cdots$ are continuous in a domain D, and if the series

$$f(z) = \sum_{n=1}^{\infty} f_n(z)$$

converges uniformly in D, then the sum $f(z)$ is again a continuous function in D.

To prove this result, we set

$$\sum_{k=1}^{n} f_k(z) = s_n(z)$$

and we write $f(z) = s_n(z) + r_n(z)$, where $r_n(z)$ is the nth remainder of the series. If z_0 is the point at which we wish to prove the continuity of $f(z)$ and z_1 is a point nearby, we have

$$f(z_1) - f(z_0) = s_n(z_1) - s_n(z_0) + r_n(z_1) - r_n(z_0),$$

and therefore,

$$|f(z_1) - f(z_0)| \leq |s_n(z_1) - s_n(z_0)| + |r_n(z_1)| + |r_n(z_0)|.$$

Given a small positive ϵ, it follows from the uniform convergence that, for sufficiently large n, $|r_n(z)| < \epsilon$, where z may be any point of D.   Hence,

$$|f(z_0) - f(z_1)| \leq |s_n(z_0) - s_n(z_1)| + 2\epsilon$$

for all z_0 and z_1 in D.   Since $s_n(z)$ is a finite sum of continuous functions, it is itself continuous.   Hence, there exists a positive δ such that $|s_n(z_0) - s_n(z_1)| < \epsilon$ if $|z_1 - z_0| < \delta$.   For such values of z_1 we obtain $|f(z_0) - f(z_1)| < 3\epsilon$, and this shows that $f(z)$ is continuous at the point $z = z_0$.

We shall see later (Chap. IV, Sec. 1) that the sum of a uniformly converging series of *analytic* functions is not only continuous but also analytic.

Exercises

1. Show that the series

$$1 + z + z^2 + \cdots + z^n + \cdots$$

converges for all values z in the disk $|z| < 1$, but that the convergence is not uniform in this domain.

2. Let D be a bounded region which has no points in common with any of the disks $|z - n| < \epsilon$, where ϵ is a small positive number and n is an integer.   Show that the series

$$f(z) = \sum_{n=-\infty}^{\infty} \frac{1}{(z - n)^2}$$

converges uniformly in D, and conclude that $f(z)$ is continuous for all finite values of z other than $z = n$, $n = 0, \pm 1, \pm 2, \cdots$.

3. If $f(z)$ is the function defined in the preceding exercise, show that the series

$$g(z) = -2 \sum_{n=-\infty}^{\infty} \frac{1}{(z - n)^3}$$

converges for non-integral values of z, and that

$$\frac{f(z + h) - f(z)}{h} - g(z) = h \sum_{n=-\infty}^{\infty} \frac{3(z - n) + 2h}{(z - n)^3(z - n + h)^2},$$

provided $z + h$ is not equal to an integer. Use this identity to prove that $f(z)$ is an analytic function which is regular for all finite values z such that $z \neq n$, $n = 0, \pm 1, \pm 2, \cdots$.

4. If D is a bounded region contained in the half-plane $\mathrm{Re}(z) > 1 + \epsilon$, where ϵ is a positive number, show that the series

$$f(z) = \sum_{n=1}^{\infty} \frac{1}{n^z}$$

converges uniformly in D and that, as a result, the function $f(z)$ is continuous at all finite points z such that $\mathrm{Re}(z) > 1$. Show that the series does *not* converge uniformly in the domain $\mathrm{Re}(z) > 1$.

9 POWER SERIES

Turning now to the consideration of power series, we observe that the series (25) assumes the form (24) if $z - a$ is replaced by z. It is therefore sufficient to study the properties of the series (24); the corresponding properties of (25) will then be obtained by substituting $z - a$ for z.

For $z = 0$, any power series of the form (24) may be regarded as convergent and as having the sum a_0. To be of any interest, however, the series must be assumed to converge also for at least one point z_0 other than 0. The following result—which we formulate for series of the form (25)—shows the implications of this assumption.

If the power series (25) converges for $z = z_0$, where $z_0 \neq a$, it necessarily converges absolutely at all points of the circular disk $|z - a| < |z_0 - a|$. In any concentric closed disk $|z - a| \leq r < |z_0 - a|$, the convergence is, moreover, uniform.

Geometrically speaking, the series converges at all points in the interior of the circle of center a which passes through the point z_0.

It is sufficient to prove this result for $a = 0$, i.e., for the series (24). If z is a point such that $|z| < |z_0|$, we have

$$\sum_{k=m+1}^{n} |a_k z^k| = \sum_{k=m+1}^{n} |a_k z_0^k| \left| \frac{z}{z^0} \right|^k.$$

The numbers $a_k z_0^k$ are the terms of a converging series, and there will therefore exist a positive constant M such that $|a_k z_0^k| < M$ for all k. Indeed, as pointed out in the preceding section, the convergence of $\Sigma \alpha_k$ implies that $\alpha_k \to 0$ for $k \to \infty$. We may thus find an integer k_0 such that $|\alpha_k| < 1$ if $k > k_0$. Since there are only a finite number of terms α_k with $k \leq k_0$, these terms have a common bound, and the assertion follows. If ρ is such that $|z| = \rho|z_0|$, we therefore have

$$(26) \qquad \sum_{k=m+1}^{n} |a_k z^k| \leq M \sum_{k=m+1}^{n} \rho^k.$$

Since $\rho < 1$, the geometric series $\sum_{k=0}^{\infty} \rho^k$ converges, and the right-hand side of (26) can therefore be made arbitrarily small by taking m large enough. Hence, the same is true of the left-hand side of (26), and it follows that $\sum_{k=0}^{\infty} |a_k z^k|$ converges.

The inequality (26) shows, moreover, that the series (24) converges uniformly for $|z| \leq r < |z_0|$. If $s_n(z)$ denotes the nth partial sum of the series, an application of (26) yields the estimate

$$|s_n(z) - s_m(z)| = \left| \sum_{k=m+1}^{n} a_k z^k \right| \leq \sum_{k=m+1}^{n} |a_k z^k|$$

$$\leq M \sum_{k=m+1}^{n} \left| \frac{z}{z_0} \right|^k \leq M \sum_{k=m+1}^{n} \left(\frac{r}{|z_0|} \right)^k.$$

Since $r < |z_0|$, the last expression can be made smaller than ϵ by choosing m large enough. As this value of m depends only on r, this estimate is valid for all z such that $|z| \leq r$, and the convergence is therefore uniform throughout this closed disk.

The fact that the convergence of the series (25) at a point z_0 implies the convergence at all points of the disk $|z - a| < |z_0 - a|$, shows that we have the following alternative: *If a power series* (25) *converges at a point* $z_0 \neq a$, *then it either converges for all finite values of* z, *or else there exists a positive number* R *such that* (25) *converges for* $|z - a| < R$ *and diverges for* $|z - a| > R$. R is called the *radius of convergence* of the power series, and the circle of center a and radius R is its *circle of convergence*. No general statement can be made regarding the convergence of the series at the points of the circumference $|z - a| = R$. The series may converge at some, or all, or none of these points.

Since a power series converges uniformly in any closed disk

which is inside, and concentric with, the circle of convergence, it follows from the last result of the preceding section that the sum of a power series is a continuous function in the interior of the circle of convergence.   However, even more is true.   We shall show that, *in the interior of its circle of convergence, a power series represents an analytic function of the complex variable z.*   We shall carry through the proof of this result for the series of the form (24); the substitution of $z - a$ for z will then yield the general result.

In order to prove that the sum of the power series

$$(27) \qquad f(z) = \sum_{n=0}^{\infty} a_n z^n, \quad |z| < R,$$

is a regular analytic function of z, we have to show that $f(z)$ has a derivative $f'(z)$ at all points z in the interior of the circle of convergence $|z| < R$.   We shall show, moreover, that $f'(z)$ is given by the power series,

$$(28) \qquad f'(z) = \sum_{n=0}^{\infty} n a_n z^{n-1}.$$

In other words, *the derivative of a power series can be found by means of term-by-term differentiation.*

We first note that the series (28) likewise converges for $|z| < R$.   Indeed, if $|z| = r < r_0 = |z_0| < R$, we have

$$\sum_{k=m+1}^{n} |k a_k z^k| = \sum_{k=m+1}^{n} |a_k z_0^k| k \left| \frac{z}{z_0} \right|^k.$$

The convergence of (27) for $z = z_0$ implies that $|a_k z_0^k| < M$ for all k. Hence,

$$\sum_{k=m+1}^{n} |k a_k z^k| < M \sum_{k=m+1}^{n} k \left(\frac{r}{r_0} \right)^k.$$

Since $r r_0^{-1} < 1$, and since the series $\Sigma k \rho^k$ converges for $0 < \rho < 1$, this proves the convergence of (28) for all z such that $|z| < R$.

Let now h be a complex number such that $r + |h| < \rho < R$, and denote the absolute value of h by ϵ.   We then have

$$\left| \frac{(z+h)^n - z^n}{h} - n z^{n-1} \right| = \left| \frac{n(n-1)}{1 \cdot 2} z^{n-2} h + \cdots + h^{n-1} \right|$$

$$\leq \frac{n(n-1)}{1 \cdot 2} r^{n-2} \epsilon + \cdots + \epsilon^{n-1} = \frac{(r + \epsilon)^n - r^n}{\epsilon} - n r^{n-1}.$$

If we write

$$g(z) = \sum_{n=0}^{\infty} n a_n z^{n-1},$$

it follows therefore that

$$\left| \frac{f(z+h) - f(z)}{h} - g(z) \right| = \left| \sum_{n=0}^{\infty} a_n \left[\frac{(z+h)^n - z^n}{h} - nz^{n-1} \right] \right|$$

$$\leq \sum_{n=0}^{\infty} |a_n| \left[\frac{(r+\epsilon)^n - r^n}{\epsilon} - nr^{n-1} \right]$$

$$= \sum_{n=0}^{\infty} |a_n| \rho^n \left[\frac{\left(\frac{r+\epsilon}{\rho}\right)^n - \left(\frac{r}{\rho}\right)^n}{\epsilon} - \frac{n}{r}\left(\frac{r}{\rho}\right)^n \right].$$

Since, for $0 < s < 1$, $\sum_{n=0}^{\infty} s^n = (1-s)^{-1}$ and $\sum_{n=0}^{\infty} ns^{n-1} = (1-s)^{-2}$, and since $|a_n|\rho^n < M$, this shows that

$$\left| \frac{f(z+h) - f(z)}{h} - g(z) \right|$$

$$\leq M \left\{ \frac{1}{\epsilon}\left[\frac{\rho}{\rho - r + \epsilon} - \frac{\rho}{\rho - r} \right] - \frac{\rho}{(\rho - r)^2} \right\} = \frac{M\epsilon}{(\rho - r)^2(\rho - r - \epsilon)}.$$

For $\epsilon = |h| \to 0$, the last expression tends to zero. In view of (1), this means that $f'(z) = g(z)$, and we have thus proved that the derivative of (27) exists and is given by (28).

Since the derivative of a power series is again a power series with the same circle of convergence, we can now differentiate the second series in order to obtain the second derivative of the original series. By repeating this process a sufficient number of times, we find that *a power series has derivatives of all orders. All these derivatives are again power series which have the same circle of convergence as the original series.* The explicit form of these series is found by the repeated application of term-by-term differentiation.

The fact that the power series

$$f(z) = \sum_{n=0}^{\infty} a_n(z-a)^n, \quad |z-a| < R,$$

has derivatives of all order makes it possible to compute the coefficient a_n by differentiating the function $f(z)$ n times and then setting $z = a$. This shows that $f^{(n)}(a) = n!a_n$. The original power series for $f(z)$ may therefore be replaced by

$$f(z) = \sum_{n=0}^{\infty} \frac{f^{(n)}(a)}{n!}(z-a)^n.$$

Thus, *a power series is the Taylor series of the function represented by it.*

It follows from the results of this section that all Taylor expansions

$$f(x) = \sum_{n=0}^{\infty} a_n (x - a)^n$$

(x, a, a_n real) known from the real calculus give rise to analytic functions of the complex variable z. In fact, all we have to do to obtain these functions is replace the real variable x by the complex variable z. If the interval of convergence of the real series was $|x - a| < R$, the complex series will converge for all z in the disk $|z - a| < R$, and it will represent there an analytic function $f(z)$. At the intersection of this disk with the real axis, this function evidently coincides with the real function $f(x)$ given by the original Taylor expansion.

For example, consider the series

$$e^x = 1 + x + \frac{x^2}{2!} + \frac{x^3}{3!} + \cdots$$

which, in the real calculus, is shown to converge for all real values of x. This series leads to the power series

$$f(z) = 1 + z + \frac{z^2}{2!} + \frac{z^3}{z!} + \cdots,$$

which, by our results, converges for all finite values of z. Hence, $f(z)$ is an analytic funcion which is regular for all finite values of z. Computing the derivative $f'(z)$ by differentiating the series term by term, we find the identity $f'(z) = f(z)$. Since it was shown in Section 4 that the only analytic function which satisfies this identity, and for which $f(0) = 1$, is the exponential function e^z, this proves that e^z has the power series expansion

(29) $$e^z = 1 + z + \frac{z^2}{2!} + \frac{z^3}{3!} + \cdots$$

for all finite values of z.

With the help of (29), and the definitions (15) and (16), we can find the power series expansions of the analytic functions $\cos z$ and $\sin z$. If we substitute $\pm iz$ for z in (29), we obtain

$$e^{\pm iz} = 1 - \frac{z^2}{2!} + \frac{z^4}{4!} - + \cdots \pm i \left[z - \frac{z^3}{3!} + \frac{z^5}{5!} - + \cdots \right],$$

and it thus follows from (15) and (16) that

$$\cos z = 1 - \frac{z^2}{2!} + \frac{z^4}{4!} - + \cdots,$$

$$\sin z = z - \frac{z^3}{3!} + \frac{z^5}{5!} - + \cdots.$$

Both of these series converge for all finite values of z.

As another example, consider the power series

$$f(z) = z - 1 - \frac{(z-1)^2}{2} + \frac{(z-1)^3}{3} - \frac{(z-1)^4}{4} + - \cdots.$$

Since the absolute value of the nth term is smaller than $|z - 1|^n$, the series will converge—and thus represent an analytic function—for $|z - 1| < 1$. Its derivative is

$$f'(z) = 1 - (z - 1) + (z - 1)^2 - (z - 1)^3 + - \cdots.$$

For $z = x$, this is a geometric progression with the ratio $-(x - 1)$. For $|x - 1| < 1$, this series converges and we thus find that, for $z = x$, $-1 < x - 1 < 1$, $f'(z)$ reduces to $[1 + (x - 1)]^{-1}$, i.e., to x^{-1}. In Section 5 it was shown that the only analytic function whose derivative reduces to x^{-1} for real x is the function $\log z$. Hence,

$$(30) \quad \log z = z - 1 - \frac{(z-1)^2}{2} + \frac{(z-1)^3}{3} - + \cdots, \quad |z - 1| < 1.$$

In its circle of convergence, the sum of a power series is evidently a single-valued function. It is therefore clear that the series (30) can represent only one particular branch of the function $\log z$. Since, for $z = 1$, the series has the sum 0, (30) is found to be a power series expansion of the principal value of the function $\log z$.

We close this section with a derivation of Cauchy's rule for the determination of the radius of convergence of a power series.

The radius of convergence of the power series

$$(31) \qquad a_0 + a_1(z - a) + a_2(z - a)^2 + \cdots$$

is

$$R = \frac{1}{A},$$

where

$$A = \limsup_{n \to \infty} \sqrt[n]{|a_n|}.$$

For a fixed value of z, we have

$$\limsup_{n \to \infty} \sqrt[n]{|a_n(z - a)^n|} = A|z - a|.$$

If $|z - a| > A^{-1}$, there will therefore exist an infinity of numbers n such that $\sqrt[n]{|a_n(z - a)^n|} > 1$, i.e., $|a_n(z - a)^n| > 1$. We thus cannot have $\lim_{n \to \infty} a_n(z - a)^n = 0$, and it follows that the series (31) cannot converge for such values of z.

On the other hand, if $|z - a| < A^{-1}$ we can find an integer N such that, for $n > N$, $\sqrt[n]{|a_n(z - a)^n|} < t$, where $A|z - a| < t < 1$. For $n > N$, the terms of the series (31) are therefore smaller in absolute value than the corresponding terms of the converging geometric progression $1 + t + t^2 + \cdots$, $0 < t < 1$. Hence, the series (31) will converge for $|z - a| < A^{-1}$.

Exercises

1. If the power series $f(z) = \sum_{n=0}^{\infty} a_n z^n$ and $g(z) = \sum_{n=0}^{\infty} b_n z^n$ both converge for $|z| < R$, show that the series $h(z) = \sum_{n=0}^{\infty} c_n z^n$, where $c_n = \sum_{\nu=0}^{n} a_\nu b_{n-\nu}$, also converges for $|z| < R$, and that $h(z) = f(z)g(z)$.

2. Assuming that the function $\tan z$ has a power series expansion of the form $a_0 + a_1 z + a_2 z + \cdots$, use the result of the preceding exercise and the identity $\sin z = \tan z \cdot \cos z$ to obtain the first three non-vanishing terms of the series.

3. Using the binomial expansion of $(z + w)^n$, prove the addition theorem $e^{z+w} = e^z e^w$ by expanding e^{z+w} according to (29) and rearranging the series in a suitable manner.

4. Find a power series expansion for the function $e^z \cos z$. *Hint:* Express $\cos z$ by means of exponentials.

5. Find a power series of the form (24) which satisfies the differential equation $zf''(z) + f'(z) + zf(z) = 0$ and the condition $f(0) = 1$. Show that this series converges for all finite values of z.

6. Find the most general power series (involving two arbitrary constants) which satisfies the differential equation $f''(z) + f(z) = 0$.

7. Show that

$$f(z) = \sum_{n=0}^{\infty} z^{2^n}$$

is the only power series of the form (24) which solves the functional equation $f(z) = z + f(z^2)$.

8. Assuming that the principal branch of the function z^α discussed in Section 6 has a power series expansion of the form $a_0 + a_1(z - 1) + a_2(z - 1)^2 + \cdots$, show that $a_0 = 1$ and that

$$a_n = \frac{\alpha(\alpha - 1)(\alpha - 2) \cdots (\alpha - n + 1)}{n!}, \quad n \geq 1$$

9. If m is a positive integer, show that the coefficients a_n of the power series expansion

$$\left(1 + \frac{z}{m}\right)^m = a_0 + a_1 z + a_2 z^2 + \cdots$$

are not larger than the corresponding coefficients of the expansion (29).

III

COMPLEX

INTEGRATION

1 LINE INTEGRALS

The properties of analytic functions discussed in the preceding chapter were all direct consequences of the requirement of differentiability. For a more penetrating study of these functions—and, indeed, for a full understanding of the implications of the condition of differentiability—it is necessary to introduce the concept of complex integration. Just as in the real calculus, the idea of integration may be approached in two different ways which, at first sight, seem to have little to do with each other. Indefinite integration is defined as the reverse of differentiation, and definite integration as the limit for $n \to \infty$ of a sum of n terms all of which tend to zero. The fact that these two definitions are essentially equivalent is largely responsible for making the calculus—whether real or complex—the useful tool it is.

The limiting process used in defining the definite integral of a function of a complex variable is easily reduced to that used in the definition of the *line integral* familiar from the real calculus. This makes it possible to define the complex integral in terms of real line integrals, and to avoid the consideration of limiting processes which are identical with those used in the ordinary calculus.

We first review the properties of line integrals which are required for our purposes. Such integrals are of the form

$$(1) \qquad I = \int_C [p(x, y) \, dx + q(x, y) \, dy],$$

where $p(x, y)$ and $q(x, y)$ are real functions of x and y which are assumed to be continuous in a domain D of the xy-plane, and C is a curve all of whose points are in D. We shall first assume that C is a *smooth arc*; this assumption will later be relaxed so as to admit continuous curves C which consist of a finite number of smooth arcs. The latter are called *piecewise smooth curves*, or *contours*. A smooth arc is one which possesses a parametric representation $x = x(t)$, $y = y(t)$, $t_0 \leq t \leq t_1$, where the functions $x(t)$ and $y(t)$ have continuous first derivatives in $[t_0, t_1]$, and $x'(t)$ and $y'(t)$ do not vanish at the same time. Geometrically, a smooth arc is such that its tangent turns continuously if the point of contact traverses the arc.

By means of the parametric representation $x = x(t)$, $y = y(t)$, the line integral can be transformed into an ordinary integral over the interval $[t_0, t_1]$. We have

$$(2) \qquad I = \int_{t_0}^{t_1} [p\{x(t), y(t)\}x'(t) + q\{x(t), y(t)\}y'(t)] \, dt.$$

The reason the line integral is generally written in the form (1), i.e., without mentioning the parameter t, is that its value depends only on the curve C and not on the particular parametric representation of C which appears in (2). Indeed, suppose C is expressed in terms of a different parameter, say s. Since C is a smooth arc, the derivative ds/dt exists and is continuous. If $s = s_0$ and $s = s_1$ correspond to $t = t_0$ and $t = t_1$, respectively, we have

$$\int_{t_0}^{t_1} p \frac{dx}{dt} \, dt = \int_{t_0}^{t_1} p \frac{dx}{ds} \frac{ds}{dt} \, dt = \int_{s_0}^{s_1} p \frac{dx}{ds} \, ds,$$

and a similar expression for the second term in the integral (2). Hence,

$$\int_{t_0}^{t_1} \left[p \frac{dx}{dt} + q \frac{dy}{dt} \right] dt = \int_{s_0}^{s_1} \left[p \frac{dx}{ds} + q \frac{dy}{ds} \right] ds,$$

and the assertion follows.

Of particular interest is the case in which the functions p and q in (1) are the partial derivatives with respect to x and y of a function $g = g(x, y)$, i.e., $p = g_x$, $q = g_y$. (If p_y and q_x exist and are continuous, this case is characterized by the relation $p_y = q_x$.) As Formula (19) of Chapter I shows, $p \, dx + q \, dy$ will then be the total differential of the function $g(x, y)$. In view of (20) (Chap. I) and (2), we thus have

$$I = \int_C \frac{dg}{dt}\, dt = g(x_1, y_1) - g(x_0, y_0),$$

where $x_0 = x(t_0)$, $y_0 = y(t_0)$, $x_1 = x(t_1)$, $y_1 = y(t_1)$. This shows that, *if $p = g_x$ and $q = g_y$, the line integral* (1) *depends only on the endpoints of the curve C, but not on the curve C itself.* Conversely, if, for any two points (x_0, y_0) and (x, y) in D, the value of the integral (1) does not depend on the particular curve in D which joins these two points, there must exist a function $g(x, y)$ such that $g_x = p$ and $g_y = q$. Indeed, if we set

$$g(x, y) = \int_{(x_0, y_0)}^{(x, y)} (p\, dx + q\, dy),$$

it follows from the postulated independence of the integral of the curve C that $g(x, y)$ is a single-valued function of x and y if the point (x_0, y_0) is kept fixed. To compute g_x, we choose a curve C which, near the point (x, y), coincides with a horizontal linear segment. This implies that $dy = 0$ near (x, y), and we obtain $g_x = p$ at the point (x, y). Similarly, the choice of a curve C which ends in a vertical segment shows that $g_y = q$.

We finally mention two elementary properties of the line integral which follow immediately from its definition. The first of these is the fact that the value of the integral (1) depends on the direction in which the point (x, y) traverses the curve C. If the direction is reversed, we obtain $-I$ instead of I. This has an important consequence in the case in which the integral depends only on the endpoints of the curve. Since a closed curve passing through the two points (x_0, y_0) and (x_1, y_1) can be decomposed into two curves, one of which goes from (x_0, y_0) to (x_1, y_1) and the other from (x_1, y_1) to (x_0, y_0), the values of the two corresponding integrals will be equal in absolute value but opposite in sign. Hence, their sum is zero, and we have the following result: *If there exists a function $g(x, y)$ such that $g_x = p$ and $g_y = q$, the value of the line integral* (1) *over a closed curve C is zero.*

The other elementary property of the line integral is its additivity, i.e., the obvious fact that the value of the integral over a curve C, which is composed of two arcs C_1 and C_2, is equal to the sum of the integrals over C_1 and C_2. Since the line integral is additive, we may extend all our results to continuous curves C which consist of a finite number of smooth arcs, i.e., to contours.

The notion of a line integral can be generalized to the case in which the functions $p(x, y)$ and $q(x, y)$ are complex-valued. If $p = p_1 + i\, p_2$, $q = q_1 + i\, q_2$ (p_1, p_2, q_1, q_2 real), we define the integral (1) by

$$(3) \quad \int_C (p\, dx + q\, dy) = \int_C (p_1\, dx + q_1\, dy) + i \int_C (p_2\, dx + q_2\, dy).$$

It is easily confirmed that all the results on line integrals obtained so far will remain true for line integrals of the form (3).

We finally point out that, if x and y are replaced by the conjugate coordinates z and $\bar{z}$ of Section 4, Chapter I, the line integral (1) takes the form

$$(4) \qquad\qquad I = \int_C (P\, dz + Q\, d\bar{z}),$$

where $dz = dx + i\, dy$, $d\bar{z} = dx - i\, dy$. P and Q are functions of the variables z and $\bar{z}$, and the reader will confirm that $2P = p - iq$, $2Q = p + iq$. Formula (2) is replaced by

$$(5) \qquad\qquad I = \int_{t_0}^{t_1} [P\, z'(t) + Q\, \overline{z'(t)}]\, dt,$$

where $z(t) = x(t) + i\, y(t)$ is the parametric representation of the curve C. If there exists a function $G(z, \bar{z})$ such that $P = G_z$ and $Q = G_{\bar{z}}$, where $\partial/\partial z$ and $\partial/\partial\bar{z}$ are the differential operators (27) (Chap. I), the integral will depend only on the endpoints $z = z(t)$, $z_0 = z(t_0)$ of the curve C, and the function G satisfies the relation

(6)

$$G(z, \bar{z}) - G(z_0, \bar{z_0}) = \int_{t_0}^{t} [G_z z'(t) + G_{\bar{z}}\overline{z'(t)}]\, dt = \int_{z_0}^{z} (G_z\, dz + G_{\bar{z}}\, d\bar{z}).$$

This follows either by a direct transformation of the corresponding results for line integrals of the form (1), or else from Formula (30) of Chapter I. If, in particular, C is a closed curve, we have

$$(7) \qquad\qquad \int_C (G_z\, dz + G_{\bar{z}}\, d\bar{z}) = 0.$$

These formulas hold for all functions G which have continuous partial derivatives G_x, G_y in D.

Exercises

1. If C is the ellipse $x = a \cos t$, $y = b \sin t$, $0 \le t < 2\pi$, show that

$$\int_C (y^3\, dx + x^3\, dy) = \frac{3\pi}{4}\, ab(a^2 - b^2).$$

2. If r, θ are polar coordinates, and if C is a closed contour which does not intersect the negative axis and does not pass through the origin, show that

$$\int_C (\log r\, dx - \theta\, dy) = 0,$$

$$\int_C (\theta\, dx + \log r\, dy) = 0.$$

3. If s is the arc-length parameter on the curve C $(ds^2 = dx^2 + dy^2)$ and L is the length of C, show that

$$\left| \int_C (p\, dx + q\, dy) \right| \leq \int_0^L \sqrt{|p|^2 + |q|^2}\, ds \leq ML,$$

where $M^2 = \max [|p|^2 + |q|^2]$.

2 INTEGRATION OF ANALYTIC FUNCTIONS

Formulas (6) and (7) become particularly simple if G is an analytic function of the complex variable z. If this function is denoted by $f(z)$, it follows from Formulas (6) and (7) of Chapter II that $f_{\bar{z}} = 0$ and $f_z = f'(z)$. As a result, (6) reduces to

$$(8) \qquad f(z) - f(z_0) = \int_{z_0}^z f'(z)\, dz,$$

and (7) shows that, for a closed curve C,

$$(9) \qquad \int_C f'(z)\, dz = 0.$$

The relation (8) expresses the fact that the operations of differentiation and integration (with z as the upper limit) are inverse to each other. If the integrand is the derivative $f'(z)$ of an analytic function, the integral does not depend on the curve connecting the points z and z_0, and it is evaluated according to the rule familiar from the real calculus.

It should be noted that our proof of (8) and (9) is valid only under the assumption that $f'(z)$ is continuous in the domain D. The use of (8) and (9) is therefore permissible only if this continuity can be verified. In the following chapter we shall see, however, that this precaution is not really necessary, since the existence of the derivative $f'(z)$ in a domain implies its continuity.

The function $f(z) = z^n$ is the derivative of $(n + 1)^{-1}z^{n+1}$, and it is continuous at all finite points of the z-plane. Formula (9) shows, therefore, that

$$(10) \qquad \int_C z^n \, dz = 0,$$

if C is an arbitrary closed contour and n is a non-negative integer. As another example, we consider the power series

$$f(z) = \sum_{n=0}^{\infty} a_n(z - a)^n, \quad |z - a| < R.$$

In accordance with the results of Section 9 of the preceding chapter, $f(z)$ is the derivative of the power series

$$F(z) = \sum_{n=0}^{\infty} \frac{a_n(z - a)^{n+1}}{n + 1},$$

which likewise converges for $|z - a| < R$. Applying (9) to the function $F(z)$, we thus find that

$$(11) \qquad \int_C f(z) \, dz = 0,$$

where C may be an arbitrary closed contour inside the disk $|z - a| < R$.

The formula (11) will evidently hold in all cases in which the analytic function $f(z)$ can be shown to be the derivative $F'(z)$ of another analytic function $F(z)$, which is regular and single-valued in a given domain D. The fact that in a *simply-connected* domain—a term which will be defined presently—there always exists a function $F(z)$ such that $F'(z) = f(z)$ and that, as a result, (11) is valid for any closed contour C in D, is the assertion of the *Cauchy integral theorem*, one of the most fundamental results of mathematical analysis. It may be noted that the validity of (11) for any closed contour in D implies the existence of the indefinite integral $F(z)$ of $f(z)$. Indeed, if we define a function $F(z)$ by

$$F(z) = \int_{z_0}^{z} f(t) \, dt,$$

where z_0 is a fixed point of D, and the integration path connecting z_0 and z is entirely contained in D, it follows from (11) and the remarks made at the end of the last section that $F(z)$ is a single-valued function of z. Hence,

$$\frac{F(z + h) - F(z)}{h} = \frac{1}{h} \int_z^{z+h} f(t)\, dt$$

$$= f(z) + \frac{1}{h} \int_z^{z+h} [f(t) - f(z)]\, dt.$$

Because of the continuity of $f(z)$, we have $|f(t) - f(z)| < \epsilon$ provided $|t - z| < \delta$. Integrating along the linear segment joining z and $z + h$ and applying the inequality (14)—to be proved at the end of this Section—we thus obtain

$$\left| \int_z^{z+h} [f(t) - f(z)]\, dt \right| < \epsilon |h|$$

$(|h| < \delta)$, and it follows that

$$\left| \frac{F(z + h) - F(z)}{h} - f(z) \right| < \epsilon$$

if $|h| < \delta$. Hence, $F'(z)$ exists, i.e., $F(z)$ is an analytic function, and $F'(z) = f(z)$. The existence of an indefinite integral and the validity of (11) for all closed contours in D are therefore equivalent to each other.

We now turn to the definition of simple connectivity. Intuitively speaking, a simply-connected domain is a domain "without holes." For instance, the circular disk $|z| < R$ is simply-connected, but the circular ring $r < |z| < R$ $(0 < r < R < \infty)$ is not, since it has the circular "hole" $|z| \leq r$. If the *complement* of a set D denotes the set of all points of the extended plane which do not belong to D, a simply-connected domain may be defined as follows: *A domain is simply-connected if its complement is connected.* For instance, the complement of the circular ring just mentioned consists of the two regions $|z| \leq r$ and $|z| \geq R$. This is not a connected set, and the ring is therefore not simply-connected. It should be noted that, in the extended z-plane (see Sec. 5, Chap. I) the set $|z| > R$ is a simply-connected domain. Indeed, it is an open and connected set, and its complement is the closed connected set $|z| \leq R$. The circumference $|z| = R$ therefore separates the extended z-plane into the two simply-connected domains, $|z| < R$ and $|z| > R$.

This property of the circumference $|z| = R$ is a special case of a general result known as the *Jordan curve theorem.* To formulate this result, we have to define the concept of a non-selfintersecting, continuous, closed curve, also called a *Jordan curve.* A curve is continuous if it has a parametric representation $x = x(t)$, $y = y(t)$, $t_0 \leq t \leq t_1$, where $x(t)$ and $y(t)$ are continuous functions of t for $t_0 \leq t \leq t_1$; it is closed, if $x(t_1) = x(t_0)$ and $y(t_1) = y(t_0)$; it is non-selfintersecting if for no two values t_2, t_3 such that $t_0 < t_2 < t_3 < t_1$ we have $x(t_2) = x(t_3)$ and $y(t_2) = y(t_3)$. We now state the Jordan curve theorem.

A Jordan curve separates the extended plane into two distinct simply-connected domains, both of which have the curve as their boundary.

One of these domains contains the point at infinity, and the other does not. The points of the first domain are said to be *outside* the curve, and the points of the second are *inside*. That a curve of this type separates the plane into two sets of points, one "inside" and one "outside," is of course intuitively clear; in fact, it takes a considerable amount of sophistication to realize that a proof of this statement is required at all. Nevertheless, the proof of the Jordan curve theorem is long and laborious. We shall therefore content ourselves to accept the truth of the theorem on the very convincing intuitive evidence.

In view of the Jordan curve theorem, the definition of a bounded simply-connected domain can be replaced by the following statement:

A bounded domain D is simply-connected if, and only if, all points in the interior of any Jordan curve, which is entirely in D, are also points of D.

The proof of the equivalence of this statement and our previous definition is left as an exercise to the reader.

We end this section with the proof of an important inequality for integrals of the type

$$(12) \qquad\qquad I = \int_C f(z)\, dz,$$

where C is a contour—open or closed—situated in a domain in which $f(z)$ is regular and single-valued. If $z = z(s)$, $s_0 \leq s \leq s_1$, is a parametric representation of C, I is defined by

$$I = \int_{s_0}^{s_1} f[z(s)] z'(s)\, ds.$$

A particularly simple parametric representation is obtained if s is taken to be the arc-length along C, counted from one end of C to the other (if C is closed, any point of C may be regarded as corresponding to $s = 0$). In this case, we have

$$|z'(s)|^2 = \left(\frac{dx}{ds}\right)^2 + \left(\frac{dy}{ds}\right)^2 = 1,$$

and thus $|f(z)z'| = |f(z)|$. If L is the length of C and $f(z)z' = Re^{i\phi}$, where $R = |f(z)|$ and $\phi = \arg [f(z)z']$, it follows that

$$I = \int_0^L Re^{i\phi}\, ds.$$

If θ is an arbitrary real constant, we have

$$e^{i\theta}I = \int_0^L Re^{i(\phi+\theta)}\, ds$$

$$= \int_0^L R\cos(\phi + \theta)\, ds + i \int_0^L R\sin(\phi + \theta)\, ds,$$

and therefore

$$\mathrm{Re}\{e^{i\theta}I\} = \int_0^L R\cos(\phi + \theta)\, ds \le \int_0^L R\, ds.$$

Except in the trivial case $I = 0$, θ can be chosen in such a way that $e^{i\theta}I$ becomes positive. We then have $e^{i\theta}I = |I|$, and the last inequality shows that

$$(13) \qquad \left|\int_C f(z)\, dz\right| \le \int_C |f(z)|\, |dz|,$$

where $|dz| = \sqrt{dx^2 + dy^2} = ds$ is the length-element on C. If $|f(z)| \le M$ at all points of C, (13) yields the estimate

$$(14) \qquad \left|\int_C f(z)\, dz\right| \le ML,$$

where L is the length of C.

Exercises

1. Let C be a contour situated in a domain in which the analytic function $f(z)$ is regular, and let $z = z(t)$, $t_0 \le t \le T$ be a parametric representation of C. If $t_0 < t_1 < t_2 \cdots < t_{n-1} < t_n = T$, $t_{\nu-1} \le t_\nu^* \le t_\nu$, $z_\nu = z(t_\nu)$, $z_\nu^* = z(t_\nu^*)$, show that

$$\lim_{n\to\infty} \sum_{\nu=1}^n f(z_\nu^*)(z_\nu - z_{\nu-1}) = \int_C f(z)\, dz,$$

provided the largest of the numbers $|z_\nu - z_{\nu-1}|$ tends to zero as $n \to \infty$.

2. Use the result of the preceding exercise to obtain the inequality (13).

3. Deduce the inequality (13) from the result of Exercise 3 of Section 1.

4. Using only the result of Exercise 1, show that $\int_C dz = 0$ for any closed contour C.

5. Show, in the same way, that $\int_C z\,dz = 0$ for a closed contour C. *Hint:* Apply Exercise 1 with $z_\nu^* = z_{\nu-1}$ and $z_\nu^* = z_\nu$.

6. Show that

$$\int_C \frac{dz}{z-a} = 2\pi i,$$

if C is a circumference $|z - a| = R$, and the point z describes C in the positive direction. *Hint:* Use polar coordinates, with the pole located at $z = a$.

7. Use (9) to show that

$$\int_C \frac{dz}{z-a} = 0$$

if C is a smooth Jordan curve whose interior does not include the point $z = a$.

8. If C is the ellipse $x = a \cos t$, $y = b \sin t$, $0 \le t < 2\pi$, $a^2 - b^2 = 1$, show that

$$i\int_C \frac{dz}{\sqrt{1-z^2}}$$

is equal to 2π or -2π, depending on which value of the radical is taken.

3   THE CAUCHY INTEGRAL THEOREM

In this section we shall prove the following version of the Cauchy integral theorem.

If the analytic function $f(z)$ is regular and single-valued in a bounded simply-connected domain D, and if C is a simple—i.e. non-selfintersecting—closed contour situated in D, then

$$(15) \qquad \int_C f(z) \, dz = 0.$$

We remark that it is not really necessary to assume that $f(z)$ be single-valued in D, since it can be shown that a function which is regular in a simply-connected domain D is also single-valued in D. This fact is known as the *monodromy theorem*. Since we shall have no occasion to use this theorem, we omit its rather difficult proof.

According to a remark made earlier, the value of a line integral depends on the direction in which the point z describes the curve; reversing the direction has the effect of multiplying the value of the integral by the factor -1. In the case of the integral (15) this is, of course, a matter of indifference. However, we shall also be concerned with integrals over closed contours whose values are different from zero, and it therefore becomes necessary to adopt a convention as to the direction of integration. If the closed contour C is simple, then, according to the Jordan curve theorem, its interior is a simply-connected domain D. We shall say that the point z describes C in the *positive sense* if, in doing so, it leaves the points of D in its immediate vicinity at its left side. If C is a circle, this evidently coincides with the usual definition of the positive, or counterclockwise, direction on C. Unless the contrary is stated, all integrations over simple closed contours will be assumed to be carried out in the positive sense.

Under the assumption that the derivative of $f(z)$ is continuous in D, Cauchy's theorem can be easily proved by an application of Green's theorem for real line integrals. As the reader will recall, Green's theorem states that

$$(16) \qquad \iint_D \left(\frac{\partial p}{\partial x} + \frac{\partial q}{\partial y} \right) dx \, dy = \int_C (p \, dy - q \, dx),$$

where D is a domain with the piecewise smooth boundary C, p and q are continuous functions of x and y in $C + D$, and the partial derivatives p_x, p_y, q_x, q_y exist and are continuous in D. If $f(x) = u(x, y) + iv(x, y)$, the left-hand side of (15) can be written in the form

$$\int_C f(z) \, dz = \int_C (u \, dx - v \, dy) + i \int_C (v \, dx + u \, dy).$$

By (16), this is equivalent to

$$\int_C f(z) \, dz = - \iint_D (u_y + v_x) \, dx \, dy - i \iint_D (v_y - u_x) \, dx \, dy,$$

where D is the domain enclosed by C. Since, in view of the Cauchy-Riemann equations, $u_y + v_x = 0$ and $v_y - u_x = 0$, the right-hand side vanishes, and we have proved (15).

A better insight into the mechanism of this proof is obtained by using a complex form of Green's theorem. If $\partial/\partial\bar{z}$ is the operator defined in Section 4 of Chapter I and $P(x, y)$ is a (real or complex) function with continuous derivatives in D, (16) shows that

$$\iint_D \frac{\partial P}{\partial \bar{z}}\, dx\, dy = \frac{1}{2} \iint_D \left(\frac{\partial P}{\partial x} + i \frac{\partial P}{\partial y} \right) dx\, dy$$

$$= \frac{1}{2} \int_C (P\, dy - i\, P\, dx) = \frac{1}{2i} \int_C P\, dz.$$

The identity

$$(17) \qquad \iint_D \frac{\partial P}{\partial \bar{z}}\, dx\, dy = \frac{1}{2i} \int_C P\, dz$$

makes Cauchy's theorem evident: If P is an analytic function in D, we have $P_{\bar{z}} = 0$, and (15) follows.

The drawback of this proof is the necessity of assuming the continuity of $f'(z)$. Since this assumption is not part of our definition of an analytic function, we have to resort to a different method of proof. This method, as well as the discovery that Cauchy's theorem can be proved without assuming the continuity of $f'(z)$, is due to E. Goursat.

We begin by establishing Cauchy's theorem in the case in which the contour C is the perimeter of a rectangle with the sides a,b. The proof is based on the repeated application of the following idea. If the midpoints of opposite sides of the rectangle are joined by linear segments, the original rectangle is decomposed into four equal rectangles with the sides $\frac{a}{2}, \frac{b}{2}$. If the perimeters of these rectangles are denoted by C_k, $k = 1, 2, 3, 4$, we have

$$(18) \qquad \sum_{k=1}^{4} \int_{C_k} f(z)\, dz = \int_C f(z)\, dz.$$

Indeed, each rectilinear component of the contours C_k which is not part of C is part of the common boundary of two of the small rectangles. Since all integrals are taken in the positive sense with respect to the enclosed areas, the integrals over these components will appear twice—but in different directions—on the left-hand side of (18). This shows that these integrations cancel out, and (18) follows.

We now assume that Cauchy's theorem does not hold for the original rectangle S, i.e., that

$$(19) \qquad \left| \int_C f(z)\, dz \right| = A > 0.$$

In view of (18), at least one of the four rectangles into which S is subdivided must be such that

$$\left| \int_{C_1} f(z)\, dz \right| \geq \frac{A}{4},$$

if C_1 denotes the perimeter of the rectangle in question. Indeed, if the absolute values of all the four terms on the left-hand side of (18) were $< \dfrac{A}{4}$, we would obtain a contradiction to (19). We now denote this rectangle by S_1, and again subdivide it into four equal rectangles. The same argument shows that among these there must be at least one rectangle S_2 such that

$$\left| \int_{C_2} f(z)\, dz \right| \geq \frac{A}{4^2},$$

where C_2 is the perimeter of S_2. Continuing in this fashion, we obtain a sequence of rectangles $S_1, S_2, \cdots$ (each of these being contained in the preceding one), such that

$$(20) \qquad \left| \int_{C_n} f(z)\, dz \right| \geq \frac{A}{4^n}.$$

If a, b are the lengths of the sides of S, it is clear that S_n has the sides $2^{-n}a$, $2^{-n}b$. Since, for $n > N$, all rectangles S_n are contained in S_N, and since the sides of S_N can be made arbitrarily small by taking N large enough, it is seen that the rectangles S_n converge to a point z_0 as $n \to \infty$.

The point z_0 is in the interior of the original rectangle S. Hence, $f'(z)$ exists for $z = z_0$, i.e., for any positive ϵ we can find a positive δ such that

$$\left| \frac{f(z) - f(z_0)}{z - z_0} - f'(z_0) \right| < \epsilon,$$

provided $|z - z_0| < \delta$. We may also write this in the form

$$(21) \qquad f(z) = f(z_0) + (z - z_0)f'(z_0) + \epsilon \eta(z),$$

where $\eta(z)$ is such that $|\eta(z)| \leq 1$. For a given ϵ, we can take n large enough so that the rectangle S_n is contained in the disk $|z - z_0| < \delta$. We now integrate both sides of (21) along the perimeter C_n of the rectangle S_n. This yields

$$\int_{C_n} f(z) \, dz = f(z_0) \int_{C_n} dz$$
$$+ f'(z_0) \int_{C_n} (z - z_0) \, dz + \epsilon \int_{C_n} (z - z_0)\eta(z) \, dz,$$

whence, in view of (10),

$$\int_{C_n} f(z) \, dz = \epsilon \int_{C_n} (z - z_0)\eta(z) \, dz.$$

Since $|\eta(z)| \leq 1$, it follows from (13) that

$$\left| \int_{C_n} f(z) \, dz \right| \leq \epsilon \int_{C_n} |z - z_0| \, |dz|.$$

The value of $|z - z_0|$ cannot exceed the length of the diagonal $2^{-n}\sqrt{a^2 + b^2}$ of S, and $\int_{C_n} |dz|$ is the perimeter $2(a + b)2^{-n}$ of S_n. Hence,

$$\left| \int_{C_n} f(z) \, dz \right| \leq \frac{2(a + b)\sqrt{a^2 + b^2}}{4^n} \epsilon.$$

A comparison with (20) shows that we must have

$$A \leq 2(a + b)\sqrt{a^2 + b^2} \, \epsilon.$$

Since ϵ was arbitrary and thus may be taken as small as we please, the assumption $A > 0$ results in a contradiction. Hence, $A = 0$, and (19) shows that this proves Cauchy's theorem for a rectangle.

With the help of this result, we are able to prove Cauchy's theorem for all closed contours C (not necessarily simple ones) which are contained in a circular disk $|z - \alpha| < R$ in which the function $f(z)$ is regular. We define a function $F(z)$ in the disk by means of the integral

$$F(z) = \int_{C_z} f(z) \, dz,$$

where the integration path C_z joins the points α and z, and consists of a horizontal segment terminating at α and a vertical segment ending at z (one of these two segments may, of course, shrink to a point). If we set $z = x + iy$, $\alpha = a + ib$, $F(z)$ is thus defined by

$$(22) \qquad F(z) = \int_a^x f(t + ib)\, dt + i \int_b^y f(x + it)\, dt.$$

In view of Cauchy's theorem for a rectangle, the value of $F(z)$ may also be computed along the path consisting of a vertical segment ending at α and a horizontal one ending at z. Clearly, the two alternative integration paths together form the perimeter of a rectangle, and the integrations must therefore lead to the same result. Accordingly, the function $F(z)$ may also be defined by

$$(22') \qquad F(z) = i \int_b^y f(a + it)\, dt + \int_a^x f(t + iy)\, dt.$$

We now compute the partial derivatives F_x and F_y. According to $(22')$ we have $F_x = f(z)$, while (22) shows that $F_y = i\, f(z)$. Hence, $F_x + i\, F_y = f(z) - f(z) = 0$. If u and v are the real and imaginary parts of $F(z)$, it follows that $0 = u_x + i\, v_x + i(u_y + i\, v_y) = u_x - v_y + i(v_x + u_y)$, i.e., $u_x - v_y = 0, v_x + u_y = 0$. The real and imaginary parts of $F(z)$ are thus found to satisfy the Cauchy-Riemann equations. Since $F_x = f(z)$ and $F_y = i\, f(z)$, and $f(z)$ is continuous, the partial derivatives of u and v are, moreover, continuous. In view of the results of Section 2, Chapter II, it follows therefore that the function $F(z) = u + iv$ is analytic at all points of the disk $|z - \alpha| < R$. To find its derivative $F'(z)$, we observe that $F'(z) = F_x(z)$ and, as shown above, $F_x = f(z)$. Hence, $F'(z) = f(z)$, and we have proved the following result.

   If $f(z)$ is analytic in the disk $|z - \alpha| < R$, there exists another analytic function $F(z)$ in $|z - \alpha| < R$ such that $F'(z) = f(z)$.

In other words, the function $f(z)$ possesses an indefinite integral $F(z)$, which is also an analytic function. If we apply the identity (9) to the function $F(z)$, we obtain

$$(23) \qquad\qquad \int_C f(z)\, dz = 0,$$

i.e., *if $f(z)$ is analytic in a disk $|z - \alpha| < R$,* (23) *holds for all closed contours inside the disk.*

We are now in a position to complete the proof of the theorem formulated at the beginning of this section. Since the closed contour C is in the interior of the domain D, we can find a small positive number d such that the disk $|z - z_1| < 2d$ is entirely contained in D if z_1 is any point of C. We now cover the domain with two sets of equidistant straight lines which are parallel to the x-axis and y-axis, respectively. If the distance between adjacent lines is taken to be d, it is clear that the network of squares of side d obtained in this way has the following property: Any square whose perimeter intersects the contour C at a point z_1 is entirely contained in the disk $|z - z_1| < 2d$. Since $f(z)$ is regular in this disk, we may therefore apply Cauchy's theorem to all closed curves which are contained in one of these squares and consist of part of the perimeter of the square and of a section of C.

If D_0 denotes the interior of C, we may divide the squares belonging to our network, and having at least two points in common with D_0, into two classes: Those whose interiors consist entirely of points of D_0, and those whose interiors also contain points of D which do not belong to D_0. If $C_1, C_2, \cdots, C_n$ denote the perimeters of the squares of the first class, and $\Gamma_1, \Gamma_2, \cdots, \Gamma_m$ denote the closed curves which are contained in a square of the second class and consist of sections of C and of parts of the perimeter of the square which are inside D_0, we have

$$(24) \qquad \int_C f(z)\, dz = \sum_{k=1}^{n} \int_{C_k} f(z)\, dz + \sum_{p=1}^{m} \int_{\Gamma_p} f(z)\, dz.$$

Indeed, by the argument used in the proof of (18), all integrations along rectilinear sections of the C_k and Γ_p inside D_0 appear twice, and in opposite directions, on the right-hand side of (24). These integrals will therefore cancel out. All that remains are the integrals over those parts of the contours Γ_p which are sections of C. Since the totality of these sections adds up to C, (24) follows.

The integrals over the C_k vanish in view of Cauchy's theorem for rectangles. The integrals over the Γ_p vanish likewise since, as pointed out above, each Γ_p is contained in a disk in which $f(z)$ is analytic, and we have already proved Cauchy's theorem for such contours. Hence, all integrals on the right-hand side of (24) are zero, and the general theorem stated at the beginning of this section is proved.

We mention, finally, that (15) remains true if the closed contour C is *not* simple, provided C is entirely contained in a simply-connected domain in which $f(z)$ is regular. We shall, however, have no occasion to use Cauchy's theorem in this more general form.

Exercises

1. Apply Cauchy's theorem to the function $f(z) = e^{-z^2}$ and the rectangle whose vertices are at $z = \pm a, \pm a + ib$ (a,b positive).

Show that the contributions to the integral along the two vertical sides tend to zero if $a \to \infty$ and b is kept constant, and prove that

$$\int_{-\infty}^{\infty} e^{-x^2} \cos 2bx \, dx = e^{-b^2} \int_{-\infty}^{\infty} e^{-x^2} \, dx = \sqrt{\pi} \, e^{-b^2}.$$

2. Apply Cauchy's theorem to the function $f(z) = e^{-z^2}$ and the sector of the circle $|z| = R$ bounded by a section of the real axis and a linear segment making the angle $\pi/4$ with the real axis. Show that the integral over the circular boundary tends to zero for $R \to \infty$, and prove that

$$\int_0^{\infty} \cos(x^2) \, dx = \int_0^{\infty} \sin(x^2) \, dx = \frac{1}{\sqrt{2}} \int_{-\infty}^{\infty} e^{-x^2} \, dx = \sqrt{\frac{\pi}{2}}.$$

3. If, in the preceding exercise, the angle $\pi/4$ is replaced by $\pi/8$, show that the same procedure leads to the result

$$\int_0^{\infty} e^{-t^2} \cos(t^2) \, dt = \frac{\sqrt{\pi}}{4} \sqrt{1 + \sqrt{2}}.$$

4. Assuming that $0 < b < 1$, and applying to the function $f(z) = (1 + z^2)^{-1}$ the procedure outlined in Exercise 1, show that

$$\int_{-\infty}^{\infty} \frac{(1 - b^2 + x^2) \, dx}{(1 - b^2 + x^2)^2 + 4b^2 x^2} = \pi.$$

5. If C is a simple closed contour, show that the area of the domain enclosed by C is given by the line integral

$$A = \frac{1}{2i} \int_C \bar{z} \, dz.$$

6. Let $f(z)$ be analytic on, and in the interior of, a simple closed contour C. Show, without using Green's formula, that the value of the integral

$$\int_C \overline{f(z)} f'(z) \, dz$$

is pure imaginary. *Hint:* Write $f(z) = Re^{i\phi}$, where R and ϕ are real.

7. Show that the result of Exercise 5 can be brought into the form

$$A = \frac{1}{2} \int_C r^2 \, d\theta,$$

where $z = re^{i\theta}$.

8. If $f(z)$ and $g(z)$ are analytic in a domain D and on its piece-wise smooth boundary C, show that

$$\iint_D \overline{f'(z)}g(z)\, dx\, dy = \frac{1}{2i} \int_C \overline{f(z)}g(z)\, dz.$$

9. If $P(z)$ is the polynomial $a_0 + a_1 z + \cdots + a_n z^n$ and D is the disk $|z| < R$, use the result of the preceding exercise to show that

$$\iint_D |P(z)|^2\, dx\, dy = \sum_{\nu=0}^{n} \frac{|a_\nu|^2}{\nu + 1} R^{2\nu+2}.$$

4 MULTIPLY-CONNECTED DOMAINS

In many applications it is necessary to consider domains which are not simply-connected, and we shall therefore need a generalization of Cauchy's theorem to the case of *multiply-connected* domains. The following definition of a domain of connectivity n is not the most general possible, but it covers all the cases encountered in the applications.

A domain is said to be of connectivity n if its boundary consists of n distinct simple closed contours.

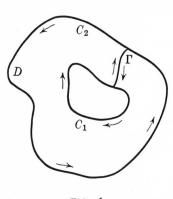

FIG. 1

For instance, the circular ring $r < |z| < R$ $(0 < r < R < \infty)$ is bounded by the circumferences $|z| = r$ and $|z| = R$, and it is therefore *doubly-connected*. An example of a domain of connectivity n is a disk $|z| < R$ with $n - 1$ circular holes, where no two of these holes have points in common. In order to obtain a form of Cauchy's theorem which is applicable to such domains, we first consider the case of a doubly-connected domain, i.e., a domain D bounded by two closed contours C_1 and C_2 (Fig. 1). If we "cut" D along a smooth non-selfintersecting arc Γ joining C_1 and C_2, we obtain a domain D' whose boundary consists of only one closed contour C'. D' is therefore simply-connected. The arrows in Fig. 1 indicate how the boundary C' is traversed in the positive sense. In this process the arc Γ is traversed twice, once in one direction and once in the opposite sense.

We now consider a function $f(z)$ which is regular and single-valued in the domain D and on its boundary (it should be noted that it is now necessary to assume explicitly that $f(z)$ is single-valued; in a multiply-connected domain a function may be regular without being single-valued). Since D' is obtained from D by the removal of the arc Γ, $f(z)$ is also regular in the domain D' and on its boundary C'. But D' is simply-connected, and we may therefore apply Cauchy's theorem. (Strictly speaking, the boundary C' of D' is not a simple closed contour, since the points of Γ appear in it twice. However, the reader will have no difficulty in showing that Cauchy's theorem remains valid for this type of boundary.) Hence,

$$\int_{C'} f(z)\, dz = 0.$$

The integration over the arc Γ is carried out twice, in opposite directions. Hence, these contributions to the integral cancel out, and the integral over C' reduces to the sum of the integrals over C_1 and C_2. A glance at Fig. 1 shows that both of these contours are traversed in such a way that the domain D remains at the left of both C_1 and C_2 if the point z moves along these curves. Accordingly, if we define the positive orientation of the boundary of a multiply-connected domain in formally the same way as in the case of a simply-connected domain, we have the following result:

If $f(z)$ is regular and single-valued in a doubly-connected domain D and on its boundary C, then

$$(25) \qquad \int_C f(z)\, dz = 0, \quad C = C_1 + C_2,$$

provided the components of C are traversed in the positive sense with respect to D.

Before we extend this result to domains of higher connectivity, we consider some important consequences of (25). If we reverse the orientation of the contour C_1 in Fig. 1, both C_1 and C_2 are oriented in the positive sense with respect to their interiors. Since the change of orientation reverses the sign of the integral, (25) takes the form

$$\int_{C_1} f(z)\, dz - \int_{C_2} f(z)\, dz = 0,$$

i.e., we have

(26)
$$\int_{C_1} f(z)\, dz = \int_{C_2} f(z)\, dz.$$

It should be kept in mind that this formula is valid only if C_1 and C_2 have the same orientation with respect to their interiors.

A very graphic way of describing the mutual relation of the contours C_1 and C_2 is by saying that C_1 can be *continuously deformed* into C_2—and vice versa—inside the domain D. Such a deformation may be visualized by the different shapes which may be given to a closed rubber band without tearing it and without introducing crossings-over. It is clear that a continuous deformation preserves the orientation of a closed contour. In this terminology, the facts expressed by (25) may be formulated as follows.

If the simple closed contour C_1 can be continuously deformed into another simple closed contour which does not intersect C_1, and if the function $f(z)$ is regular and single-valued in the closure of the doubly-connected domain D bounded by C_1 and C_2, then (26) holds.

A different way of describing this situation is to say that *the value of*

$$\int_C f(z)\, dz$$

over a simple closed contour C_1 remains unchanged if C_1 is continuously deformed into a simple closed contour C_2 in such a way that at no time a singularity of the integrand is crossed.

As an application, we compute the value of

$$\int_C \frac{dz}{z - a},$$

where C is a simple closed contour, and a is a point of the domain D enclosed by C. If we choose a positive number r such that the circumference $|z - a| = r$ is inside D, the domain bounded by C and this circumference is doubly-connected. Hence, (26) applies, and we have

$$\int_C \frac{dz}{z - a} = \int_{C_r} \frac{dz}{z - a},$$

where C_r is the circumference. It is therefore sufficient to compute the integral along C_r. Introducing polar coordinates $z = a + re^{i\theta}$, we have $dz = ire^{i\theta}\, d\theta$ and $z - a = re^{i\theta}$. Thus,

$$\int_{C_r} \frac{dz}{z-a} = i \int_0^{2\pi} d\theta = 2\pi i,$$

and our result is

(27)
$$\int_C \frac{dz}{z-a} = 2\pi i.$$

It is worthy of note that the integral on the left-hand side of (27) makes it possible to test whether or not a given point a, which is not on C, is inside the domain enclosed by C. If it is inside, the value of the integral is $2\pi i$. If it is not inside the domain, the integrand in (27) is regular, and it follows from Cauchy's theorem that the value of the integral is zero.

The extension of Cauchy's theorem to the case of domains of higher connectivity is carried out by an obvious generalization of the procedure used in the doubly-connected case. Fig. 2

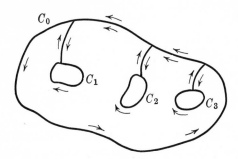

FIG. 2

illustrates this procedure for $n = 4$. We "cut" the domain along $n - 1$ smooth arcs which join the outer boundary C_0 with each of the inner boundaries C_ν, $\nu = 1, \cdots, n - 1$. This transforms the original domain D into a simply-connected domain D', and Cauchy's theorem for simply-connected domains may be applied to the boundary C' of D'. As before, the integrals over the cuts are taken twice, each time in a different direction, and it follows that they cancel out. We thus again obtain (25), where D now has the connectivity n, and where C consists of the closed contours C_ν, $\nu = 0, 1, \cdots, n - 1$. All of these contours are described in the positive sense with respect to D.

If we reverse the orientation of the inner boundary contours, we obtain the following generalization of the formula (26).

Let C_0 be the outer boundary contour of a bounded domain D of connectivity n, and let $C_\nu, \nu = 1, \cdots, n - 1$ be its inner boundary contours. If the function $f(z)$ is regular and single-valued in the closure of D, then

(28)
$$\int_{C_0} f(z) \, dz = \sum_{\nu=1}^{n-1} \int_{C_\nu} f(z) \, dz,$$

provided all the contours are positively oriented with respect to their interiors.

EXERCISES

1. Show that Green's formula (17) remains valid if the domain D is multiply-connected, and if C is taken to be the positively oriented boundary of D.

2. If $P(z)$ is the polynomial $\prod_{\nu=1}^{n} (z - a_\nu)$, and if C is a simple closed contour whose interior contains all the points a_ν, show that

$$\int_C \frac{P'(z)}{P(z)} \, dz = 2\pi i n.$$

IV

APPLICATIONS OF

CAUCHY'S THEOREM

1 THE CAUCHY INTEGRAL FORMULA

Suppose that the analytic function $f(z)$ is regular on a simple closed contour C and in its interior D, and consider the integral

$$\int_C \frac{f(z)}{z - \zeta}\, dz,$$

where ζ is a point of D. Since the integrand is evidently not continuous at the point ζ, this integral cannot be evaluated by means of Cauchy's theorem for simply-connected domains. However, if we remove from D a small closed disk $|z - r| \le r$ which is entirely contained in D, we obtain a doubly-connected domain D_r in which the integrand is regular and single-valued. We therefore may apply Cauchy's theorem to the boundary of D_r. This boundary consists of C and of the circumference C_r of the deleted disk. Using Cauchy's theorem in the formulation (26) (Chapter III), we thus have

$$\int_C \frac{f(z)}{z - \zeta}\, dz = \int_{C_r} \frac{f(z)}{z - \zeta}\, dz,$$

where both C and C_r are positively oriented with respect to their interiors.

In the integral on the right-hand side we introduce polar coordinates $z = \zeta + re^{i\theta}$. Since r is constant, we have $dz = ire^{i\theta}\, d\theta$, and thus

$$\int_C \frac{f(z)}{z - \zeta}\, dz = i \int_0^{2\pi} f(\zeta + re^{i\theta})\, d\theta.$$

The function $f(z)$ is continuous at the point ζ. Hence, if ϵ is an arbitrarily small given positive number, we have

$$|f(\zeta + re^{i\theta}) - f(\zeta)| < \epsilon$$

provided r is taken small enough. It follows that

$$\int_0^{2\pi} f(\zeta + re^{i\theta}) = \int_0^{2\pi} f(\zeta)\, d\theta + \delta = 2\pi f(\zeta) + \delta,$$

where

$$|\delta| = \left| \int_0^{2\pi} [f(\zeta + re^{i\theta}) - f(\zeta)]\, d\theta \right|$$

$$\leq \int_0^{2\pi} |f(\zeta + re^{i\theta}) - f(\zeta)|\, d\theta \leq 2\pi\epsilon.$$

Hence,

$$\int_C \frac{f(z)}{z - \zeta}\, dz = 2\pi i f(\zeta) + i\delta$$

i.e.,

$$\left| \int_C \frac{f(z)}{z - \zeta}\, dz - 2\pi i f(\zeta) \right| \leq \epsilon.$$

Since ϵ may be taken arbitrarily small, this proves the identity

$$(1) \qquad\qquad f(\zeta) = \frac{1}{2\pi i} \int_C \frac{f(z)}{z - \zeta}\, dz,$$

known as the *Cauchy integral formula*.

Formula (1) reveals a very remarkable fact concerning the nature of an analytic function of a complex variable. In order to compute the integral on the right-hand side, it is only necessary to know the values of $f(z)$ on the contour C. Since ζ may be any point of the domain D enclosed by C, (1) shows therefore that *the values of the function $f(z)$ in D are completely determined by its values on the boundary of D.*

With the help of the Cauchy integral formula we are able to prove that *the derivative of an analytic function is again an analytic function.* To put it differently, if $f(z)$ possesses a derivative $f'(z)$ in a domain, then $f'(z)$ is necessarily continuous there and possesses a derivative, $f''(z)$. Applying the same argument to $f'(z)$, we find that $f''(z)$ must also have a derivative, $f'''(z)$. Evidently, we may continue in this manner, inferring the existence of derivatives of higher and higher order, and we thus obtain the result that *an analytic function which is regular in a domain possesses there derivatives of all orders.* This state of affairs has no parallel in the theory of function of a real variable x. If $f(x)$ is differentiable in an interval, its derivative $f'(x)$ is not necessarily continuous, let alone differentiable.

To prove this result, we choose a positive number ϵ such that the point $\zeta + h$ is inside the domain D provided $|h| < \epsilon$. Formula (1) may then be applied to the point $\zeta + h$, and we obtain

$$\frac{f(\zeta + h) - f(\zeta)}{h} = \frac{1}{2\pi i h} \int_C f(z) \left[\frac{1}{z - \zeta - h} - \frac{1}{z - \zeta} \right] dz$$

$$= \frac{1}{2\pi i} \int_C \frac{f(z) \, dz}{(z - \zeta)(z - \zeta - h)}.$$

In view of

$$\frac{1}{(z - \zeta)(z - \zeta - h)} = \frac{1}{(z - \zeta)^2} + \frac{h}{(z - \zeta)^2(z - \zeta - h)},$$

this may be brought into the form

$$(2) \quad \frac{f(\zeta + h) - f(\zeta)}{h} - \frac{1}{2\pi i} \int_C \frac{f(z)}{(z - \zeta)^2} \, dz$$

$$= \frac{h}{2\pi i} \int_C \frac{f(z) \, dz}{(z - \zeta)^2(z - \zeta + h)}.$$

The function $|f(z)|$ is continuous on C, and there will therefore exist a positive constant M such that $|f(z)| \leq M$ at all points of C. If d denotes the smallest distance between ζ and any point of C, and if we take ϵ smaller than $d/2$, we have $|z - \zeta|^{-2} \leq d^{-2}$ and $|z - \zeta - h| \geq |z - \zeta| - |h| \geq d - d/2 = d/2$, i.e.,

$$|z - \zeta - h|^{-1} \leq 2d^{-1}.$$

Estimating the integral on the right-hand side of (2) by means of the inequality (14) of Chapter III, we thus obtain

$$(3) \quad \left| \frac{f(\zeta + h) - f(\zeta)}{h} - \frac{1}{2\pi i} \int_C \frac{f(z)}{(z - \zeta)^2} \, dz \right| \leq \frac{\epsilon L}{\pi d^3},$$

where L is the length of C. For $h \to 0$, this yields

$$\left| f'(\zeta) - \frac{1}{2\pi i} \int_C \frac{f(z)}{(z - \zeta)^2} \, dz \right| \leq \frac{\epsilon L}{\pi d^3}.$$

Since ϵ may be taken arbitrarily small, this proves the formula

$$(4) \qquad f'(\zeta) = \frac{1}{2\pi i} \int_C \frac{f(z)}{(z - \zeta)^2} \, dz.$$

A comparison with (1) shows that this is precisely what we would have obtained by differentiating the right-hand side of (1) under the integral sign.

Our proof, however, shows more than this. If all we had known about the function $f(\zeta)$ were the fact that it can be represented by the right-hand side of (1), our argument would have established the existence of the derivative $f'(\zeta)$ of $f(\zeta)$. Indeed, if we let h tend to zero in (3) in any specified way, our argument shows that the limit of $h^{-1}[f(z + h) - f(z)]$ exists, and is the same, regardless of the manner in which h approaches zero. The function represented by the integral on the right-hand side of (1) is therefore necessarily analytic in D. We now remark that the function (4) may be treated in exactly the same way. If we consider the expression

$$\frac{f'(\zeta + h) - f'(\zeta)}{h},$$

and express $f'(\zeta + h)$ and $f'(\zeta)$ by means of the Formula (4), a trivial modification of the preceding argument shows that the limit of this expression for $h \to 0$ exists, and is independent of the manner in which h tends to zero. This proves that the derivative $f'(\zeta)$ of an analytic function $f(\zeta)$ is again an analytic function, and that its derivative $f''(\zeta)$ is given by the formula

$$f''(\zeta) = \frac{2}{2\pi i} \int_C \frac{f(z)}{(z - \zeta)^3} \, dz.$$

Integral representations for the higher derivatives of $f(\zeta)$ are obtained by applying the same argument successively to $f''(\zeta)$, $f'''(\zeta)$, etc. The carrying out of these steps is left as a useful exercise to the reader. The general result is

$$(5) \qquad f^{(n)}(\zeta) = \frac{n!}{2\pi i} \int_C \frac{f(z)}{(z - \zeta)^{n+1}} \, dz,$$

i.e., the nth derivative of $f(\zeta)$ may be computed by differentiating the right-hand side of (1) n times under the integral sign.

The fact that the derivative of an analytic function is again an analytic function can be used to prove the following converse of Cauchy's theorem, known as Morera's theorem.

If the function $f(z)$ is continuous in a simply-connected domain D and if, for every closed contour C in D,

(6)
$$\int_C f(z) \, dz = 0,$$

then $f(z)$ is analytic in D.

As pointed out in Section 2 of the preceding chapter, the assumption (6) is equivalent to the existence of an analytic function $F(z)$ in D such that $F'(z) = f(z)$. Since $f(z)$ is thus shown to be the derivative of an analytic function, it is itself analytic, and Morera's theorem is proved.

As an application of Morera's theorem, we prove the following result concerning infinite series whose terms are analytic functions.

If the analytic functions $f_1(z), f_2(z), \cdots, f_n(z), \cdots$ are all regular in the same simply-connected domain D, and if the series

(7)
$$f(z) = \sum_{n=1}^{\infty} f_n(z)$$

converges uniformly in D, then its sum $f(z)$ is also a regular analytic function in D.

As shown in Section 8 of Chapter I, the sum of a uniformly converging series of continuous functions is itself continuous. The function $f(z)$ is therefore continuous in D and $\int_C f(z) \, dz$ exists for any closed contour in D. Moreover, because of the uniform convergence, the value of this integral can be found by term-by-term integration of the series (7). Indeed, since the convergence is uniform there exists, for any positive ϵ, an integer $N = N(\epsilon)$ such that

$$|r_N| = \left| \sum_{n=N+1}^{\infty} f_n(z) \right| < \epsilon,$$

if z is any point of D. Hence,

$$\left| \int_C f(z) \, dz - \sum_{n=1}^{N} \int_C f_n(z) \, dz \right| = \left| \int_C r_N \, dz \right| \leq \epsilon L,$$

where L is the length of C. But ϵ may be taken arbitrarily small, and it follows that

(8)
$$\int_C f(z) \, dz = \sum_{n=0}^{\infty} \int_C f_n(z) \, dz.$$

If the contour C is situated in the interior of a disk D_0 which is contained in D then, as shown in Sec. 3, Chap. III, all the integrals on the right-hand side of (8) are zero. We thus have

$$\int_C f(z) \, dz = 0$$

for all closed contours in D_0, and it follows from Morera's theorem that $f(z)$ is a regular analytic function at all points of D_0. Hence, $f(z)$ is regular at all points of D.

We end this section with the proof of *Liouville's theorem* concerning entire functions, i.e., analytic functions which are regular and single-valued for all finite values of z.

An entire function cannot be bounded unless it reduces to a constant.

Suppose that $f(z)$ is bounded, i.e., that there exists a positive constant M such that $|f(z)| \le M$ for all finite z. If ζ is a fixed complex number and C denotes the circumference $|z - \zeta| = R$, an application of (4) and of the inequality (14) (Chap. III, Sec. 2) shows that

$$|f'(\zeta)| = \left| \frac{1}{2\pi i} \int_C \frac{f(z)}{(z - \zeta)^2} \, dz \right| \le \frac{ML}{2\pi R^2} = \frac{M}{R}.$$

Since $f(z)$ is an entire function, R may be taken arbitrarily large, and we have thus shown that the assumption $|f(z)| \le M$ leads to $f'(\zeta) = 0$. Since ζ was an arbitrary complex number, the derivative of $f(z)$ vanishes identically, and $f(z)$ must therefore reduce to a constant.

Exercises

1. Let $f(z)$ be regular for $|z| \le 1$, and assume that $f(0) = 1$. By evaluating the integral

$$\frac{1}{2\pi i} \int_{|z|=1} \left[2 + e^{i\alpha}z + \frac{e^{-i\alpha}}{z} \right] f(z) \frac{dz}{z}$$

(α real) both by means of (4) and by introducing polar coordinates, show that

$$\frac{2}{\pi} \int_0^{2\pi} f(e^{i\theta}) \cos^2 \frac{\alpha + \theta}{2} \, d\theta = 2 + e^{i\alpha} f'(0).$$

Use this result in order to prove the following statement: If $f(z)$ is regular and $\text{Re}[f(z)] \geq 0$ for $|z| \leq 1$, and if $f(0) = 1$, then $|f'(0)| \leq 2$.

2. The Legendre polynomial $P_n(z)$ is defined by

$$P_n(z) = \frac{1}{2^n n!} \frac{d^n}{dz^n} [(z^2 - 1)^n].$$

Use (5) to show that $P_n(z)$ can be represented by the integral

$$P_n(z) = \frac{1}{2\pi i} \int_C \frac{(t^2 - 1)^n}{2^n (t - z)^{n+1}} dt,$$

where C is a simple closed contour surrounding the point z. Taking C to be the circle of center z and radius $\sqrt{|z^2 - 1|}$, deduce Laplace's formula

$$P_n(z) = \frac{1}{\pi} \int_0^\pi (z + \sqrt{z^2 - 1} \cos \theta)^n d\theta.$$

3. Using the methods of this section, show that a power series represents an analytic function in the interior of its circle of convergence.

4. With the help of Formula (5), obtain the following generalization of Liouville's theorem: If n is a positive integer, and if an entire function $f(z)$ is such that $|f(z)| \leq M|z|^n$ for all finite z, then $f(z)$ must be a polynomial whose degree does not exceed n. *Hint:* Show that $f^{(n+1)}(z) \equiv 0$.

5. If the points $z = a$ and $z = b$ are inside the domain bounded by the simple closed contour C, show that

$$\int_C \frac{dz}{(z - a)(z - b)} = 0.$$

6. Show that the Cauchy integral formula (1) remains valid if C is the complete boundary of a multiply-connected domain D and $f(z)$ is regular and single-valued in D.

7. Show that the following formulation of Morera's theorem is valid for a general (i.e., not necessarily simply-connected) domain D: If $f(z)$ is continuous in D and if, for every point z_0 in D, there is a disk containing z_0 such that (6) holds for every closed contour in the disk, then $f(z)$ is analytic in D.

2   THE TAYLOR SERIES

In Chapter II (Sec. 9) we saw that a power series represents an analytic function in the interior of its circle of convergence. We are now in a position to prove that, conversely, any analytic function which is regular in a disk can be expanded into a converging power series. To show that this is the case, we first note that the function $(t - z)^{-1}$ can be expanded into a power series of the form $\sum_{n=0}^{\infty} a_n(z - a)^n$, where a is any point of the z-plane other than t, and the series converges in the disk $|z - a| < |t - a|$. Indeed,

(9)
$$\frac{1}{t - z} = \frac{1}{t - a - (z - a)} = \frac{1}{t - a} \frac{1}{1 - \left(\dfrac{z - a}{t - a}\right)}$$

$$= \frac{1}{t - a} \sum_{n=0}^{\infty} \left(\frac{z - a}{t - a}\right)^n = \sum_{n=0}^{\infty} \frac{(z - a)^n}{(t - a)^{n+1}},$$

where the geometric progression converges for $\left|\dfrac{z - a}{t - a}\right| < 1$, i.e., for $|z - a| < |t - a|$. We also recall from Chapter II that a power series converges uniformly in any closed disk interior to, and concentric with, the circle of convergence. If R_0 is a number such that $0 < R_0 < |t - a| = R$, the convergence of our geometric series will thus be uniform for $|z - a| \leq R_0$.

Let now $f(z)$ be an analytic function which is regular for $|z - a| \leq R$. If C denotes the circumference $|z - a| = R_0$, it follows from (1) and (9) that

(10) $f(z) = \dfrac{1}{2\pi i} \displaystyle\int_C \frac{f(t)}{t - z} dt = \frac{1}{2\pi i} \int_C f(t) \left[\sum_{n=0}^{\infty} \frac{(z - a)^n}{(t - a)^{n+1}} \right] dt.$

On C, the convergence of the series (9) is uniform and, as the reader will easily confirm, the uniformity of the convergence is not affected by the multiplication of each term by the continuous function $f(t)$. As shown in the preceding section, the integral of a uniformly converging series of continuous functions may be evaluated by means of term-by-term integration. If these remarks are applied to the last integral in (10), we find that $f(z)$ can be written as the sum of the infinite series

$$(11) \qquad f(z) = \sum_{n=0}^{\infty} a_n(z - a)^n, \quad |z - a| \leq R_0 < R,$$

where the coefficients a_n are given by the formula

$$(12) \qquad a_n = \frac{1}{2\pi i} \int_C \frac{f(t)\, dt}{(t - a)^{n+1}}.$$

Since R_0 may be chosen arbitrarily close to R, we thus have the following result.

An analytic function $f(z)$ which is regular in a disk $|z - a| < R$ can be expanded there into a converging power series of the form (11) whose coefficients are given by the formula (12), where C is a circumference $|z - a| = R_0$, $0 < R_0 < R$.

The fact that, under these conditions, an analytic function can be expanded into a Taylor series is known as *Taylor's theorem*. In the case in which $a = 0$, the series (11) is also called a *Maclaurin series*.

It was shown in Section 9, Chapter II, that every power series is necessarily the Taylor series of the function $f(z)$ represented by it, i.e., we must have

$$(13) \qquad a_n = \frac{f^{(n)}(a)}{n!}.$$

This fact can also be directly confirmed by comparing Formulas (5) and (12). Formula (13) shows that, in the interior of a circle $|z - a| < R$ in which $f(z)$ is regular, $f(z)$ is completely determined by the values of the derivatives of $f(z)$ at the point $z = a$. Since for the computation of these derivatives it is only necessary to know the values of $f(z)$ along a small linear segment passing through the point $z = a$, it follows that two analytic functions which have the same values at the points of such a segment must coincide at all points of the circle of convergence. `In particular, if a is a real number and if two functions are regular, and have the same values, on a section of the real axis containing the point $z = a$, these functions are regular in the same disk $|z - a| < R$ and take there the same values. This shows that the extension of a real function $f(x)$ to an analytic function $f(z)$ of the complex variable z is uniquely determined by the values of $f(x)$. If such an extension is possible at all, it is possible in only one way. For instance, there can be only one analytic function which, for real values of z (i.e., for $z = x$), coincides with the real exponential function e^x.

Just as in the case of a real power series, the value of the Taylor series (11) as a computational tool depends on our ability to estimate the largest possible error committed if we replace the infinite series by a finite number of terms. If we write

$$f(z) = \sum_{n=0}^{m} a_n(z - a)^n + r_m(z),$$

we thus have to find an estimate for the largest possible value of $r_m(z)$. By (11) and (12), we have

$$r_m(z) = \frac{1}{2\pi i} \int_C \left[\sum_{n=m+1}^{\infty} \left(\frac{z - a}{t - a} \right)^n \right] \frac{f(t)\,dt}{t - a}.$$

Since, in view of (9),

$$\sum_{n=m+1}^{\infty} \left(\frac{z - a}{t - a} \right)^n = \left(\frac{z - a}{t - a} \right)^{m+1} \sum_{n=0}^{\infty} \left(\frac{z - a}{t - a} \right)^n = \frac{(z - a)^{m+1}}{(t - a)^m(t - z)},$$

we obtain

$$(14) \qquad r_m(z) = \frac{(z - a)^{m+1}}{2\pi i} \int_C \frac{f(t)\,dt}{(t - a)^{m+1}(t - z)}.$$

To estimate $|r_m(z)|$, we take C to be the circumference $|t - a| = R_0$, and we denote the maximum of $|f(t)|$ on R_0 by $M(R_0)$. Since the length of C is $2\pi R_0$, and since $|t - z| = |t - a - (z - a)| \geq |t - a| - |z - a| = R_0 - |z - a|$, (14) leads to the inequality

$$(15) \qquad |r_m(z)| \leq \frac{|z - a|^{m+1} M(R_0)}{R_0^m(R_0 - |z - a|)}, \quad |z - a| < R_0 < R.$$

In our discussion of power series (Sec. 9, Chap. II), we obtained a rule for determining the radius of convergence of a power series (11) from its coefficients a_n. The results of the present section enable us to give a much more elegant rule, with the help of which we can often find the radius of convergence without any computation at all. This rule is based on the fact, implied by our results, that *on the circumference of the circle of convergence of a power series there must be at least one singular point of the function represented by the series.* Indeed, if there were no singularity on the circumference $|z - a| = R$ of the radius of convergence, the function $f(z)$ would be regular in a disk $|z - a| < R + \epsilon$, where ϵ is a sufficiently small positive number. But from this it would follow that the series (11) must converge in the disk $|z - a| < R + \epsilon$, and this contradicts the assumption that $|z - a| < R$ is the circle of convergence. The circle of convergence of the series (11) may therefore be determined by the following rule: *The circumference of the circle of convergence of the expansion* (11) *of an analytic function* $f(z)$ *which is regular at* a *passes through the singularity of* $f(z)$ *which is closest to* a. The radius of convergence is thus equal to the distance between a and the nearest singularity of the function.

If we know where the singularities of a function $f(z)$ are, we therefore also know the radii of convergence of all power series expansions (11) of $f(z)$. As an example, let us consider the function $f(z) = \log z$, whose only finite singularity is at the point $z = 0$. If a is any complex number other than zero, a given branch of the function may therefore be expanded into a power series of the form (11), and the radius of convergence R of this series must be equal to the distance of the point a from the origin, that is, $R = |a|$. The explicit form of the expansion is, in this case,

$$\log z = \log a - \sum_{n=1}^{\infty} (-1)^n \frac{(z - a)^n}{a^n}$$

(proof ?), where $\log a$ is one of the values of the function $\log z$ at the point $z = a$. The reader will easily confirm that the radius of convergence of this series is indeed equal to $|a|$.

The above rule for finding the region of convergence of a power series points up the fact that the behavior of a power series cannot be properly understood without the use of complex variables. There does not exist a corresponding "real" rule for determining the interval of convergence of a real power series with the help of the properties of the function. For instance, the real power series

$$\frac{1}{1 + x^2} = 1 - x^2 + x^4 - x^6 + - \cdots$$

converges only in the interval $-1 < x < 1$, although the function represented by it is continuous, and has derivatives of all orders, for all real values of x. The reason for this behavior is, of course, that the *complex* function $(1 + z^2)^{-1}$ has singularities at the points $z = \pm i$, and that these singularities "stop" the convergence of the series. The series converges therefore only for $|z| < 1$, and this restricts the convergence of the real series to the interval $-1 < x < 1$.

If $f(z)$ is an entire function, all of its Taylor expansions must converge for all finite values of z. The radius of convergence of these series is therefore infinitely large. For instance, the coefficients a_n of the expansion $\sum\limits_{n=0}^{\infty} a_n z^n$ of the entire function $f(z) = e^z$ are found from (13) to be $a_n = (n!)^{-1}$. Hence, e^z has the expansion

$$e^z = \sum_{n=0}^{\infty} \frac{z^n}{n!}$$

(where we set $0! = 1$), and it is clear a priori that this expansion must converge for all finite values of z.

From Formula (12) we can obtain an estimate of the absolute value of the coefficient a_n, which is often useful. Setting, for convenience, $a = 0$, we assume that $f(z)$ is regular for $|z| < R$ and that $|f(z)| \le M(r)$ for $|z| = r$. If C is the circumference $|z| = r$, the length of C is $2\pi r$, and (12) shows that

$$(16) \qquad |a_n| \le \frac{M(r)}{r^n}.$$

This estimate is known as *Cauchy's coefficient inequality*.

More precise information regarding the magnitude of the coefficients can be obtained by means of *Parseval's identity*

$$(17) \qquad \frac{1}{2\pi} \int_0^{2\pi} |f(re^{i\theta})|^2 \, d\theta = \sum_{n=0}^{\infty} |a_n|^2 r^{2n},$$

which is interesting in its own right and has many useful applications in the theory of functions. To prove (17), we note that $|f(re^{i\theta})|^2 = f(re^{i\theta})\overline{f(re^{i\theta})}$, and that the series

$$f(re^{i\theta}) = \sum_{n=0}^{\infty} a_n r^n e^{in\theta}$$

converges uniformly in θ. Hence,

$$(17') \qquad \int_0^{2\pi} |f(re^{i\theta})|^2 \, d\theta = \int_0^{2\pi} \overline{f(re^{i\theta})} \left[\sum_{n=0}^{\infty} a_n r^n e^{in\theta} \right] d\theta$$

$$= \sum_{n=0}^{\infty} a_n r^n \int_0^{2\pi} \overline{f(re^{i\theta})} e^{in\theta} \, d\theta.$$

But

$$\int_0^{2\pi} \overline{f(re^{i\theta})} e^{in\theta} \, d\theta = \int_0^{2\pi} e^{in\theta} \left[\sum_{m=0}^{\infty} \overline{a_m} r^m e^{-im\theta} \right] d\theta$$

$$= \sum_{m=0}^{\infty} \overline{a_m} r^m \int_0^{2\pi} e^{i(n-m)\theta} \, d\theta,$$

and the latter integrals are all zero for $m \neq n$. For $m = n$, the value of the integral is 2π, and it follows that

$$\int_0^{2\pi} \overline{f(re^{i\theta})} e^{in\theta} d\theta = 2\pi \overline{a_n} r^n.$$

In view of (17'), this proves (17).

If $|f(z)| \leq M(r)$ for $|z| = r$, we have

$$\frac{1}{2\pi} \int_0^{2\pi} |f(re^{i\theta})|^2 \, d\theta \leq M^2(r),$$

and (17) shows that (16) can be replaced by the stronger inequality

(18) $$\sum_{n=0}^{\infty} |a_n|^2 r^{2n} \leq M^2(r).$$

Exercises

1. If z is a complex number such that $|z| < R$, and if the function e^z is replaced by the finite sum

$$1 + z + \frac{z^2}{2!} + \cdots + \frac{z^{n-1}}{(n-1)!},$$

show that the absolute value of the error committed cannot exceed

$$\frac{|z|^n e^R}{R^{n-1}(R - |z|)}.$$

For a given z, how has R to be chosen in order to make this quantity as small as possible?

2. If $f(z)$ is the principal branch of the function $(1 - z)^\alpha$ (i.e., if we assume $f(0) = 1$), show that $f(z)$ has an expansion of the form

$$f(z) = \sum_{n=0}^{\infty} a_n z^n$$

which converges for $|z| < 1$, and find the coefficients a_n.

3. Show that the function

$$f(z) = e^{z^2} \int_0^z e^{-z^2} \, dz$$

satisfies the differential equation $f'(z) = 1 + 2z f(z)$ with the initial condition $f(0) = 0$, and use this fact to obtain the power series expansion

$$f(z) = \sum_{n=0}^{\infty} \frac{n!2^{2n-1}}{(2n)!} z^{2n-1}.$$

(As this example illustrates, Formula (13) does not necessarily provide the easiest way of computing the Taylor coefficients of a given function $f(z)$. Whenever it can be shown that $f(z)$ satisfies a simple differential equation, this furnishes a convenient method for the successive determination of the coefficients.)

4. If t is a real number such that $-1 < t < 1$, show that the power series

$$\frac{1}{\sqrt{1 - 2tz + z^2}} = 1 + \sum_{n=1}^{\infty} P_n(t)z^n$$

converges for $|z| < 1$, and that $P_n(t)$ is a polynomial in t of degree n.

5. Use (12) to show that

$$\left(\frac{z^n}{n!}\right)^2 = \frac{1}{2\pi i} \int_C \frac{z^n e^{zt}}{n!t^n} \frac{dt}{t},$$

where C is a circumference whose center is at the origin. With the help of this result, prove that

$$\sum_{n=0}^{\infty} \left(\frac{z^n}{n!}\right)^2 = \frac{1}{2\pi} \int_0^{2\pi} e^{2z \cos \theta} \, d\theta.$$

6. If $f(z)$ is regular for $|z| < 1$ and

$$|f(z)| \le \frac{1}{1 - |z|},$$

show that the coefficients of the expansion $f(z) = \sum_{n=0}^{\infty} a_n z^n$ are subject to the inequality

$$|a_n| \le (n + 1)\left(1 + \frac{1}{n}\right)^n < e(n + 1).$$

7. If $f(z)$ is regular for $|z| < R$, and if $f(z)$ is an *odd function*, i.e., if $f(-z) = -f(z)$, show that in its Taylor expansion $f(z) = \sum_{n=0}^{\infty} a_n z^n$ all coefficients a_n of even index n are zero. Similarly, show that the expansion of an even function, i.e., a function for which $f(-z) = f(z)$, has non-zero coefficients only for even values of n.

8. Let

$$f(z) = \sum_{n=0}^{\infty} a_n z^n, \quad |z| < R,$$

and denote by ω the mth root of unity $e^{2\pi i/m}$ (see Sec. 3, Chap. I). Show that

$$\frac{1}{m} \sum_{\nu=1}^{m} f(\omega^\nu z) = \sum_{p=0}^{\infty} a_{pm} z^{pm}.$$

More generally, if k is an integer such that $0 \leq k < m$, show that

$$\frac{1}{m} \sum_{\nu=1}^{m} \frac{f(\omega^\nu z)}{\omega^{k\nu}} = \sum_{p=0}^{\infty} a_{pm+k} z^{pm+k}.$$

9. If $f(z)$ is regular for $|z| < R$, and if $f(x)$ is real for $-R < x < R$, show that the coefficients a_n of the expansion $f(z) = \sum_{n=0}^{\infty} a_n z^n$ must all be real. Show also that, for $|z| < R$, $f(z)$ satisfies the identity $f(\bar{z}) = \overline{f(z)}$.

10. If $a_n = \alpha_n + i\beta_n$ (α_n, β_n real), and if the series $f(z) = \sum_{n=0}^{\infty} a_n z^n$ converges for $|z| < R$, show that $f(z) = g(z) + ih(z)$, where

$$g(z) = \frac{1}{2}[f(z) + \overline{f(\bar{z})}] = \sum_{n=0}^{\infty} \alpha_n z^n$$

and

$$h(z) = \frac{1}{2i}[f(z) - \overline{f(\bar{z})}] = \sum_{n=0}^{\infty} \beta_n z^n$$

11. Suppose the function $g(z)$ is regular for $|z| \leq 1$ and that $g(x)$ is real for $-1 \leq x \leq 1$. Applying Cauchy's theorem first to the boundary of the upper and then to the lower half of the unit circle, show that

$$\int_{-1}^{1} |g(x)|^2 \, dx = \int_{-1}^{1} g^2(x) \, dx \leq \int_{0}^{\pi} |g(e^{i\theta})|^2 \, d\theta$$

and

$$\int_{-1}^{1} g^2(x) \, dx \leq \int_{\pi}^{2\pi} |g(e^{i\theta})|^2 \, d\theta,$$

and therefore

$$\int_{-1}^{1} g^2(x) \, dx \leq \frac{1}{2} \int_{0}^{2\pi} |g(e^{i\theta})|^2 \, d\theta.$$

12. If $f(z)$ is a function regular for $|z| \leq 1$, use the decomposition $f(z) = g(z) + ih(z)$ of Exercise 10, and the result of Exercise 11, to prove the inequality

$$\int_{-1}^{1} |f(x)|^2 \, dx \leq \frac{1}{2} \int_{0}^{2\pi} |f(e^{i\theta})|^2 \, d\theta.$$

13. If $f(z)$ is a polynomial $a_0 + a_1 z + \cdots + a_n z^n$, show that

$$\int_0^1 |f(x)|^2 \, dx = \sum_{\nu=0}^n \sum_{\mu=0}^n \frac{a_\nu \overline{a_\mu}}{\nu + \mu + 1}.$$

14. Using Parseval's identity and the results of the two preceding exercises, show that

$$\sum_{\nu=1}^n \sum_{\mu=1}^n \frac{a_\nu \overline{a_\mu}}{\nu + \mu + 1} \leq \pi \sum_{\nu=1}^n |a_\nu|^2,$$

where $a_0, a_1, \cdots, a_n$ are arbitrary complex constants.

15. Applying Parseval's identity to the function $f(z) = (1 - z)^{-1}$, show that

$$\frac{1}{2\pi} \int_0^{2\pi} \frac{d\theta}{1 - 2\rho \cos \theta + \rho^2} = \frac{1}{1 - \rho^2}, \quad 0 \leq \rho < 1.$$

16. Applying Parseval's identity to the function

$$1 + z + z^2 + \cdots + z^{n-1} = \frac{z^n - 1}{z - 1},$$

deduce the formula

$$\int_0^{2\pi} \left(\frac{\sin \frac{1}{2} n\theta}{\sin \frac{1}{2}\theta} \right)^2 d\theta = 2\pi n.$$

17. Use Cauchy's inequality (16) to give an alternative proof of Liouville's theorem.

3 THE LAURENT SERIES

If a function $f(z)$ is regular and single-valued in a circular ring $0 < r < |z - a| < R$, but not in the entire disk $|z - a| < R$, $f(z)$ cannot be expanded into a Taylor series about the point a. Indeed, such a series would represent a regular analytic function in the disk $|z - a| < R$, contrary to our assumption. Nevertheless, $f(z)$ can be expanded in $r < |z - a| < R$ into a series proceeding by integral powers of $z - a$, provided we also admit *negative* powers. An expansion of this type is known as a *Laurent series*, and the fact that a function which is regular and single-valued in a circular ring can be expanded into a Laurent series is referred to as *Laurent's theorem*.

We suppose that z is a point in this circular ring, and that the positive number ϵ is chosen small enough so that $r + \epsilon < |z - a| < R - \epsilon$. If we denote the circumferences $|z - a| = R - \epsilon$ and $|z - a| = r + \epsilon$ by C_1 and C_2, respectively, the function $f(z)$ is regular and single-valued in the closure of the ring bounded by C_1 and C_2. Since the point z is inside this ring, and since the validity of the Cauchy integral formula does not depend on the connectivity of the domain, we have

$$(19) \qquad f(z) = \frac{1}{2\pi i} \int_{C_1} \frac{f(t)\,dt}{t - z} - \frac{1}{2\pi i} \int_{C_2} \frac{f(t)}{t - z}\,dt.$$

Indeed, C_1 and C_2 constitute the entire boundary of the ring, and the negative sign before the second integral takes account of the fact that the negative direction on the circle C_2 is the positive direction with respect to the interior of the ring.

The Laurent expansion of $f(z)$ is obtained by replacing the function $(t - z)^{-1}$ in both integrals (19) by their expansions in terms of powers of $z - a$, and then integrating the resulting series term-by-term. In the case of the integral over C_1, this procedure is identical with that used in the proof of Taylor's theorem. Indeed, if t is on C_1 we have $|z - a| < |t - a| = R - \epsilon$, and $(t - z)^{-1}$ has the expansion (9). It follows therefore, in complete analogy to the argument leading from (10) to (11) and (12), that

$$(20) \qquad f_1(z) = \frac{1}{2\pi i} \int_{C_1} \frac{f(t)}{t - z}\,dt = \sum_{n=0}^{\infty} a_n(z - a)^n$$

where

$$a_n = \frac{1}{2\pi i} \int_{C_1} \frac{f(t)\,dt}{(t - a)^{n+1}}, \quad n = 0, 1, 2, \cdots.$$

On C_2, however, we have $r + \epsilon = |t - a| < |z - a|$ and the expansion (9) does not converge. To obtain a converging series for $(t - z)^{-1}$, we write

$$\frac{1}{t - z} = \frac{1}{t - a - (z - a)} = -\frac{1}{z - a} \frac{1}{1 - \dfrac{t - a}{z - a}}.$$

Since $\left| \dfrac{t - a}{z - a} \right| < 1$ on C_2, the last fraction can be expanded into a geometric progression. Hence,

$$\frac{1}{t - z} = -\sum_{n=1}^{\infty} \frac{(t - a)^{n-1}}{(z - a)^n}.$$

The convergence is uniform in t, and we may therefore employ this series for the evaluation of the second integral in (19). Our result is

$$(21) \qquad f_2(z) = -\frac{1}{2\pi i}\int_{C_2}\frac{f(t)}{t-z}\,dt = \sum_{n=1}^{\infty}\frac{a_{-n}}{(z-a)^n},$$

where the coefficients a_{-n} are given by

$$a_{-n} = \frac{1}{2\pi i}\int_{C_2}f(t)(t-a)^{n-1}\,dt, \quad n = 1, 2, \cdots.$$

We note that in the integrals defining a_n and a_{-n} we may replace the circles C_1 and C_2 by any closed curve which can be obtained from them by continuous deformation within the ring (see Sec. 4). In particular, we may replace both C_1 and C_2 by a circle C which is concentric with them and situated in the interior of the ring. Collecting our results, and observing that the number ϵ can be taken arbitrarily small, we arrive at Laurent's theorem:

If $f(z)$ is regular and single-valued in the circular ring $r < |z - a| < R$, it can be expanded there into a series of the form

$$(22) \qquad f(z) = \sum_{n=-\infty}^{\infty} a_n(z-a)^n,$$

where

$$(23) \qquad a_n = \frac{1}{2\pi i}\int_C \frac{f(t)\,dt}{(t-a)^{n+1}}, \quad n = 0, \pm1, \pm2, \cdots,$$

and C is a circumference $|z - a| = \rho, r < \rho < R$.

We may also state this result by saying that the function $f(z)$ can be written as the sum of two functions $f_1(z)$ and $f_2(z)$, defined by (20) and (21), which may be expanded into series proceeding by positive and negative powers of $z - a$, respectively. The expansion (20) is an ordinary power series. Therefore, it will converge at all points of a disk if it converges at a point of the boundary of the disk. Hence, $f_1(z)$ is regular for $|z - a| < R$. The expansion (21) is also a power series, if it is regarded as a function of the variable $(z - a)^{-1}$. If such a series converges at a point z_0, it will therefore converge at all points z such that $|z - a|^{-1} < |z_0 - a|^{-1}$, i.e., $|z - a| > |z_0 - a|$. Hence, the series (21) will converge for all values z such that $|z - a| > r$, i.e., its domain of convergence is the *exterior* of a circle. Laurent's theorem shows therefore that *a function $f(z)$ which is regular and single-valued in a*

circular ring $r < |z - a| < R$, *has a decomposition of the form*
$f(z) = f_1(z) + f_2(z)$, *where* $f_1(z)$ *and* $f_2(z)$ *are regular for* $|z - a| < R$
and $|z - a| > r$, *respectively.*

The reader will notice that the last statement asserts that the function $f_2(z)$ is *regular at* $z = \infty$. This is justified by the observation that a power series of the form

$$(24) \qquad g(z) = \sum_{n=0}^{\infty} \frac{b_n}{(z - a)^n},$$

which converges for $|z - a| > r$, has a derivative

$$g'(z) = - \sum_{n=1}^{\infty} \frac{n b_n}{(z - a)^{n+1}}$$

at all points in $|z - a| > r$, including the point $z = \infty$. Indeed, the last formula shows that $g'(\infty) = 0$. The assertion of Taylor's theorem, according to which an analytic function $g(z)$ can be expanded into a power series in the neighborhood of any point $z = a$ at which $g(z)$ is regular, will therefore also hold for the point $z = \infty$. The only formal difference is that, in this case, the series proceeds by negative powers, and that a neighborhood of $z = \infty$ is interpreted as the exterior of a large circle.

A function $g(z)$ which is regular at $z = \infty$ possesses expansions of the form (24), where a may be any finite number. In particular, it has an expansion of the form

$$g(z) = \sum_{n=0}^{\infty} \frac{c_n}{z^n},$$

which converges in some neighborhood $|z| > \rho$ of $z = \infty$. If, in this expansion, the variable z is replaced by z^{-1}, we obtain an ordinary power series. This series represents a regular function at all points z such that $|z| < \rho^{-1}$, including the point $z = 0$. We thus have the following simple characterization of the regularity of a function at the point $z = \infty$: *The function* $g(z)$ *is regular at* $z = \infty$ *if, and only if, the function* $g(z^{-1})$ *is regular at* $z = 0$.

EXERCISES

1. Show that, for $1 < |z| < 2$,

$$\frac{1}{(1 - z)(2 - z)} = \sum_{n=1}^{\infty} \frac{1}{z^n} + \sum_{n=0}^{\infty} \frac{z^n}{2^{n+1}}.$$

2. If a is a complex number such that $\mathrm{Re}(a) > 1$, show that

$$\frac{2}{1 - z^2} = \sum_{n=1}^{\infty} (-1)^n \frac{(a-1)^{n-1}}{(z-a)^n} + \sum_{n=0}^{\infty} (-1)^n \frac{(z-a)^n}{(a+1)^{n+1}}$$

for $|a - 1| < |z - a| < |a + 1|$.

3. The Bessel function $J_n(z)$ is defined as the nth coefficient ($n \geq 0$) of the "generating function"

$$e^{z\left(t - \frac{1}{t}\right)} = \sum_{n=-\infty}^{\infty} J_n(z) t^n.$$

Use Laurent's theorem to show that

$$J_n(z) = \frac{1}{\pi} \int_0^{\pi} \cos{(n\theta - z\sin\theta)}\, d\theta.$$

4. If $J_n(z)$ is the function defined in the preceding exercise, show by writing

$$e^{z\left(t - \frac{1}{t}\right)} = e^{zt}\, e^{-\frac{z}{t}}$$

and multiplying out the terms of the two exponential series that

$$J_n(z) = \sum_{\nu=0}^{\infty} \frac{(-1)^\nu (z/2)^{n+2\nu}}{\nu!\,(n+\nu)!}.$$

5. Suppose that a function $f(z)$ is regular and single-valued in the ring $r < |z| < r^{-1}$, and satisfies there the functional relation $f\left(\dfrac{1}{\bar{z}}\right) = \overline{f(z)}$. If the constants a_n are its Laurent coefficients (23) (for $a = 0$), show that $a_{-n} = \bar{a}_n$. Show also that $f(z)$ takes real values for $|z| = 1$.

6. If $f(z)$ is regular and single-valued and $|f(z)| < M$ for $r < |z - a| < R$, show that the coefficients (23) are subject to the inequalities

$$|a_n| \leq \frac{M}{R^n}, \quad n = 0, 1, \cdots,$$

$$|a_{-n}| \leq M r^n, \quad n = 0, 1, \cdots.$$

7. Using the preceding inequality for $|a_{-n}|$, prove the following theorem: If a function is known to be regular and single-valued at all points of a disk $|z - a| < R$ except at its center $z = a$, and if there exists a positive constant M such that $|f(z)| < M$ for $0 < |z - a| < R$, then $f(z)$ is also regular at $z = a$.

8. If the analytic function $f(t)$ is regular for $|t| < 5/2$, show that the function $f\left(z + \dfrac{1}{z}\right)$ must have a Laurent expansion $\displaystyle\sum_{n=-\infty}^{\infty} a_n z^n$ which converges for $\dfrac{1}{2} < |z| < 2$.

4 ISOLATED SINGULARITIES

If the function $f(z)$ is regular and single-valued at all points of a disk $|z - a| < R$ except at its center $z = a$, it follows from Laurent's theorem that the series

$$(25) \quad f(z) = \cdots + \frac{a_{-2}}{(z-a)^2} + \frac{a_{-1}}{z-a}$$
$$+ a_0 + a_1(z-a) + a_2(z-a)^2 + \cdots$$

will converge for all z such that $0 < |z - a| < R$. If all the coefficients a_{-n} $(n = 1, 2, \cdots)$ are zero, (25) reduces to a Taylor series, and $f(z)$ is regular at the point $z = a$. If at least one of these coefficients is not zero, then $z = a$ is a singular point of the function $f(z)$. Since in a sufficiently small neighborhood $|z - a| < \epsilon$ there are no further singularities of the function, we say that $z = a$ is an *isolated singularity* of $f(z)$.

It is not difficult to construct examples of singularities which are not isolated. For instance, the function

$$f(z) = \frac{1}{\sin \dfrac{1}{z}}$$

has such a singularity at $z = 0$. Indeed, since $\sin \pi n = 0$ for all integral values of n, $f(z)$ is not continuous at the points $z = (\pi n)^{-1}$. Any neighborhood of $z = 0$ will therefore contain singularities of $f(z)$. The point $z = 0$ is the limit point of an infinity of singular points, and is therefore also a singular point (and thus a non-isolated one). To see the truth of the last remark, we have only to recall that regularity at a point was defined as regularity in some neighborhood of the point.

The isolated singularities $z = a$ in whose neighborhood the function $f(z)$ has an expansion (25) can be divided into two categories.   The first of these corresponds to the case in which only a finite number of the coefficients a_{-n} $(n = 1, 2, \cdots)$ are different from zero.   In this case, (25) can be written in the form

(26)

$$f(z) = \frac{a_{-m}}{(z - a)^m} + \cdots + \frac{a_{-1}}{z - a} + a_0 + a_1(z - a) + \cdots, \quad a_{-m} \neq 0,$$

and the function $f(z)$ is said to have a *pole of order m* at $z = a$.   The rational function

$$\frac{a_{-m}}{(z - a)^m} + \cdots + \frac{a_{-1}}{z - a}$$

is called the *principal part,* or the *meromorphic part* of the function $f(z)$ at the pole $z = a$.   If the expansion (25) has an infinity of non-vanishing coefficients a_{-n}, $f(z)$ is said to have an *essential singularity* at $z = a$.

These two classes of isolated singularities can also be defined at the point $z = \infty$.   If, in Laurent's theorem, we have $r \geq 0$ and $R = \infty$, the expansion (22) will be valid for $r < |z - a| < \infty$. The terms giving rise to singularities at $z = \infty$ are now, of course, the positive powers of $z - a$; if only negative powers appear, the series has the form (24) and $z = \infty$ is a regular point.   In the case in which only a finite number of the positive powers have non-zero coefficients, $z = \infty$ is a pole of the function.   If we take $a = 0$ (which we may do without loss of generality), the expansion will then have the form

$$(27) \quad f(z) = a_m z^m + \cdots + a_1 z + a_0 + \frac{a_{-1}}{z} + \frac{a_{-2}}{z^2} + \cdots, \quad a_m \neq 0.$$

As before, we say that $z = \infty$ is a pole of order m of $f(z)$.   If an infinity of positive powers appear explicitly, $z = \infty$ is said to be an essential singularity of $f(z)$.   According to this definition, a polynomial of nth order has an nth order pole at $z = \infty$, and this is evidently the only singularity of the polynomial.   Any entire function which does not reduce to a polynomial has an essential singularity at $z = \infty$.

The behavior of an analytic function in the neighborhood of a pole is easy to describe.   If we write (26) in the form

$$f(z) = \frac{P_m(z)}{(z - a)^m} + f_1(z),$$

where $P_m(z)$ is the polynomial

$$P_m(z) = a_{-m} + a_{-m+1}(z - a) + \cdots + a_{-1}(z - a)^{m-1}, \quad a_{-m} \neq 0,$$

and $f_1(z)$ is regular at $z = a$, it becomes clear that $f(z) \to \infty$ for $z \to a$, regardless of the path along which a is approached. A pole may therefore be characterized as a point at which the function takes the value ∞. As we shall see later, no such simple statement can be made for an essential singularity.

If we multiply (26) by the factor $(z - a)^m$, the resulting function

$$g(z) = (z - a)^m f(z) = a_{-m} + a_{-(m-1)}(z - a) + \cdots$$

is represented by a converging power series and is therefore regular in the neighborhood of $z = a$. Since $a_{-m} \neq 0$ we have $g(a) \neq 0$ and it follows from the continuity of $g(z)$ that $g(z) \neq 0$ in a certain neighborhood $|z - a| < \epsilon$ of $z = a$. Indeed, if ϵ is such that $|g(a) - g(z)| < \frac{1}{2}|g(a)|$ in $|z - a| < \epsilon$, we have

$$|g(z)| = |g(a) - [g(a) - g(z)]|$$
$$\geq |g(a)| - |g(a) - g(z)| > |g(a)| - \tfrac{1}{2}|g(a)| = \tfrac{1}{2}|g(a)| > 0.$$

The function $[g(z)]^{-1}$ will thus be continuous in $|z - a| < \epsilon$, and its derivative is $-g'(z)g^{-2}(z)$. The function is therefore analytic in $|z - a| < \epsilon$, and it follows from Taylor's theorem that there exists a converging expansion

$$\frac{1}{(z - a)^m f(z)} = \frac{1}{g(z)} = b_0 + b_1(z - a)$$
$$+ b_2(z - a)^2 + \cdots, \quad |z - a| < \epsilon,$$

where b_0 is evidently different from zero. Hence,

$$\frac{1}{f(z)} = b_0(z - a)^m + b_1(z - a)^{m+1} + \cdots.$$

In other words, *if $f(z)$ has a pole of order m at $z = a$, then $1/f(z)$ is regular at $z = a$ and has there a zero of order m.* Here, a zero of order m is defined as a point at which both the function and its derivatives up to the $(m - 1)$st order vanish. We may also say that a zero of order m is a point $z = a$ at which the first non-vanishing coefficient of the Taylor expansion $\sum\limits_{n=0}^{\infty} a_n(z - a)^n$ is a_m. It may be remarked that the converse of the above statement is also true: If $1/f(z)$ has a zero of order m, then $f(z)$ has a pole of order m.

The behavior of an analytic function in the neighborhood of an essential singularity is of a much more complicated nature. An idea of what happens near such a point is given by the following theorem.

In any neighborhood of an isolated essential singularity, an analytic function approaches any given value arbitrarily closely.

To put it differently, if $|z - a| < \epsilon$ is an arbitrarily small neighborhood of the point $z = a$, and if α is any complex number, there will always exist points z_0 in this neighborhood such that $|f(z_0) - \alpha| < \delta$, where δ may be taken as small as we please. If this assertion were false, there would exist a number α such that $|f(z) - \alpha| \geq m$ in $|z - a| < \epsilon$, where m is a fixed positive number. We would then have

$$\left| \frac{1}{f(z) - \alpha} \right| \leq \frac{1}{m}$$

in this neighborhood. The only possible singularity of the function $[f(z) - \alpha]^{-1}$ is at $z = a$. However, since the function has just been shown to be bounded near this point, it follows from Exercise 7 of the preceding section that it is regular in $|z - a| < \epsilon$. Its reciprocal, $f(z) - \alpha$ is therefore either regular in this disk, or else it has a pole there. But this contradicts our assumption that $z = a$ was an *essential* singularity, and we have proved that there cannot exist a positive constant m such that $|f(z) - \alpha| \geq m$ in $|z - a| < \epsilon$. Since α was arbitrary, this completes the proof of the theorem.

With the help of more advanced analytical methods, even more can be shown. It can be proved that, in any neighborhood of an isolated essential singularity, an analytic function actually takes every finite value, with one possible exception. That such an exception can actually occur is shown by the function $e^{1/z}$, which has an essential singularity at $z = 0$, and which never takes the value zero.

Exercises

1. If the function $f(z)$ has a pole of mth order at $z = a$, and if $P(w)$ is a polynomial of degree n, show that the function $P[f(z)]$ has a pole or order nm at $z = a$.

2. Find the principal part of the function

$$f(z) = \frac{1}{(1 + z^2)^3}$$

at the point $z = i$.

3. Find the principal part of the function

$$f(z) = \frac{1}{\sin^2 z}$$

at the point $z = \pi n$, where n is an integer.

4. Show that in an arbitrarily small disk $|z| < \epsilon$ the function

$$f(z) = e^{1/z}$$

takes every non-zero value infinitely often.

5. If the function $f(z)$ has a pole of order $2m$ at a point $z = a$, show that the function $g(z) = \sqrt{f(z)}$ has a pole of order m at this point. State and prove a corresponding result for zeros of order $2m$.

5 RATIONAL FUNCTIONS

We recall that a rational function $f(z)$ is a function of the form

$$(28) \qquad f(z) = \frac{P(z)}{Q(z)},$$

where

$$P(z) = \alpha_0 + \alpha_1 z + \cdots + \alpha_n z^n, \quad \alpha_n \neq 0,$$

and

$$Q(z) = \beta_0 + \beta_1 z + \cdots + \beta_m z^m, \quad \beta_m \neq 0$$

are polynomials of degree n and m, respectively. We may assume that $P(z)$ and $Q(z)$ have no common zeros. Indeed, if $P(z_0) = 0$ we have $P(z) = (z - z_0)^{k_1} P_1(z)$, where $P_1(z)$ is a polynomial, $P_1(z_0) \neq 0$, and k_1 is a positive integer. Similarly, it follows from $Q(z_0) = 0$ that $Q(z) = (z - z_0)^{k_2} Q_1(z)$, where $Q_1(z_0) \neq 0$. By cancelling a suitable number of the factors $z - z_0$ we can therefore replace (28) by the quotient of two polynomials which do not both vanish at $z = z_0$.

The results of the preceding section make it possible to characterize a rational function by the nature of its singularities. We shall show that *a single-valued function is rational if, and only if, all its singularities are poles.*

To prove this assertion we note that, since both $P(z)$ and $Q(z)$

are regular for all finite values of z, the finite singularities of (28) can be located only at the points at which $Q(z)$ takes the value zero. Since the zeros of $P(z)$ and $Q(z)$ do not coincide, the function $1/f(z)$ will be regular at these points and will vanish there. We may therefore conclude from the results of the preceding section that these singularities are poles. In order to study the behavior of $f(z)$ near $z = \infty$, we write (28) in the form

$$f(z) = z^{n-m} \left[\frac{\alpha_n + \dfrac{\alpha_{n-1}}{z} + \cdots + \dfrac{\alpha_0}{z^n}}{\beta_m + \dfrac{\beta_{m-1}}{z} + \cdots + \dfrac{\beta_0}{z^m}} \right], \quad \alpha_n \neq 0, \quad \beta_m \neq 0.$$

The expression in the bracket is regular for large $|z|$, and we have therefore

$$f(z) = z^{n-m} \left(c_0 + \frac{c_1}{z} + \frac{c_2}{z^2} + \cdots \right), \quad c_0 \neq 0,$$

where the power series converges for $|z| > R$ if R is taken large enough. This makes it clear that the behavior of $f(z)$ near $z = \infty$ depends on the value of $n - m$. If $n - m \leq 0$, the Laurent expansion of $f(z)$ near $z = \infty$ does not contain positive powers of z, and $f(z)$ is therefore regular at $z = \infty$. If $n - m > 0$, the point $z = \infty$ is a pole of order $n - m$. We have thus proved that all singularities of a rational function are poles.

Postponing for a moment the proof of the fact that a function which has no singularities but poles is necessarily rational, we first use the present result to prove the possibility of decomposing a rational function into a polynomial and a sum of partial fractions. The reader is familiar with elementary cases of this decomposition, such as

$$\frac{1}{1 - x^2} = \frac{1}{2} \frac{1}{1 - x} + \frac{1}{2} \frac{1}{1 + x},$$

from the real calculus, where they are used as an aid in the integration of rational functions. In general, such a decomposition is not possible without the use of complex numbers, even if the coefficients of the polynomials $P(z)$ and $Q(z)$ are real (consider, for instance, $f(z) = (1 + z^2)^{-1}$).

We assume that the poles of $f(z)$ are located at the points $a_1, a_2, \cdots, a_p, \infty$, and we denote by $M(z, a_1), \cdots, M(z, a_p)$, $M(z, \infty)$ the meromorphic parts of $f(z)$ at these points. The functions M are of the form

(29) $$M(z, a_k) = \frac{A_{m_k,k}}{(z - a_k)^{m_k}} + \cdots + \frac{A_{1,k}}{z - a_k},$$

(29') $$M(z, \infty) = A_\sigma z^\sigma + \cdots + A_1 z,$$

where m_k and σ are the orders of the poles at the points $z = a_k$ and $z = \infty$, respectively. We now consider the function

(30) $$F(z) = f(z) - \sum_{k=1}^{p} M(z, a_k) - M(z, \infty).$$

Since $f(z)$, $M(z, a_k)$ and $M(z, \infty)$ are rational functions, the same is true of $F(z)$. As just shown, the only possible singularities of $F(z)$ are therefore poles, and it is clear that these poles cannot be located at points other than $a_1, \cdots, a_p, \infty$. However, since the function (29) is defined by the condition that $f(z) - M(z, a_k)$ is regular at $z = a_k$, the function (30) is regular at all the points a_k, and therefore at all finite points of the plane. If, finally, the pole at $z = \infty$ is removed by subtracting the function $M(z, \infty)$, the resulting function (30) will be a rational function without poles, i.e., a function which is regular at all points of the extended plane.

It is easy to see that such a function $F(z)$ must reduce to a constant. Indeed, since $F(z)$ is regular for all z, $F(z)$ has a Taylor expansion which converges for all finite z, i.e., we have

$$F(z) = \sum_{n=0}^{\infty} a_n z^n.$$

But, as shown in the preceding section, $F(z)$ will have a singularity at $z = \infty$ unless all the coefficients a_n are zero for $n \geq 1$. Hence, the series reduces to its first term, and it follows that $F(z)$ is a constant. Denoting this constant by C, we thus conclude from (30) that

(31) $$f(z) = C + \sum_{k=1}^{P} M(z, a_k) + M(z, \infty),$$

where the functions M are defined by (29) and (29'). This is the desired decomposition of a rational function into a polynomial and a sum of partial fractions. Whenever the degree of the numerator of (28) does not exceed the degree of the denominator, the polynomial $M(z, \infty)$ will reduce to a constant.

The same argument also proves that a function $f(z)$ all of whose singularities are poles must be rational. If the meromorphic parts belonging to these poles are given by (29) and (29'), the function (30) is left without singularities. It thus reduces to a constant, and $f(z)$ must therefore be of the form (31). If, in (31), the functions M are replaced by their explicit representations (29) and (29'), the result can evidently be brought into the form (28), where $P(z)$ and $Q(z)$ are polynomials. Hence, (31) is a rational function, and our result is proved.

The fact that a rational function without poles is a constant can be used for a short proof of the *fundamental theorem of algebra*, according to which the equation

$$(32) \qquad \alpha_0 + \alpha_1 z + \cdots + \alpha_n z^n = 0, \quad \alpha_n \neq 0, \quad n \geq 1,$$

has exactly n roots. If $P(z) = \alpha_0 + \alpha_1 z + \cdots + \alpha_n z^n$, we have to show that there exist n numbers, $z_1, \cdots, z_n$, such that $P(z_k) = 0$, $k = 1, \cdots, n$. We first assume that the polynomial $P(z)$ does not vanish at all, and we consider the rational function $1/P(z)$. Since $P(z) \neq 0$, this function has no finite poles, and it is clearly regular for $z = \infty$. Hence, it must reduce to a constant, and $P(z)$ must therefore also be a constant. But, since $\alpha_n \neq 0$ and $n \geq 1$, this is impossible, and the assumption $P(z) \neq 0$ has thus led to a contradiction. There must therefore exist a number z_1 such that $P(z_1) = 0$. Expanding $P(z)$ in powers of $z - z_1$, we obtain

$$P(z) = C_1(z - z_1) + C_2(z - z_1)^2 + \cdots + C_n(z - z_1)^n,$$

and this shows that $P(z) = (z - z_1)P_1(z)$, where $P_1(z)$ is a polynomial of degree $n - 1$.

If $n - 1 \geq 1$, and we apply to $P_1(z)$ the argument just applied to $P(z)$, we find that there exists a number z_2 such that $P_1(z_2) = 0$ and $P_1(z) = (z - z_2)P_2(z)$, where $P_2(z)$ is a polynomial of degree $n - 2$. Hence, $P(z) = (z - z_1)(z - z_2)P_2(z)$. This process can be continued as long as the remaining polynomial is of positive degree. Since a polynomial of degree zero is a constant, we have thus proved that

$$(33) \qquad P(z) = C(z - z_1)(z - z_2) \cdots (z - z_n),$$

where C is a constant. Since $P(z_k) = 0$ for $k = 1, 2, \cdots, n$, this proves the fundamental theorem of algebra. The numbers $z_1, \cdots, z_n$ are not necessarily all different. If m of these numbers coincide, we say that the corresponding root is of mth order, or of *multiplicity m*. The statement that Equation (32) has n roots will, of course, be true only if each root is counted as many times as its multiplicity indicates.

With the help of the fundamental theorem of algebra we can show that *a rational function takes all values exactly the same number of times.* Indeed, if $f(z)$ is the function (28), and β is an arbitrary complex number, the equation $f(z) = \beta$ is equivalent to $P(z) - \beta Q(z) = 0$. If $m \neq n$ and $\beta \neq 0, \infty$, the polynomial $P(z) - \beta Q(z)$ is always of the same degree, regardless of the value of β. The number of solutions of the equation $P(z) - \beta Q(z)$ is therefore independent of the value of β. If $m = n$, it is easy to see that

$$\frac{P(z)}{Q(z)} = \frac{P_1(z)}{Q(z)} + \gamma,$$

where γ is a constant, and $P_1(z)$ is a polynomial of degree $n - 1$. The preceding argument may therefore be applied to the function P_1/Q, and this proves the result in the case $n = m$. The discussion of the cases $\beta = 0$ and $\beta = \infty$ is left as an exercise to the reader.

EXERCISES

1. Let $a_0, a_1, \cdots, a_n, A_0, A_1, \cdots, A_n$ be given complex numbers, and suppose that the numbers a_k are all different. Show that there cannot exist more than one polynomial $P(z)$ of degree n for which $P(a_k) = A_k, k = 0, 1, \cdots, n$.

2. If $P_k(z)$ is the product of n factors,

$$P_k(z) = \prod_{\nu \neq k} (z - a_\nu),$$

show that the polynomial of the preceding exercise is given by the *Lagrange interpolation formula*

$$P(z) = \sum_{k=0}^{n} A_k \frac{P_k(z)}{P_k(a_k)}.$$

3. If $\omega = e^{\frac{2\pi i}{n+1}}$, the numbers $\omega, \omega^2, \cdots, \omega^{n+1}$ are the roots of unity of degree $n + 1$ (Chap. I, Sec. 3). Show that the polynomial $P(z)$ of degree n for which $P(\omega^\nu) = A_\nu$ can be written in the form

$$P(z) = \frac{1}{n+1} \sum_{\nu=0}^{n} \omega^\nu A_\nu \left(\frac{z^{n+1} - 1}{z - \omega^\nu} \right).$$

4. If $\omega = e^{2\pi i/n}$, show that

$$\prod_{\nu=1}^{n} (1 - \omega^\nu z) = 1 - z^n$$

and

$$\prod_{\nu=1}^{n-1} (1 - \omega^\nu z) = 1 + z + z^2 + \cdots + z^{n-1}.$$

5. Setting $z = 1$ in the preceding formula, prove the identity

$$\prod_{\nu=1}^{n-1} \sin \frac{\pi\nu}{n} = \frac{n}{2^{n-1}}.$$

6. If all the zeros and poles of a rational function $f(z)$ are of even order, show that $f(z) = [g(z)]^2$, where $g(z)$ is another rational function.

7. If $z_1, \cdots, z_n$ are the zeros of a polynomial $P(z)$ of degree n, show that

$$\frac{P'(z)}{P(z)} = \sum_{k=1}^{n} \frac{1}{z - z_k} = \sum_{k=1}^{n} \frac{\bar{z} - \bar{z}_k}{|z - z_k|^2}.$$

Combining this with the result of Exercise 13, Chapter I, Section 3, prove the following theorem: The zeros of the derivative $P'(z)$ of a polynomial $P(z)$ lie in the smallest convex polygon which contains the zeros of $P(z)$.

8. Let $f(z)$ be a rational function all of whose zeros and poles are simple. If its zeros are located at the points $\alpha_1, \cdots, \alpha_n$ and its poles at $\bar{\alpha}_1^{-1}, \cdots, \bar{\alpha}_n^{-1}$, where $|\alpha_k| \neq 1$, show that $|f(z)|$ has a constant value on the circumference $|z| = 1$. *Hint:* Show that $|z - \alpha| = |1 - \bar{\alpha}z|$ for $|z| = 1$.

9. Show that, for a given rational function $f(z)$, it is always possible to find another rational function $g(z)$ which has no poles in the disk $|z| < 1$, and for which $|g(z)| = |f(z)|$ on the circumference $|z| = 1$.

6   THE RESIDUE THEOREM

As shown before, a function $f(z)$ which has an isolated singularity at a point $z = a$ (and is single-valued in the neighborhood of this point) can be expanded into a Laurent series (22), whose coefficients are given by (23). The coefficient a_{-1} of this expansion is of particular interest. As (23) shows, we have

$$(34) \qquad\qquad a_{-1} = \frac{1}{2\pi i} \int_C f(z)\, dz,$$

where C is a simple closed contour surrounding the point $z = a$, and $f(z)$ is regular on C and at all points of the interior of C with the exception of $z = a$. The coefficient a_{-1} is called the *residue* of the function $f(z)$ at the singular point $z = a$. Its importance is due to the fact that, except for a numerical factor, it is equal to the value of the integral of $f(z)$ over the closed contour C. In those cases in which the value of a_{-1} can be determined by some other method, equation (34) will thus make it possible to evaluate this integral without actually using an integration process, and without the knowledge of the indefinite integral of $f(z)$.

This method of evaluating integrals over closed curves is easily extended to the case in which there is a finite number of isolated singularities $a_1, a_2, \cdots, a_n$ in the interior of C. Since these singular points are isolated, we can draw small circles $C_1, \cdots, C_n$ about $a_1, \cdots, a_n$ which are entirely in the interior of C and which do not overlap. The contour C and the circumferences $C_1, \cdots, C_n$ form the boundary of a domain of connectivity $n + 1$, in the interior of which the function $f(z)$ is regular and single-valued. We may therefore apply the identity (28) of the preceding chapter. Hence,

$$\int_C f(z)\, dz = \sum_{\nu=1}^n \int_{C_\nu} f(z)\, dz.$$

To each of the integrals on the right-hand side we may apply (34). If R_{a_ν} is the residue of the function $f(z)$ at the point $z = a_\nu$, we thus have

$$(35) \qquad \int_C f(z)\, dz = 2\pi i \sum_{\nu=1}^n R_{a_\nu}.$$

The result expressed by this formula is known as the *residue theorem*. It should be kept in mind that the validity of (35) was proved under the following conditions: $f(z)$ is regular and single-valued on the simple closed contour C and in its interior, except at the points $a_1, \cdots, a_n$, which are isolated singularities of $f(z)$.

The residue theorem has many applications in complex analysis. One of these, as pointed out above, is its use in the "integration-less" evaluation of integrals over closed curves. In these cases we must, of course, be able to find the residues R_a by some method which does *not* involve integration. Since R_a is the coefficient of $(z - a)^{-1}$ in the Laurent expansion about the point $z = a$, R_a will be known whenever this Laurent expansion is known explicitly. This expansion—and, in particular, the value of the residue—can be obtained without too much effort whenever the singularity in question is a pole. If the point $z = a$ is an essential singularity of the function, it is in general not possible to find the residue R_a without the use of integration.

The computation of the residue R_a is particularly simple if $z = a$ is a pole of first order or, as we also say, a *simple pole* of the function $f(z)$. In this case, the Laurent expansion of $f(z)$ has the form

$$f(z) = \frac{R_a}{z - a} + A_0 + A_1(z - a) + \cdots,$$

and this shows that

$$(36) \qquad R_a = \lim_{z \to a} (z - a)f(z).$$

In the case of a double pole, a convenient way of computing the residue is obtained by observing that, because of

$$f(z) = \frac{A_{-2}}{(z - a)^2} + \frac{R_a}{z - a} + A_0 + A_1(z - a) + \cdots,$$

we have

$$(z - a)^2 f(z) = A_{-2} + R_a(z - a) + A_0(z - a)^2 + \cdots,$$

and therefore

$$(37) \qquad R_a = \lim_{z \to a} [(z - a)^2 f(z)]'.$$

The reader will have no difficulty in obtaining similar formulas for poles of higher order. It should, however, be noted that the validity of these formulas depends on the correct value of the order of the pole. For instance, (36) will give the residue only if the pole is simple; if the pole is of higher order, this limit is infinite. Similarly, (37) can be used only if the order of the pole does not exceed 2.

We now consider some classes of real definite integrals which can be evaluated with the help of the residue theorem. We begin with integrals of the form

$$\int_0^{2\pi} F(\cos \theta, \sin \theta) \, d\theta,$$

where $F(s, t)$ is a rational function of s and t. If we write $z = e^{i\theta}$, the integration interval $0 \leq \theta \leq 2\pi$ is transformed into the circumference $|z| = 1$ in the complex z-plane. Since

$$\cos \theta = \frac{1}{2}\left(e^{i\theta} + e^{-i\theta}\right) = \frac{1}{2}\left(z + \frac{1}{z}\right),$$

$$\sin \theta = \frac{1}{2i}\left(e^{i\theta} - e^{-i\theta}\right) = \frac{1}{2i}\left(z - \frac{1}{z}\right),$$

and since $dz = ie^{i\theta}\, d\theta = iz\, d\theta$, the original integral is transformed into the contour integral

$$\frac{1}{i}\int_C F\left[\frac{1}{2}\left(z + \frac{1}{z}\right), \frac{1}{2i}\left(z - \frac{1}{z}\right)\right]\frac{dz}{z},$$

where C is the circumference $|z| = 1$. Clearly, the integrand is a rational function of z. According to the residue theorem, its value will therefore be $2\pi i$ times the sum of the residues at the poles of the integrand in the disk $|z| < 1$ (there can be no poles on $|z| = 1$ if the original integral exists). As an example, we consider the integral

$$I = \int_0^{2\pi} \frac{d\theta}{a + b \cos \theta}, \quad 0 < b < a.$$

Introducing the complex variable z, we obtain

$$I = \frac{2}{i}\int_C \frac{dz}{bz^2 + 2az + b} = \frac{2}{ib}\int_C \frac{dz}{(z - \alpha)(z - \beta)},$$

where

$$\alpha = \frac{-a + \sqrt{a^2 - b^2}}{b}, \quad \beta = \frac{-a - \sqrt{a^2 - b^2}}{b}.$$

Since $|\alpha| < |\beta|$ and $\alpha\beta = 1$, only the point $z = \alpha$ is in the unit disk. To evaluate the integral we thus only have to find the residue of

$$\frac{1}{(z - \alpha)(z - \beta)}$$

at the point $z = \alpha$. But this is a simple pole, and (36) shows therefore that the residue is $(\alpha - \beta)^{-1}$. Applying now the residue theorem, we find that

$$I = \frac{4\pi}{b(\alpha - \beta)} = \frac{2\pi}{\sqrt{a^2 - b^2}}.$$

As an example of an integrand with a double pole, we consider

$$I = \int_0^{2\pi} \frac{d\theta}{(a + b \cos \theta)^2}, \quad 0 < b < a.$$

Introduction of the complex variable z leads to

$$I = \frac{4}{i} \int_C \frac{z \, dz}{(bz^2 + 2az + b)^2} = \frac{4}{ib^2} \int_C \frac{z \, dz}{(z - \alpha)^2(z - \beta)^2},$$

where α and β have the same meaning as before. To find the residue of

$$\frac{z}{(z - \alpha)^2(z - \beta)^2}$$

at the double pole $z = \alpha$, we use (37). Since $[z(z - \beta)^{-2}]' = -(z + \beta)(z - \beta)^{-3}$, (37) shows that the residue is $-(\alpha + \beta)(\alpha - \beta)^{-3}$. Hence,

$$I = -\frac{8\pi(\alpha + \beta)}{b^2(\alpha - \beta)^3} = \frac{2\pi a}{(a^2 - b^2)^{3/2}}.$$

A simple example involving a pole of higher order is

$$I = \int_0^{2\pi} \cos^{2n} \theta \, d\theta,$$

where n is a positive integer. This integral transforms into

$$I = \frac{1}{2^n i} \int_C \left(z + \frac{1}{z}\right)^{2n} \frac{dz}{z}.$$

The integrand is $z^{-(2n+1)}(1 + z^2)^{2n}$, and its residue at its pole of order $2n + 1$ at $z = 0$ is clearly equal to the coefficient of z^{2n} in the binomial expansion of $(1 + z^2)^{2n}$. Hence,

$$I = \frac{\pi(2n)(2n - 1) \cdots (n + 1)}{2^{n-1}(n!)} = \frac{\pi(2n)!}{2^{n-1}(n!)^2}.$$

In the integrals considered so far, the given integration interval was automatically transformed into a closed contour in the z-plane, and this enabled us to apply the residue theorem. We now turn to the discussion of cases in which the integration curves are not closed a priori. In order to make the residue theorem applicable, it becomes necessary to replace the given integration curves by equivalent ones which are closed. As a first illustration of how this is done, we consider the integral

(38) $$\int_{-\infty}^{\infty} R(x) \, dx,$$

where $R(x)$ is a rational function of x for which $\int_{-\infty}^{\infty} |R(x)| \, dx$ exists. Clearly, $R(z)$ must have no poles on the real axis and, if $R(z)$ is written in the form (28), the degree of the denominator of $R(z)$ must exceed the degree of the numerator by at least 2.

We first compute the integral

$$\int_C R(z)\, dz,$$

where the closed contour C consists of the real segment $-r \leq z \leq r$ and the half-circle $z = re^{i\theta}, 0 < \theta < \pi$. Since the rational function $R(z)$ has only a finite number of poles, there exists a number r_0 such that for $r > r_0$, all the poles of $R(z)$ are situated in the disk $|z| < r$. The contour C will then contain in its interior all the poles a_ν of $R(z)$ for which $\mathrm{Im}(a_\nu) > 0$, and it follows from the residue theorem that

$$2\pi i \sum_\nu R_{a_\nu} = \int_C R(z)\, dz = \int_{-r}^{r} R(x)\, dx + \int_{C'} R(z)\, dz,$$

where the summation is extended over the poles in the upper half-plane, and where C' is the half-circle. In view of our assumptions about $R(z)$, we have $|z^2 R(z)| < M$ for large $|z|$, where M is a positive constant. On C', we have $dz = ire^{i\theta}\, d\theta$, and therefore

$$\left| \int_{C'} R(z)\, dz \right| = \left| ir \int_{C'} R(re^{i\theta})e^{i\theta}\, d\theta \right| \leq \frac{\pi M}{r}.$$

It follows that

$$\left| 2\pi i \sum_\nu R_{a_\nu} - \int_{-r}^{r} R(x)\, dx \right| \leq \frac{\pi M}{r}.$$

and thus, for $r \to \infty$,

$$(39) \qquad \int_{-\infty}^{\infty} R(x)\, dx = 2\pi i \sum_\nu R_{a_\nu}.$$

In using this formula, it must be remembered that only the residues of poles in the upper half-plane appear in the summation.

For instance, to compute the integral corresponding to $R(x) = (1 + x^2)^{-1}$, we note that the only pole of

$$(1 + z^2)^{-1} = [(z + i)(z - i)]^{-1}$$

in the upper half-plane is the simple pole at $z = i$. By (36), the residue is $2i$, and it follows that

$$\int_{-\infty}^{\infty} \frac{dx}{1 + x^2} = \pi.$$

As a less elementary example, consider the integrand

$$R(x) = (1 + x^4)^{-1}.$$

We have

$$\frac{1}{z^4 + 1} = \frac{1}{(z^2 + i)(z^2 - i)} = \frac{1}{(z + i\sqrt{i})(z - i\sqrt{i})(z + \sqrt{i})(z - \sqrt{i})},$$

where $\sqrt{i}$ is one of the two values denoted by this symbol. If we set $\sqrt{i} = e^{\pi i/4} = 2^{-1/2}(1 + i)$, the integrand will have two simple poles, at $z = \sqrt{i}$ and $z = i\sqrt{i}$, in the upper half-plane. By (36), the residues at these points are found to be $(4i\sqrt{i})^{-1}$ and $(4\sqrt{i})^{-1}$, respectively. The sum of these two numbers is $(2\sqrt{2}\,i)^{-1}$, and it thus follows that

$$\int_{-\infty}^{\infty} \frac{dx}{1 + x^4} = \frac{\pi}{\sqrt{2}}.$$

The procedure used to compute the integral (38) can be extended to integrals of the type

$$\int_{-\infty}^{\infty} R(x)\cos \alpha x \, dx, \quad \int_{-\infty}^{\infty} R(x)\sin \alpha x \, dx, \quad \alpha > 0,$$

where the rational function $R(x)$ is real for real x, and otherwise has the same properties as before. Since $R(x)$ is real, the two integrals are the real and imaginary parts of

$$\int_{-\infty}^{\infty} R(x)e^{i\alpha x} \, dx,$$

and it is sufficient to evaluate this integral. If C is the closed contour used before, we consider the integral

$$\int_C R(z)e^{i\alpha z} \, dz.$$

Since, at all points of C, $|e^{i\alpha z}| = |e^{i\alpha x - \alpha y}| = e^{-\alpha y} \leq 1$, we have $|R(z)e^{i\alpha z}| \leq |R(z)|$, and the previous estimates become applicable. The only difference is that now the relevant residues are those of the function $R(z)e^{i\alpha z}$. The result corresponding to (39) is therefore

$$\int_{-\infty}^{\infty} R(x)e^{i\alpha x} \, dx = 2\pi i \sum_{\nu} R_{\alpha_\nu},$$

where the summation is extended over all residues of $R(z)e^{i\alpha z}$ in the upper half-plane.

As an application, we compute

$$\int_{-\infty}^{\infty} \frac{\cos \alpha x \, dx}{a^2 + x^2}, \quad a > 0.$$

In the upper half-plane, the function $e^{i\alpha z}(a^2 + z^2)^{-1}$ has a simple pole at $z = ai$, and its residue at this point is $(2iae^{\alpha a})^{-1}$. Hence

$$2 \int_0^\infty \frac{\cos dx}{a^2 + x^2}\, dx = \int_{-\infty}^\infty \frac{\cos \alpha x}{a^2 + x^2}\, dx = \int_{-\infty}^\infty \frac{e^{i\alpha x}}{a^2 + x^2}\, dx = \frac{\pi}{a} e^{-\alpha a}.$$

The imaginary part of the integral is zero, since the integrand is an odd function of x.

It is worth keeping in mind that from a known definite integral which depends on one or more arbitrary parameters, other definite integrals can be obtained by differentiating or integrating with respect to these parameters. This will often be easier than evaluating these new integrals by the residue method. For instance, differentiation of the identity

$$(40) \qquad\qquad \int_0^\infty \frac{\cos \alpha x}{a^2 + x^2}\, dx = \frac{\pi}{2a} e^{-\alpha a}$$

with respect to α yields

$$\int_0^\infty \frac{x \sin \alpha x}{a^2 + x^2}\, dx = \frac{\pi}{2} e^{-a\alpha}.$$

For $\alpha = 1$ and $a \to 0$ (prove the legitimacy of this passage to the limit!), we obtain the well-known formula

$$\int_0^\infty \frac{\sin x}{x}\, dx = \frac{\pi}{2}.$$

If (40) is differentiated with respect to a, the result is

$$\int_0^\infty \frac{\cos x\, dx}{(a^2 + x^2)^2}\, dx = \frac{\pi(1 + a\alpha)}{4a^3} e^{-a\alpha},$$

and additional differentiations with respect to a will successively yield the values of

$$\int_0^\infty \frac{\cos x\, dx}{(a^2 + x^2)^n}\, dx$$

for all positive integers n.

Another general type of integral which can be evaluated with the help of residues is

$$(41) \qquad\qquad \int_0^\infty x^{\alpha-1} R(x)\, dx,$$

where $R(z)$ is a rational function of z. If the function $x^{\alpha-1}R(x)$ is to be integrable over the interval $(0, \infty)$, we must require that $R(z)$

be free of poles on the positive axis, and that $|z^\alpha R(z)| \to 0$ for $|z| \to 0$ and $|z| \to \infty$.

The technique of evaluating this integral is the same as before. We compute the integral

$$\int_C z^{\alpha-1} R(z) \, dz$$

over a suitable closed path C, and a passage to the limit will then yield the value of (41). In choosing C, we must take into account the fact that the origin is a branch-point of the integrand and that, as a result, the integrand will not be single-valued in a domain containing the origin. In order to be able to apply the residue theorem, we have to use a contour C which forms the boundary of a domain D in which the integrand is single-valued. In view of the properties of the function z^α discussed in Chapter II, Section 6, a suitable domain D is obtained by cutting the circular ring $\rho < |z| < r$ along the linear segment $\rho < z < r$. Clearly, D is simply-connected, and its boundary C consists of the following four sections: the circumference $|z| = r$, the circumference $|z| = \rho$, the upper edge of the cut $\rho < z < r$, and the lower edge of this cut. The function $R(z)$ has a finite number of poles in $0 < |z| < \infty$, and we may therefore choose ρ and r in such a way that all these poles are in $\rho < |z| < r$. It then follows from the residue theorem that

$$(42) \qquad \int_C z^{\alpha-1} R(z) \, dz = 2\pi i \sum_\nu R_{a_\nu},$$

where the summation is extended over all poles of $R(z)$ in $0 < |z| < \infty$.

The values of the integrals over $|z| = \rho$ and $|z| = r$ tend to zero for $\rho \to 0$ and $r \to \infty$. Indeed, since $|z^\alpha R(z)| \to 0$ for $|z| \to 0$ and $|z| \to \infty$, we have on these circumferences

$$\left| \int z^{\alpha-1} R(z) \, dz \right| \leq \int_0^{2\pi} |z^\alpha R(z)| \, d\theta \to 0.$$

If the value of the integrand on the upper edge of the cut is $z^{\alpha-1} R(z)$, its value on the lower edge is $e^{2\pi i \alpha} z^{\alpha-1} R(z)$; this follows from the properties of the function z^α discussed in Chapter II, and from the fact that we pass from the upper edge to the lower by describing $|z| = \rho$ in the positive direction. The latter remark also makes it clear that a point traversing C in the positive direction will go over the upper edge from ρ to r, and on the lower edge from r to ρ.

If all this is taken into account, and if ρ and r are made to tend to 0 and ∞, respectively, (42) takes the form

$$\int_0^\infty x^{\alpha-1} R(x)\, dx - e^{2\pi i\alpha} \int_0^\infty x^{\alpha-1} R(x)\, dx = 2\pi i \sum_\nu R_{a_\nu},$$

i.e.,

$$(43) \qquad \int_0^\infty x^{\alpha-1} R(x)\, dx = \frac{2\pi i \sum\limits_\nu R_{a_\nu}}{1 - e^{2\pi i\alpha}}.$$

This is the desired formula. Its validity does not depend on the branch of the function z^α used in the computation. If α is a real number, it will of course be convenient to choose the branch of x^α which is positive on the upper edge.

To illustrate the use of (43), we compute the integral

$$\int_0^\infty \frac{x^{\alpha-1}}{x + a}\, dx, \quad 0 < \alpha < 1,$$

where the number a is not negative, but otherwise arbitrary. The integrand has a simple pole at $z = -a$, and its residue at this point is $(-a)^{\alpha-1}$. It thus follows from (43) that

$$\int_0^\infty \frac{x^{\alpha-1}}{x + a}\, dx = \frac{2\pi i (-a)^{\alpha-1}}{1 - e^{2\pi i\alpha}}.$$

In view of

$$(-a)^{\alpha-1} = (ae^{\pi i})^{\alpha-1} = a^{\alpha-1} e^{\pi i(\alpha-1)} = a^{\alpha-1} e^{\pi i\alpha} e^{-\pi i} = -a^{\alpha-1} e^{\pi i\alpha}$$

and

$$\frac{e^{\pi i\alpha}}{1 - e^{2\pi i\alpha}} = \frac{1}{e^{-\pi i\alpha} - e^{\pi i\alpha}} = \frac{i}{2\sin \pi\alpha},$$

this can be brought into the form

$$(44) \qquad \int_0^\infty \frac{x^{\alpha-1}}{x + a}\, dx = \frac{\pi a^{\alpha-1}}{\sin \pi\alpha}.$$

By differentiating, or integrating, this identity with respect to the parameters a and α, many related definite integrals can be obtained. For instance, a differentiation with respect to a yields

$$\int_0^\infty \frac{x^{\alpha-1}\, dx}{(x + a)^2} = \frac{\pi(1 - \alpha)a^{\alpha-2}}{\sin \pi\alpha}, \quad 0 < \alpha < 2,$$

and further differentiations lead to the integrals

$$\int_0^\infty x^{\alpha-1}(x + a)^{-n}\, dx, \quad n = 2, 3, \cdots.$$

If we set $a = ic$ ($c > 0$) in (44), we have

$$\int_0^\infty \frac{x^{\alpha-1}}{x + ic}\, dx = \int_0^\infty \frac{x^{\alpha-1}(x - ic)}{x^2 + c^2}\, dx = \frac{\pi(ic)^{\alpha-1}}{\sin \pi\alpha}.$$

Observing that $i^{\alpha-1} = e^{\frac{\pi i}{2}(\alpha-1)} = -ie^{\frac{\pi i \alpha}{2}}$, and separating real and imaginary parts, we find that

$$\int_0^\infty \frac{x^\alpha}{x^2 + c^2}\, dx = \frac{\pi c^{\alpha-1}}{2 \cos \dfrac{\pi \alpha}{2}}.$$

This identity may again serve as a point of departure for the computation of additional definite integrals.

As these examples illustrate, the computation of a complicated definite integral—especially one involving poles of higher order—by residue methods is not necessarily the most economical way of getting the result. A considerable amount of computational labor can often be saved by first computing a similar integral of simpler type—say, an integral involving a simple pole—and then obtaining the value of the desired integral by differentiation with respect to a parameter, by separating real and imaginary parts, or by other analytic manipulations. For instance, instead of computing

$$\int_{-\infty}^\infty \frac{dx}{(1 + x^2)^n}$$

by finding the residue of $(1 + z^2)^{-n}$ at $z = i$, it is easier to differentiate the identity

$$\int_{-\infty}^\infty \frac{dx}{a + x^2} = \frac{\pi}{\sqrt{a}}$$

$n - 1$ times. This gives

$$(-1)^{n-1}(n - 1)! \int_{-\infty}^\infty \frac{dx}{(a + x^2)^n} = \pi \frac{(-1)^{n-1}}{a^{n-1/2}} \cdot \frac{1}{2} \cdot \frac{3}{2} \cdots \frac{(2n - 3)}{2},$$

and thus

$$\int_{-\infty}^\infty \frac{dx}{(1 + x^2)^n} = \frac{\pi(2n - 2)!}{2^{2n-2}[(n - 1)!]^2}.$$

The differentiation under the integral sign can be justified by an elementary argument.

EXERCISES

Evaluate the integrals in Exercises 1 through 10 by the residue method.

1. $\displaystyle\int_0^{2\pi} \frac{d\theta}{a^2 \cos^2\theta + b^2 \sin^2\theta} = \frac{\pi}{2ab}$, $(a,b$ real$)$.

2. $\displaystyle\int_0^{2\pi} \frac{\cos^3 3\theta}{1 - 2a\cos\theta + a^2} \, d\theta = \pi\frac{1 - a + a^2}{1 - a}$, $0 < a < 1$.

3. $\displaystyle\int_0^{2\pi} e^{2\cos\theta} \, d\theta = 2\pi \sum_{n=0}^{\infty} \frac{1}{(n!)^2}$

4. $\displaystyle\int_{-\infty}^{\infty} \frac{dx}{(a^2 + x^2)(b^2 + x^2)} = \frac{\pi}{ab(a + b)}$

5. $\displaystyle\int_{-\infty}^{\infty} \frac{x^2 - x + 2}{x^4 + 10x^2 + 9} \, dx = \frac{5\pi}{12}$

6. $\displaystyle\int_{-\infty}^{\infty} \frac{dx}{1 + x^6} = \frac{2\pi}{3}$

7. $\displaystyle\int_{-\infty}^{\infty} \frac{\cos \alpha x}{a^4 + x^4} \, dx = \frac{\pi}{\sqrt{2a^3}} e^{-a\alpha/2} \left(\cos \frac{a\alpha}{\sqrt{2}} + \sin \frac{a\alpha}{\sqrt{2}}\right)$

8. $\displaystyle\int_{-\infty}^{\infty} \frac{x \sin \alpha x}{a^4 + x^4} \, dx = \frac{\pi}{a^2} e^{-a\alpha/\sqrt{2}} \sin \frac{a\alpha}{\sqrt{2}}$.

9. $\displaystyle\int_0^{\infty} \frac{x^{-\alpha}dx}{1 + 2x\cos\theta + x^2} = \frac{\pi}{\sin \pi\alpha} \frac{\sin \alpha\theta}{\sin \theta}$,
$$-1 < \alpha < 1, \quad -\pi < \theta < \pi.$$

10. $\displaystyle\int_0^{\infty} \frac{x^{\alpha-1} dx}{1 + x^4} = \frac{\pi}{8 \sin \dfrac{\pi\alpha}{4}}$, $0 < \alpha < 4$.

11. Using the result of Exercise 1, show that

$$\int_0^{2\pi} \frac{d\theta}{(a^2 \cos^2\theta + b^2 \sin^2\theta)^2} = \frac{\pi(a^2 + b^2)}{4a^3b^3}, \quad (a,b \text{ real}).$$

12. Using the result of Exercise 4, show that

$$\int_{-\infty}^{\infty} \frac{dx}{(a^2 + x^2)^2(b^2 + x^2)^2} = \frac{\pi(a^2 + 3ab + b^2)}{2a^3b^3(a + b)^3}.$$

13. If

$$f(z) = \sum_{n=0}^{\infty} a_n z^n, \quad |z| \leq r,$$

$$g(z) = \sum_{n=0}^{\infty} b_n z^n, \quad |z| < \rho,$$

show that

$$\sum_{n=0}^{\infty} a_n b_n z^n = \frac{1}{2\pi i} \int_{|t|=r} f(t) g\left(\frac{z}{t}\right) \frac{dt}{t}, \quad |z| < \rho r.$$

14. Let the functions $f(z)$ and $g(z)$ be regular at the point $z = a$. If $f(a) \neq 0$, $g(a) = 0$, $g'(a) \neq 0$, show that the residue of the function $f(z)/g(z)$ at $z = a$ is

$$\frac{f(a)}{g'(a)}.$$

15. If $f(z)$ is regular in $|z| \leq 1$, show that

$$(1 - |z|^2) f(z) = \frac{1}{2\pi i} \int_{|t|=1} f(t) \left(\frac{1 - \bar{z}t}{t - z}\right) dt,$$

and conclude that

$$(1 - |z|^2)|f(z)| \leq \frac{1}{2\pi} \int_0^{2\pi} |f(e^{i\theta})| \, d\theta.$$

16. Let $f(z) = \sum_{\nu=0}^{\infty} a_\nu z^\nu$ be regular in $|z| \leq R$. If $s_n(z)$ is the partial sum

$$s_n(z) = \sum_{\nu=0}^{n} a_\nu z^\nu,$$

show that

$$s_n(z) = \frac{1}{2\pi i} \int_{|z|=R} f(t) \left(\frac{t^{n+1} - z^{n+1}}{t - z}\right) \frac{dt}{t^{n+1}}.$$

17. Let $P(z)$ be the polynomial $(z - z_1)(z - z_2) \cdots (z - z_n)$, where $z_\nu \neq z_\mu$ for $\nu \neq \mu$. If C is the boundary of a domain D containing the points z_ν, and if $f(z)$ is regular and single-valued in $C + D$, show that

$$Q(z) = \frac{1}{2\pi i} \int_C \frac{f(t)}{P(t)} \frac{P(t) - P(z)}{t - z} \, dt$$

is a polynomial of order $n - 1$, and that $f(z_\nu) = Q(z_\nu)$, $\nu = 1$, $2, \cdots, n$.

18. If the rational function $R(z)$ is the derivative of another rational function, show that all the residues of $R(z)$ must be zero.

19. If, near $z = \infty$, the Laurent expansion of the rational function $R(z)$ is

$$R(z) = A_n z^n + A_{n-1} z^{n-1} + \cdots + A_0 + \frac{A_{-1}}{z} + \frac{A_{-2}}{z^2} + \cdots,$$

the quantity $-A_{-1}$ is called *the residue of $R(z)$ at $z = \infty$*. Using this definition, prove that *the sum of all the residues of a rational function is zero*. (*Hint:* Integrate $R(z)$ over a circle $|z| = r$ which contains all the finite poles of the function.)

20. Applying the preceding result to the function

$$\frac{P'(z)}{P(z)},$$

where $P(z)$ is a polynomial of degree n, give an alternative proof of the fundamental theorem of algebra.

21. Let r be a positive number, and let a be non-real. By computing the integral

$$\int_{-r}^{r} \left(\sum_{\nu=1}^{m} \frac{A_\nu}{(z-a)^\nu} \right) dz$$

and letting $r \to \infty$, show that the value of

$$\int_{-\infty}^{\infty} \left(\sum_{\nu=1}^{m} \frac{A_\nu}{(z-a)^\nu} \right) dz$$

is $\pi i A_1$ if $\text{Im}(a) > 0$, and $-\pi i A_1$ if $\text{Im}(a) < 0$.

22. Using the decomposition of a rational function into a sum of partial fractions (Sec. 5) and the results of Exercises 19 and 21, give an alternative proof of Formula (39).

7 THE ARGUMENT PRINCIPLE

An analytic function $f(z)$ which is regular at a point $z = a$ and has there a zero of order k can be written in the form

$$f(z) = (z-a)^k g(z),$$

where the function $g(z)$ is regular at $z = a$, and $g'(a) \neq 0$. This implies the relation

$$\frac{f'(z)}{f(z)} = \frac{k}{z-a} + \frac{g'(z)}{g(z)}$$

$$= \frac{k}{z-a} + \text{terms regular at } z = a,$$

which shows that the logarithmic derivative $f'(z)/f(z)$ of $f(z)$ has at

$z = a$ a simple pole with the residue k. This property of the logarithmic derivative gives rise to a simple formula for the total number of zeros N of an analytic function in a domain D. Let C be a simple closed contour, D its interior, and let $f(z)$ be regular in $D + C$. If $f(z) \neq 0$ on C, it follows from the residue theorem that

$$(45) \qquad N = \frac{1}{2\pi i} \int_C \frac{f'(z)}{f(z)} \, dz,$$

if all the zeros in D are counted with their multiplicities. Indeed, the zeros of $f(z)$ are the only singularities of f'/f and, as just shown, the residue corresponding to a given zero is equal to its multiplicity.

This formula can be generalized to the case in which the function $f(z)$ has a finite number of poles in D. If $f(z)$ has a pole of order m at $z = b$, $f(z)$ can be written

$$f(z) = \frac{h(z)}{(z - b)^m},$$

where $h(z)$ is regular at $z = b$, and $h(b) \neq 0$. Hence,

$$\frac{f'(z)}{f(z)} = -\frac{m}{z - b} + \frac{h'(z)}{h(z)},$$

and we see that, at a pole of order m, the logarithmic derivative has a simple pole with the residue $-m$. If P is the total number of the poles of $f(z)$ in D, we have therefore

$$(46) \qquad N - P = \frac{1}{2\pi i} \int_C \frac{f'(z)}{f(z)} \, dz,$$

if both the zeros and the poles of $f(z)$ in D are counted with their multiplicities. If $f(z)$ is regular in D, (46) reduces to (45).

At the first glance it may seem surprising that the integral on the right-hand side of (46) is always equal to an integer. In order to see why this should be the case—and also in order to gain a fuller understanding of the facts expressed by (46)—we replace $f(z)$ by its polar representation $f(z) = Re^{i\phi}$, where $R = |f(z)|$ and $\phi = \arg [f(z)]$. In view of $f'(z)dz = df(z) = d(Re^{i\phi}) = e^{i\phi}(dR + iR d\phi)$, (46) transforms into

$$N - P = \frac{1}{2\pi i} \int_C \left(\frac{dR}{R} + i d\phi \right) = \frac{1}{2\pi i} \int_C \frac{dR}{R} + \frac{1}{2\pi} \int_C d\phi.$$

Since

$$\int_C \frac{dR}{R} = [\log R]_C,$$

and since $\log R$ returns to its initial value if the point z traverses the entire contour C, this integral has the value zero. Hence,

$$(47) \qquad N - P = \frac{1}{2\pi} \int_C d\phi.$$

Again, we have

$$(48) \qquad \int_C d\phi = [\phi]_C,$$

but this time we cannot conclude that the integral is zero, since the argument ϕ does not necessarily return to its initial value if z traverses the entire contour C. If z_0 is a point of C, we can replace (48) by

$$\int_C d\phi = \phi^*(z_0) - \phi(z_0) = [\arg f(z_0)]^* - \arg f(z_0),$$

where $\phi^*(z_0)$ is the value of the argument *after* the contour C has been traversed. Since the various possible values of the argument of a complex number can differ from each other only by an integral multiple of 2π, it is clear that

$$\Delta_C \arg f(z) = [\arg f(z_0)]^* - \arg f(z_0),$$

the *variation of arg f(z) along the contour* C, must be an integral multiple of 2π. Because of (47), Formula (46) is equivalent to

$$(49) \qquad N - P = \frac{1}{2\pi} \Delta_C \arg f(z),$$

and this makes it plain why the right-hand side of (46) is always equal to an integer.

The formula (49), which makes it possible to compute the number $N - P$ from the variation of the argument of $f(z)$ along the boundary C, is known as the *argument principle*. Before we illustrate the application of this principle by a number of examples, we point out that Formulas (46) and (49) may also be used to count the number of times, N_α, a function $f(z)$ takes the value α. Indeed, since $f(z) - \alpha$ is zero if $f(z) = \alpha$, it follows from (46) that

$$(50) \qquad N_\alpha - P = \frac{1}{2\pi i} \int_C \frac{f'(z)}{f(z) - \alpha} \, dz.$$

Similarly, (49) shows that

$$(51) \qquad N_\alpha - P = \frac{1}{2\pi} \Delta_C \arg [f(z) - \alpha].$$

As a first application of the argument principle we prove the following useful result, known as *Rouché's theorem*.

Let $f(z)$ and $g(z)$ be regular in a domain D and on its boundary C. If, at all points of C, $|f(z)| > |g(z)|$, then the function $f(z) + g(z)$ has exactly as many zeros in D as the function $f(z)$.

Since, for any two non-zero complex numbers α and β, we have $\arg (\alpha\beta) = \arg \alpha + \arg \beta$, it follows from

$$f(z) + g(z) = f(z) \left[1 + \frac{g(z)}{f(z)} \right]$$

that

$$\arg [f(z) + g(z)] = \arg f(z) + \arg \left[1 + \frac{g(z)}{f(z)} \right],$$

where z is a point of C. The variations of these arguments along the contour C are therefore related by the formula

$$\Delta_C \arg [f(z) + g(z)] = \Delta_C \arg f(z) + \Delta_C \arg \left[1 + \frac{g(z)}{f(z)} \right].$$

Our assumptions imply that

$$(52) \qquad \Delta_C \arg \left[1 + \frac{g(z)}{f(z)} \right] = 0.$$

Indeed, since $|g(z)| < |f(z)|$ on C, the points

$$w = 1 + \frac{g(z)}{f(z)}$$

are subject to the inequality

$$|w - 1| = \left| \frac{g(z)}{f(z)} \right| < 1,$$

and this shows that w remains in the disk $|w - 1| < 1$ as the point z moves along the contour C. Since this disk is in the interior of the domain obtained by cutting the plane along the negative axis, $\arg w$ is single-valued in the disk. If z traverses the entire contour C, $\arg w$ must therefore return to its initial value, and (52) follows. Hence,

$$\Delta_C \arg [f(z) + g(z)] = \Delta_C f(z),$$

and a glance at the argument principle (49) shows that the value of $N - P$ must be the same for $f(z)$ and $f(z) + g(z)$. Since these functions are regular in D, we have $P = 0$, and we have proved that the function $f(z) + g(z)$ has as many zeros in D as the function $f(z)$.

We notice, incidentally, that, except for the last remark, our proof is also valid for functions $f(z)$ and $g(z)$ which have poles in D. In this case, the conclusion is that the difference $N - P$ between the number of zeros and the number of poles is the same for $f(z) + g(z)$ as it is for $f(z)$.

Rouché's theorem often provides a convenient means for estimating the number of roots of an equation in a given domain. Consider, for instance, the equation $z^5 + 15z + 1 = 0$. On the circle $|z| = 2$, we have $|z|^5 = 32$ and $|15z + 1| \leq 31$. Hence, the function $z^5 + 15z + 1$ has as many zeros in $|z| < 2$ as the function z^5. Since the latter function has a zero of order 5 at $z = 0$, it follows therefore from Rouché's theorem that all the five roots of $z^5 + 15z + 1 = 0$ must be in $|z| < 2$. On the other hand, since, for $|z| = \frac{3}{2}$,

$$|z^5 + 1| < \frac{243}{32} + 1 < \frac{45}{2} = |15z|,$$

the function $z^5 + 15z + 1$ has as many zeros in $|z| < \frac{3}{2}$ as the function $15z$, i.e., it has exactly one zero there. Accordingly, four of the zeros of our equation are in the ring $\frac{3}{2} < |z| < 2$.

Rouché's theorem also leads to a short proof of the fundamental theorem of algebra. If R is taken sufficiently large, we have

$$|z|^n > |a_{n-1}z^{n-1} + \cdots + a_1 z + a_0|$$

for $|z| = R$; indeed, if $|z| > 1$ we have

$$|a_{n-1}z^{n-1} + \cdots + a_0| < |z|^{n-1}[|a_{n-1}| + \cdots + |a_0|],$$

and this is smaller than $|z|^n$ for $R > |a_{n-1}| + \cdots + |a_0|$. By Rouché's theorem, the function $z^n + a_{n-1}z^{n-1} + \cdots + a_0$ will thus have as many zeros in $|z| < R$ as the function z^n. Since the latter has a zero of order n at $z = 0$, the theorem is proved.

As an example for the application of Rouché's theorem to functions which have poles, we determine the number of solutions of the equation

$$(53) \qquad\qquad \tan z = \alpha z$$

in the interior of the square with the vertices $\pm \pi n \pm i\pi n$, where n is a positive integer and α is a complex constant. On the perimeter C of the square we have

$$|\tan z| < \frac{1 + e^{-2n}}{1 - e^{-2n}};$$

the proof of this inequality follows from the definition

$$\tan z = \frac{e^{2iz} - 1}{i(e^{2iz} + 1)}$$

and is left as an exercise to the reader. Since $|\alpha z| \geq \pi n|\alpha|$ on C, we shall have $|\alpha z| > |\tan z|$ provided

$$(54) \qquad \pi n|\alpha| > \frac{1 + e^{-2n}}{1 - e^{-2n}}.$$

In the interior of this square, the difference $N - P$ between the number of zeros and the number of poles will be the same for αz and for $\alpha z - \tan z$. Since αz has one zero and no poles, we conclude that $N - P = 1$ for the function $\alpha z - \tan z$. The poles of $\tan z$ are at the points $z = \pm \frac{\pi}{2}, + \frac{3\pi}{2}, \cdots$, and they are all simple. There are thus $2n$ poles in the square, and it follows that $N = 2n + 1$. Our result is therefore that in the square with the corners $\pm \pi n \pm i\pi n$, where n and $|\alpha|$ are related by (54), the equation (53) has precisely $2n + 1$ roots. We note incidentally that, for real α, Equation (53) can easily be shown to have $2n + 1$ roots in the interval $-n < x < n$. Our result shows therefore that, for real α, all roots of (53) are real.

As a last application of the argument principle we prove that *an analytic function which is regular on and within a simple closed contour C, and which takes real values at all points of C, must reduce to a constant.* Let $\alpha = a + ib$ ($b \neq 0$) be a non-real complex number, and consider the values of $w = f(z) - \alpha = f(z) - a - ib$ as z describes C. If $b > 0$, we have $\operatorname{Im} [f(z) - a - ib] = -b$, and this shows that the point w remains in the lower half-plane. In this half-plane, $\arg w$ is single-valued, and it follows that $\Delta_C \arg w = \Delta_C \arg [f(z) - \alpha] = 0$. Since $f(z)$ has no poles, we conclude from (51) that the function $f(z)$ does not take the value α in the interior of C. But α was an arbitrary number such that $\operatorname{Im}(\alpha) > 0$, and it follows that $f(z)$ takes no values whose imaginary part is positive. The same argument also shows that $f(z)$ cannot take values whose imaginary part is negative. Hence, $f(z)$ must be real throughout the domain bounded by C. But, as shown earlier (Chap. II, Sec. 3), such a function must reduce to a constant, and the result follows.

EXERCISES

1. Show that the equation

$$ze^{a-z} = 1, \quad a > 1,$$

has precisely one root in the circle $|z| \le 1$. Show also that this root must be positive.

2. Show that the equation

$$z + e^{-z} = a, \quad a > 1,$$

has one (real) root in the half-plane $\text{Re}(z) \ge 0$.

3. If α is a complex number such that $|\alpha| < 1$, show that the function

$$f(z) = \frac{z - \alpha}{1 - \bar{\alpha}z}$$

takes in the disk $|z| < 1$ every value a for which $|a| < 1$ exactly once, and it takes no values a such that $|a| > 1$. *Hint:* Show that $|f(z)| = 1$ for $|z| = 1$, and apply Rouché's theorem to $f(z) - a$.

4. If $|\alpha_\nu| < 1$, $\nu = 1, 2, \cdots, n$, generalize the result of the preceding exercise to show that the function

$$f(z) = \prod_{\nu=1}^{n} \left(\frac{z - \alpha_\nu}{1 - \bar{\alpha}_\nu z} \right)$$

takes in $|z| < 1$ every value of modulus less that unity exactly n times, and takes no value whose modulus exceeds unity.

5. If $|\alpha| < 1$, $|\beta| < 1$, show that the function

$$f(z) = \left(\frac{z - \alpha}{1 - \bar{\alpha}z} \right) \left(\frac{1 - \bar{\beta}z}{z - \beta} \right)$$

takes in $|z| < 1$ every value a such that $|a| \ne 1$ exactly once.

6. Use Rouché's theorem to show that a rational function which has n poles in the extended z-plane takes every complex value exactly n times. *Hint:* Take C to be a small circle about one of the poles, and split off the principal part.

7. Show that the function

$$f(z) = z^m + \frac{1}{z^m},$$

where m is a positive integer, takes in $|z| < 1$ every non-real value m times.   *Hint:* Observe the behavior of $f(z)$ for $|z| = 1$.

8. If $P(z)$ and $Q(z)$ are polynomials, show that the curve, or curves, given by the equation

$$P(z) = \overline{Q(z)}$$

cannot be closed.   If the degrees of $P(z)$ and $Q(z)$ do not exceed 2, show that these curves are either hyperbolas or straight lines.

9. Let $f(z)$ be regular in a domain D and on its boundary C, and let $|f(z)|$ be constant on C.   Applying Rouché's theorem to the function $f(z) - a$, show that unless $f(z)$ reduces to a constant, it must have at least one zero in D.

8 THE MAXIMUM PRINCIPLE

Let D be a domain bounded by one or more simple closed contours C, and let $f(z)$ be regular and single-valued in $D + C$. Since $f(z)$ is continuous in the closed set $D + C$, the same is true of its absolute value $|f(z)|$, and it follows that $|f(z)|$ must attain its maximum at some point, or points, of $D + C$.   The *maximum principle*—or *maximum modulus principle*—asserts that these points cannot be in D, but must lie on the boundary C.   Before we prove this assertion, we state it in such a way as to make it applicable to functions which are only assumed to be regular in D; no assumption is made as to the regularity, or even existence, of the function $f(z)$ on the boundary of D.

If $f(z)$ is regular and single-valued in a domain D, then $|f(z)|$ cannot attain its maximum in D at an interior point of D unless $f(z)$ reduces to a constant.

If we apply the maximum principle to a domain consisting of a small neighborhood $|z - z_0| < \epsilon$ of a point z_0 at which the non-constant function $f(z)$ is regular, we see that the inequality $|f(z)| \leq |f(z_0)|$ could not possibly hold at all points z such that $|z - z_0| < \epsilon$.   In other words, $|f(z)|$ cannot have a *local maximum* at a point z_0 at which $f(z)$ is regular.   Conversely, the proof of the maximum principle can be reduced to showing that $|f(z)|$ cannot have a local maximum.   Indeed, suppose the maximum principle is not true, and there exist points z_0 in D such that $|f(z)| \leq |f(z_0)|$ for all z in D. If S denotes the set of all such points z_0, there are two possibilities: Either S coincides with D—i.e., $|f(z)|$ is constant throughout D—or S has boundary points which are interior points of D. Since, as shown in Chapter II, Section 3, $|f(z)|$ cannot be constant in a domain unless $f(z)$ itself is constant, only the second case is of interest. If z_0 is a boundary point of S which is inside D, we can find a positive ϵ such that the disk $|z - z_0| < \epsilon$ is in D. We then have $|f(z)| \leq |f(z_0)|$ at all points of the disk—i.e., we have a local maximum at z_0—and we know, moreover, that every circumference $|z - z_0| = r < \epsilon$ contains points z such that $|f(z)| < |f(z_0)|$; if this were not true, z_0 would not be a boundary point of S.

We now apply the Cauchy integral formula to the contour $|t - z_0| = r$. Writing $t = z_0 + re^{i\theta}$, we have $dt = ire^{i\theta}\, d\theta$, and therefore

$$f(z_0) = \frac{1}{2\pi i} \int_{|t - z_0| = r} \frac{f(t)}{t - z}\, dt = \frac{1}{2\pi} \int_0^{2\pi} f(z_0 + re^{i\theta})\, d\theta.$$

Hence,

$$|f(z_0)| \leq \frac{1}{2\pi} \int_0^{2\pi} |f(z_0 + re^{i\theta})|\, d\theta.$$

Since, by assumption, $|f(z_0 + re^{i\theta})| \leq |f(z_0)|$, the right-hand side cannot be larger than $|f(z_0)|$, and it follows that

$$|f(z_0)| = \frac{1}{2\pi} \int_0^{2\pi} |f(z_0 + re^{i\theta})|\, d\theta,$$

i.e.,

$$\frac{1}{2\pi} \int_0^{2\pi} [|f(z_0)| - |f(z_0 + re^{i\theta})|]\, d\theta = 0.$$

Since the integrand is continuous and non-negative, this is possible only if $|f(z_0)| - |f(z_0 + re^{i\theta})| = 0$ for all $0 \leq \theta < 2\pi$. Hence, there can be no points on $|z - z_0| = r$ at which $|f(z)| < |f(z_0)|$. The assumption that the set S has boundary points which are interior points of D has thus produced a contradiction, and it follows that S coincides with D, i.e., $f(z)$ has a constant value throughout D. This completes the proof of the maximum principle.

The minimum of $|f(z)|$ may very well be attained at an interior point of D; this will evidently happen whenever $f(z)$ takes the value zero at a point of D. However, if $f(z) \neq 0$ at all points of D, then $|f(z)|$ cannot have a minimum at an interior point. Indeed, the function $g(z) = [f(z)]^{-1}$ is regular in D if $f(z)$ has no zeros, and a minimum of $|f(z)|$ would correspond to a maximum of $|g(z)|$. If we apply the maximum principle to the function $g(z)$, the result follows.

Similar results hold for real harmonic functions $u(x, y)$. As shown in Chapter II, Section 3, every real function $u(x, y)$ which is harmonic in a domain D is the real part of a function $f(z) = u(x, y) + iv(x, y)$ analytic in D. The function

$$F(z) = e^{f(z)} = e^{u(x,y)+iv(x,y)}$$

is likewise analytic in D. Since

$$|F(z)| = e^{u(x,y)},$$

and since the real exponential function is an increasing function of its argument, a local maximum of $u(x, y)$ corresponds to a local maximum of $|F(z)|$. Since the latter is excluded by the maximum principle, this proves that $u(x, y)$ cannot have a maximum at an interior point of D. If we observe that $-u(x, y)$ is also a harmonic function, and that a maximum of $-u(x, y)$ corresponds to a minimum of $u(x, y)$, we can conclude that $u(x, y)$ can also not attain its minimum in D at an interior point of D. Hence, *a real non-constant function which is harmonic in a domain D cannot have a maximum or a minimum at a point in the interior of D.*

EXERCISES

1. If the analytic function $f(z)$ is regular for $|z| < R$, and if $M(r)$ denotes the maximum of $|f(z)|$ for $|z| = r$, show that $M(r)$ is a strictly increasing function of r in the interval $0 \leq r < R$.

2. Derive the result of Exercise 9 of the preceding section by using the maximum principle rather than Rouché's theorem.

3. If $f(z)$ is regular in $|z| \leq 1$ except for a pole of order m at $z = \alpha$ ($|\alpha| < 1$), and if $|f(z)| \leq 1$ on the circumference $|z| = 1$, show that

$$|f(z)| \leq \left| \frac{1 - \bar{\alpha}z}{z - \alpha} \right|^m$$

at all points of $|z| \leq 1$ other than α.

4. Let $f(z)$ be regular and $|f(z)| \leq 1$ for $|z| \leq 1$. If, moreover, $f(0) = 0$, show that the inequality $|f(z)| \leq 1$ can be strengthened to

$$|f(z)| \leq |z|.$$

5. Let $P_1, \cdots, P_n$ be n arbitrary points of the plane, and let $\overline{PP_\nu}$ denote the distance between P_ν and a variable point P. If P is confined to the closure of a domain D, show that the product $\prod\limits_{\nu=1}^{n} \overline{PP_\nu}$ attains its maximum if P is some point of the boundary of D.

6. Prove the fundamental theorem of algebra by applying the maximum principle to the function

$$f(z) = (a_0 + a_1 z + \cdots + a_n z^n)^{-1}$$

(which would be regular if the theorem were false) in the region $|z| \leq R$, and letting $R \to \infty$.

7. Let $P(z)$ be a polynomial of degree n, and consider the points z for which

$$|P(z)| = C,$$

where C is a positive constant. Show that these points form one or more closed curves, depending on the value of C. Show that the number of these closed curves cannot exceed n.

9   THE POISSON INTEGRAL

According to the Cauchy integral formula of Section 1, an analytic function $f(z)$ which is regular for $|z| \leq R$ can be represented in the disk $|z| < R$ in the form

$$(55) \qquad f(z) = \frac{1}{2\pi i} \int_C \frac{f(t)}{t - z}\, dt,$$

where C is the circumference $|z| = R$. If z^* is a value for which $|z^*| > R$, the function

$$\frac{f(t)}{t - z^*}$$

is regular in $|t| \leq R$, and it follows therefore from Cauchy's theorem that

$$\frac{1}{2\pi i} \int_C \frac{f(t)}{t - z^*}\, dt = 0.$$

The value of the right-hand side of (55) will thus remain unchanged by the subtraction of this integral, and we may replace (55) by

$$(56) \qquad f(z) = \frac{1}{2\pi i} \int_C f(t) \left[\frac{1}{t - z} - \frac{1}{t - z^*} \right] dt,$$

where z^* is such that $|z^*| > R$.

Since $|z| < R$, the number $z^* = R^2/\bar{z}$ will satisfy this condition, and it may be used in (56). To simplify (56), we introduce polar coordinates $t = Re^{i\theta}$. Since $dt = iRe^{i\theta} d\theta$, we have

$$\left[\frac{1}{t - z} - \frac{1}{t - z^*} \right] dt = \frac{(z - z^*) dt}{(t - z)(t - z^*)} = \frac{iR\left(z - \dfrac{R^2}{\bar{z}}\right) e^{i\theta} d\theta}{(Re^{i\theta} - z)\left(Re^{i\theta} - \dfrac{R^2}{\bar{z}}\right)}$$

$$= \frac{i(R^2 - |z|^2) d\theta}{(Re^{i\theta} - z)(Re^{-i\theta} - \bar{z})} = \frac{i(R^2 - |z|^2) d\theta}{|Re^{i\theta} - z|^2}.$$

Substituting this in (56), we obtain

$$f(z) = \frac{R^2 - |z|^2}{2\pi} \int_0^{2\pi} \frac{f(Re^{i\theta}) d\theta}{|Re^{i\theta} - z|^2}.$$

Except for the expression $f(Re^{i\theta})$, all the terms on the right-hand side are real. Taking the real part on both sides of this formula, we therefore have

$$(57) \qquad \mathrm{Re}[f(z)] = \frac{R^2 - |z|^2}{2\pi} \int_0^{2\pi} \frac{\mathrm{Re}[f(Re^{i\theta})] d\theta}{|Re^{i\theta} - z|^2}.$$

Since the real part u of an analytic function $f(z) = u + iv$ is a harmonic function, we have thus obtained a representation of a harmonic function in the disk $|z| < R$ in terms of its boundary values on the circumference $|z| = R$. If we introduce polar coordinates r, φ in the z-plane and write $u = u(r, \varphi)$, Formula (57) can be further simplified. Noting that

$$(58) \quad |t - z|^2 = |Re^{i\theta} - re^{i\varphi}|^2 = (Re^{i\theta} - re^{i\varphi})(Re^{-i\theta} - re^{-i\varphi})$$

$$= R^2 - rR(e^{i(\theta - \varphi)} + e^{i(\varphi - \theta)}) + r^2$$

$$= R^2 - 2rR \cos(\theta - \varphi) + r^2,$$

we arrive at the equivalent expression

$$(59) \quad u(r, \varphi) = \frac{R^2 - r^2}{2\pi} \int_0^{2\pi} \frac{u(R, \theta) d\theta}{R^2 - 2rR \cos(\theta - \varphi) + r^2}.$$

(59) is known as the *Poisson formula,* or the *Poisson integral formula.* The expression

$$(60) \qquad K(R, \theta; r, \varphi) = \frac{R^2 - r^2}{R^2 - 2rR \cos (\theta - \varphi) + r^2}$$

is referred to as the *Poisson kernel.*

The Poisson formula (59) was derived under the assumption that the values $u(R, \theta)$ are the boundary values of a known harmonic function $u(r, \varphi)$. The right-hand side of (59) will, however, also represent a function of r and φ if $u(R, \theta)$ is replaced by an arbitrary continuous function $U(\theta)$ of θ. As the following result shows, the function thus obtained will always be harmonic, and its boundary values for $r = R$, $\varphi = \theta$ will coincide with the values of $U(\theta)$.

If the function $U(\theta)$ is continuous for $0 \le \theta \le 2\pi$ except for a finite number of finite jumps, then the function

$$(61) \qquad u(r, \varphi) = \frac{R^2 - r^2}{2\pi} \int_0^{2\pi} \frac{U(\theta) \, d\theta}{R^2 - 2rR \cos (\theta - \varphi) + r^2}$$

is harmonic in the disk $r < R$, and

$$(62) \qquad \lim_{r \to R} u(r, \theta) = U(\theta)$$

at all points of continuity of $U(\theta)$.

At a point at which $U(\theta)$ has a jump, (62) has no meaning, since the limit ceases to be uniquely defined.

In order to show that the right-hand side of (61) is a harmonic function for $r < R$, we compute the real part of the analytic function $(t + z)(t - z)^{-1}$, where $t = Re^{i\theta}$ and $z = re^{i\varphi}$. Since

$$\frac{t + z}{t - z} = \frac{(t + z)(\bar{t} - \bar{z})}{|t - z|^2} = \frac{|t|^2 - |z|^2 + z\bar{t} - t\bar{z}}{t - z^2}$$

$$= \frac{R^2 - r^2}{|t - z|^2} + 2i \frac{\operatorname{Im}(z\bar{t})}{|t - z|^2},$$

(58) shows that

$$(63) \qquad K(R, \theta; r, \varphi) = \operatorname{Re}\left[\frac{t + z}{t - z}\right] = \operatorname{Re}\left[\frac{2t}{t - z}\right] - 1,$$

where K is the Poisson kernel (60). We may therefore replace (61) by the equivalent formula

$$(64) \qquad u(r, \varphi) = \operatorname{Re}\left[\frac{1}{\pi} \int_0^{2\pi} \frac{tU(\theta) \, d\theta}{t - z}\right] - \frac{1}{2\pi} \int_0^{2\pi} U(\theta) \, d\theta.$$

As shown in detail in Section 1, an integral of the type

$$\int_0^{2\pi} \frac{g(\theta)\, d\theta}{t - z}$$

can be differentiated with respect to z under the integral sign, and it therefore represents an analytic function of z for $|z| < R$. Hence, the first term on the right-hand side of (64) is the real part of an analytic function, i.e., it is a harmonic function. Since the second term is a constant, we have proved that the function $u(r, \varphi)$ defined by (61) is harmonic for $r < R$.

To show that $u(r, \varphi)$ takes the proper boundary values, we first consider the case in which $U(\theta) = 0$ at the points of an arc α of the boundary. If β is the complementary arc, (61) reduces to

$$(65) \qquad u(r, \varphi) = \frac{R^2 - r^2}{2\pi} \int_\beta \frac{U(\theta)\, d\theta}{R^2 - 2rR \cos (\theta - \varphi) + r^2}.$$

If $r \to R$ and φ tends to a value θ_0, the integrand will become infinite only if the point (R, θ_0) is in β. Hence, the integrand remains finite if (R, θ_0) is a point in the interior of α, and the factor $R^2 - r^2$ will thus make the right-hand side of (65) tend to zero. This shows that $u(r, \varphi)$ has the correct boundary behavior at the points of the arc α.

We next consider the function $u_\alpha(r, \varphi)$ which corresponds to a function $U_\alpha(\theta)$ vanishing at the points of α and having the value 1 at the points of β. If $u_\beta(r, \varphi)$ and $U_\beta(\theta)$ are the corresponding functions for the arc β, we have $U_\alpha(\theta) + U_\beta(\theta) = 1$ for all θ in $[0, 2\pi]$. It follows therefore from (61) that

$$(66) \quad u_\alpha(r, \varphi) + u_\beta(r, \varphi) = \frac{R^2 - r^2}{2\pi} \int_0^{2\pi} \frac{d\theta}{R^2 - 2r \cos (\theta - \varphi) + r^2}.$$

As an application of Poisson's formula (59) shows, the expression on the right-hand side represents the harmonic function 1. Hence,

$$u_\alpha(r, \varphi) + u_\beta(r, \varphi) = 1.$$

Since $u_\alpha(r, \varphi)$ has just been shown to have the boundary values 0 if (r, φ) approaches a point of α (and, similarly, $u_\beta(r, \varphi) \to 0$ if (r, φ) tends to a point of β), this makes it clear that $u_\alpha(r, \varphi)$ and $u_\beta(r, \varphi)$ tend to 1 if (r, φ) approaches a point of β or α, respectively. This proves the correctness of (62) in the case in which $U(\theta) = 0$ on an arc of $r = R$, and $U(\theta) = 1$ on the rest of the circumference.

To prove (62) in the case of a general function $U(\theta)$, we denote by θ_0 a value at which $U(\theta)$ is continuous, and we denote by δ a small positive number with the property that $|U(\theta) - U(\theta_0)| < \epsilon$ if $|\theta - \theta_0| < \delta$, where ϵ is a given positive number. It is sufficient to establish (62) under the assumption that $U(\theta) = 0$ for points outside the arc α defined by $|\theta - \theta_0| < \delta$. Indeed, if $U^*(\theta) = U(\theta)$ on α and $U^* = 0$ elsewhere, we have $U^*(\theta) - U(\theta) = 0$ on α and, as shown above, the corresponding function $u^*(r, \varphi) - u(r, \varphi)$ will tend to zero if $(r, \varphi) \rightarrow (R, \theta_0)$. The functions $u(r, \varphi)$ and $u^*(r, \varphi)$ thus approach the same boundary value at this point. Assuming, then, that $U(\theta) = 0$ unless $|\theta - \theta_0| < \delta$, and applying (61) we have

$$u(r, \varphi) = \frac{1}{2\pi} \int_\alpha K U(\theta)\, d\theta,$$

where K denotes the Poisson kernel (60). Writing this in the form

$$u(r, \varphi) = \frac{1}{2\pi} \int_\alpha K[U(\theta) - U(\theta_0)]\, d\theta + \frac{U(\theta_0)}{2\pi} \int_\alpha K\, d\theta,$$

and noting that, in view of (61),

$$\frac{1}{2\pi} \int_\alpha K\, d\theta$$

is the harmonic function $u_\alpha(r, \theta)$ discussed above, we have

$|u(r, \varphi) - U(\theta_0)|$
$$= \left| \frac{1}{2\pi} \int_\alpha K[U(\theta) - U(\theta_0)]\, d\theta + U(\theta_0)[u_\alpha(r, \varphi) - 1] \right|.$$

On α, we have $|U(\theta) - U(\theta_0)| < \epsilon$, and thus

$$|u(r, \varphi) - U(\theta_0)| \leq \frac{\epsilon}{2\pi} \int_\alpha K\, d\theta + |U(\theta_0)|\, |u_\alpha(r, \varphi) - 1|.$$

Since K is positive, and since the right-hand side of (66) has the value 1, it follows that

$$\frac{1}{2\pi} \int_\alpha K\, d\theta \leq \frac{1}{2\pi} \int_0^{2\pi} K\, d\theta = 1,$$

and therefore

$$|u(r, \varphi) - U(\theta_0)| \leq \epsilon + |U(\theta_0)|\, |u_\alpha(r, \varphi) - 1|.$$

If we now use the fact that $u_\alpha(r, \varphi)$ tends to 1 as the point (r, φ) approaches the point (R, θ_0) on α, we can conclude from this inequality that

$$\limsup_{(r,\varphi)\rightarrow(R,\theta_0)} |u(r, \varphi) - U(\theta_0)| \leq \epsilon.$$

Since ϵ was arbitrary, and may be taken as small as we please, it follows that

$$\lim_{(r,\varphi)\to(R,\theta_0)} |u(r,\varphi) - U(\theta_0)| = 0,$$

and this completes the proof of (62).

The problem of finding a function which is harmonic in a domain and takes given values at the points of the boundary, is known as the *boundary value problem of the first kind*, or the *Dirichlet problem*. Our proof shows that, for the circle, the Poisson formula (61) provides the explicit solution of the Dirichlet problem.

In practice, the direct computation of the integral (61) for a given function $U(\theta)$ may present serious difficulties, and it is often easier to obtain the function $u(r,\varphi)$ by expanding the right-hand side of (61) into an infinite series. Since, for $|z| < |t|$,

$$\frac{t+z}{t-z} = \frac{1+\dfrac{z}{t}}{1-\dfrac{z}{t}} = 1 + 2 \sum_{n=1}^{\infty} \left(\frac{z}{t}\right)^n = 1 + 2 \sum_{n=1}^{\infty} \left(\frac{r}{R}\right)^n e^{in(\varphi-\theta)},$$

the Poisson kernel (63) has the expansion

$$K = \mathrm{Re}\left[1 + 2 \sum_{n=1}^{\infty} \left(\frac{r}{R}\right)^n e^{in(\varphi-\theta)}\right] = 1 + 2 \sum_{n=1}^{\infty} \left(\frac{r}{R}\right)^n \cos n(\varphi - \theta)$$

$$= 1 + 2 \sum_{n=1}^{\infty} \left(\frac{r}{R}\right)^n (\cos n\theta \cos n\varphi + \sin n\theta \sin n\varphi).$$

For $r < R$, the convergence is uniform in θ, and term-by-term integration is permissible. In view of (60), (61) may therefore be replaced by

$$(67) \qquad u(r,\varphi) = \frac{a_0}{2} + \sum_{n=1}^{\infty} \left(\frac{r}{R}\right)^n (a_n \cos n\varphi + b_n \sin n\varphi),$$

where

$$(68) \qquad a_n = \frac{1}{\pi} \int_0^{2\pi} U(\theta) \cos n\theta \, d\theta$$

and

$$(68') \qquad b_n = \frac{1}{\pi} \int_0^{2\pi} U(\theta) \sin n\theta \, d\theta.$$

If the coefficients (68) are computed with the help of the given boundary values $U(\theta)$, the expansion (67) will give the solution of the Dirichlet problem in question.

As an example, we construct a harmonic function $u(r,\theta)$ in the unit circle, with the boundary values $U(\theta) = u(1, \theta) = 1$ for $-\frac{\pi}{2} < \theta < \frac{\pi}{2}$ and $U(\theta) = u(1, \theta) = -1$ for $\frac{\pi}{2} < \theta < \frac{3\pi}{2}$. An elementary computation shows that $b_n = 0$ for all n, and that $a_{2m} = 0$, $a_{2m+1} = 4(-1)^m[\pi(2m+1)]^{-1}$, $m = 0, 1, \cdots$. It thus follows from (67) that

$$u(r, \varphi) = \frac{4}{\pi} \sum_{m=0}^{\infty} \frac{(-1)^m}{2m+1} r^{2m+1} \cos(2m+1)\varphi.$$

Because of

$$r^n \cos n\varphi = \operatorname{Re}(z^n), \quad z = re^{i\varphi},$$

we have

$$u(r, \varphi) = \operatorname{Re}\left[\frac{4}{\pi} \sum_{m=0}^{\infty} (-1)^m \frac{z^{2m+1}}{2m+1}\right],$$

and this shows that

(69) $$u(r, \varphi) = \frac{4}{\pi} \operatorname{Re}[\arctan z].$$

The Dirichlet problem is not the only boundary value problem of importance in the applications. Another such problem is the so-called *boundary value problem of the second kind*, or *Neumann problem*. This calls for the construction of a harmonic function u in a domain from the values of its normal derivative $\partial u/\partial n$ (i.e., the directional derivative in the direction given by the outwards pointing normal) at the points of the boundary. In the case of the disk $r < R$, this amounts to constructing a harmonic function $u(r, \varphi)$ such that

(70) $$\left[\frac{\partial u(r, \theta)}{\partial r}\right]_{r=R} = V(\theta),$$

where $V(\theta)$ is a given function of θ. Since we know that $u(r, \varphi)$ must have an expansion of the form (67), we can solve our problem by determining the coefficients a_n and b_n from the condition (70). Assuming that $u(r, \theta)$ is harmonic for $0 \leq r \leq R$, we find that

$$a_n = \frac{R}{\pi n} \int_0^{2\pi} V(\theta) \cos n\theta \, d\theta$$

and

$$b_n = \frac{R}{\pi n} \int_0^{2\pi} V(\theta) \sin n\theta \, d\theta$$

for $n = 1, 2, \cdots$, while a_0 remains arbitrary. The verification of these formulas is recommended to the reader as an exercise.

Exercises

1. If $u(r, \varphi)$ is a harmonic function for $r < R$, show that $u(r, \varphi)$ is subject to the *mean-value theorem*

$$u(0) = \frac{1}{2\pi r} \int_0^{2\pi} u(r, \varphi) \, ds,$$

where ds is the length-element on the circle about the origin of radius r.

2. Deduce from Exercise 1 the area mean-value theorem

$$u(0) = \frac{1}{\pi r^2} \iint_{\rho < r} u(\rho, \varphi) \, d\omega,$$

where $d\omega$ is the area element.

3. Use the mean-value theorem of Exercise 1 to prove the maximum principle for harmonic functions.

4. The Laplace equation in polar coordinates is

$$\frac{1}{r} \frac{\partial}{\partial r} \left(r \frac{\partial u}{\partial r} \right) + \frac{1}{r^2} \frac{\partial^2 u}{\partial \theta^2} = 0.$$

Integrating this equation over θ from 0 to 2π (for fixed r) show that, for a function $u(r, \theta)$ which is harmonic for $r_0 < r < R$,

$$\int_0^{2\pi} u(r, \theta) \, d\theta = A \log r + B, \quad r_0 < r < R,$$

where A and B do not depend on r. Use this result to obtain an alternative proof of the mean-value theorem of Exercise 1.

5. Find a harmonic function $u(r, \theta)$ which has the boundary values $u(1, \theta) = \theta/2$ for $-\pi < \theta < \pi$. [Answer:

$$u(r, \theta) = \text{Re}\{\log (1 + z)\}, \quad z = re^{i\theta}].$$

6. If the function $u(r, \theta)$ is harmonic for $0 \leq r \leq R$ and $V(\theta)$ is defined by (70), show that

$$\int_0^{2\pi} V(\theta) \, d\theta = 0.$$

7. If the analytic function $f(z)$ is regular for $|z| \leq R$ and if $u(r, \varphi) = \text{Re}[f(z)]$ for $z = re^{i\varphi}$, show that

$$f(z) = \frac{1}{2\pi} \int_0^{2\pi} \frac{Re^{i\theta} + z}{Re^{i\theta} - z} u(R, \theta) \, d\theta, \quad 0 \leq |z| < R.$$

8. Using the results of Exercises 1 and 7, prove the following theorem: If $f(z)$ is regular and $\text{Re}[f(z)] \geq 0$ for $|z| \leq R$, and if $f(0)$ is real, then

$$|f(z)| \leq f(0)\left[\frac{R + |z|}{R - |z|}\right], \quad |z| < R.$$

9. Construct a harmonic function in the unit circle whose normal derivative $\partial u/\partial r$ has the boundary values 1 for $-\frac{\pi}{2} < \theta < \frac{\pi}{2}$, and -1 for $\frac{\pi}{2} < \theta < \frac{3\pi}{2}$. [Answer:

$$u(r, \varphi) = \frac{4}{\pi} \sum_{n=0}^{\infty} \frac{(-1)^n}{(2n + 1)^2} r^{2n+1} \cos (2n + 1)\varphi].$$

V

CONFORMAL

MAPPING

1 BASIC PROPERTIES

It is shown in analytic geometry that a real function $y = f(x)$ of a real variable x determines a curve in the xy-plane, if x and y are interpreted as rectangular coordinates. This geometric aspect of the functional relationship between x and y is a valuable aid in the investigation of real functions. This is true in particular in those cases in which the graph of the function is a curve of simple type, such as a straight line or a conic, whose properties can be taken in at one glance. In the case of an analytic function $w = f(z)$ of a complex variable z, no such simple geometric interpretation is possible. As both z and w are complex numbers, a geometric representation of the function would require four real coordinates. Since our direct geometric intuition fails in a space of more than three dimensions, nothing much would be gained by such a procedure.

There exists, however, another possibility of visualizing the behavior of an analytic function $w = f(z)$. We may regard the points z and w as points in two different planes—the z-plane and the w-plane—and we can then interpret the functional relationship $w = f(z)$ as a *mapping* of points in the z-plane onto points in the w-plane. To any set of points S in the z-plane at which $f(z)$ is regular there will thus correspond a set of points S' in the w-

plane.   We call S' the *map*, or the *image*, of the set S as given by
the function $w = f(z)$.

If the function $f(z)$ is regular and single-valued in a domain
D, it is easy to see that the image of a continuous arc in D under
the mapping $w = f(z)$ is again a continuous arc.   Indeed, if $z =
x + iy$, $w = u(x, y) + iv(x, y)$, the image of the arc $x = x(t)$,
$y = y(t)$ $(t_1 \leq t \leq t_2)$ is the arc $u = u[x(t), y(t)]$, $v = v[x(t), y(t)]$.
Since $u(x, y)$ and $v(x, y)$ are continuous functions of x and y, u and
v are clearly continuous in t if $x(t)$ and $y(t)$ are continuous.   From
the differentiability of $f(z)$ it follows, in a similar way, that the
image of a smooth arc in D is again a smooth arc.   It should,
however, be noted that the image of a non-selfintersecting arc
may very well be an arc which intersects itself.   It is clear that
this will happen whenever the original arc passes through two
points, z_1 and z_2, in D which are such that $f(z_1) = f(z_2)$.

One of the fundamental properties of a mapping given by an
analytic function is the fact that it is angle-preserving, or *conformal*.   By this we mean that two smooth arcs in D which
intersect and form the angle α, are mapped into two smooth arcs
in the w-plane which intersect under the same angle α.   In other
words, although the mapping may considerably distort the shape
of the two arcs, it will not change the angle under which they
intersect.   We shall also see that the conformality of the mapping
is a characteristic property of analytic functions; that is, a mapping cannot be conformal at all points of a domain unless it is the
mapping given by some analytic function $w = f(z)$ regular in this
domain.

In order to prove that the mapping associated with an
analytic function $w = f(z)$ is conformal, we consider a smooth
arc $x = x(t)$, $y = y(t)$—or, in complex notation, $z = z(t)$—which
terminates at a point $z_0 = z(t_0)$ at which $f(z)$ is regular.   If we
write $w_0 = f(z_0)$ and $w = w(t) = f[z(t)]$, we have

(1) $$w - w_0 = \frac{f(z) - f(z_0)}{z - z_0} (z - z_0),$$

and therefore

(2) $$\arg (w - w_0) = \arg \left[\frac{f(z) - f(z_0)}{z - z_0} \right] + \arg (z - z_0).$$

$\arg (z - z_0)$ is the angle between the positive axis and the vector
pointing from z_0 to z.   If z tends to z_0 along the smooth arc $z(t)$,

it thus follows that $\lim \arg (z - z_0)$ is the angle θ between the positive axis and the tangent to the arc at z_0. Similarly, $\arg (w - w_0)$ tends to the angle ϕ between the positive axis and the tangent to $w(t)$ at the point w_0. Hence, a passage to the limit $z \to z_0$ in (2) yields the result

$$(3) \qquad\qquad \phi = \arg f'(z_0) + \theta,$$

provided $f'(z_0)$ is not zero. The latter proviso is necessary since $\arg f'(z_0)$ ceases to be defined if $f'(z_0) = 0$.

Formula (3) shows that the difference $\phi - \theta$ depends only on the point z_0 and not on the particular smooth arc $z = z(t)$ for which the angles θ and ϕ were computed. If $z = z_1(t)$ is another smooth arc terminating at z_0, and if the corresponding tangential directions are given by the angles θ_1 and ϕ_1, it follows therefore that $\phi_1 - \theta_1 = \phi - \theta$, i.e.,

$$(4) \qquad\qquad \phi_1 - \phi = \theta_1 - \theta.$$

Since $\theta_1 - \theta$ is the angle between the arcs $z = z_1(t)$ and $z = z(t)$ and $\phi_1 - \phi$ is the angle between the images of these arcs (where the angle between two smooth arcs is defined as the angle between their tangents at the point of intersection), (4) shows that the angle between two arcs is not changed by the mapping $w = f(z)$, provided $f' \neq 0$ at the point of intersection. The relation (4) shows, moreover, that the *sense* of the angle is also preserved in this mapping (i.e., $\phi_1 - \phi$ is equal to $\theta_1 - \theta$, and not to $\theta - \theta_1$). A mapping which preserves both the size and the sense of angles is called *conformal*. Our result is, therefore, that the mapping given by an analytic function $w = f(z)$ is conformal at all points at which $f(z)$ is regular and $f'(z) \neq 0$.

We next show that a mapping $(x, y) \to (u, v)$, where $z = x + iy$, $w = u + iv$, cannot be conformal in a domain in which the partial derivatives u_x, u_y, v_x, v_y exist and are continuous, unless it is a mapping given by an analytic function $u + iv = w = f(z)$. Indeed, if f is a function of x and y with continuous partial derivatives, and if $z = z(t)$ is a smooth arc, we have (by Formula (30), Chap. I, Sec. 4)

$$\frac{df}{dt} = \frac{\partial f}{\partial z} z'(t) + \frac{\partial f}{\partial \bar{z}} \overline{z'(t)}.$$

If $z(t)$ is the linear segment $z(t) = z_0 + e^{i\theta}t$, where θ is a fixed angle, this takes the form

$$\frac{df}{dt} = e^{i\theta}\frac{\partial f}{\partial z} + e^{-i\theta}\frac{\partial f}{\partial \bar{z}}$$

$$= e^{i\theta}\left[\frac{\partial f}{\partial z} + e^{-2i\theta}\frac{\partial f}{\partial \bar{z}}\right].$$

Since arg $[df/dt] = \phi$, where ϕ is the angle between the positive axis and the tangent to the image of the linear segment, it follows that

(5) $$\phi = \theta + \arg[f_z + e^{-2i\theta}f_{\bar{z}}].$$

If θ_1 is the angle corresponding to another linear segment ending at z_0 and ϕ_1 is the associated angle of the image of this segment, the conformality of the mapping requires that $\phi_1 - \phi = \theta_1 - \theta$. Since this must be true for an arbitrary choice of the angle θ_1, (5) shows that the value of arg $[f_z + e^{-2i\theta}f_{\bar{z}}]$ must be the same for all θ such that $0 \leq \theta < 2\pi$. Since the point $\zeta = f_z + e^{-2i\theta}f_{\bar{z}}$ describes the circle of center f_z and radius $f_{\bar{z}}$ if θ varies from 0 to π, arg ζ can remain constant only if the radius of the circle is zero, i.e., if

$$\frac{\partial f}{\partial \bar{z}} = 0.$$

A comparison with Formula (6) of Chapter II shows that this is the complex form of the Cauchy-Riemann equations. We have therefore proved that at a point at which the mapping is conformal the mapping function satisfies the Cauchy-Riemann equations. Since the derivatives f_x and f_y are, moreover, continuous, the function $f(z)$ is differentiable at z_0 (cf. Chap. II, Sec. 2). If the mapping is conformal at all points of a domain D, $f(z)$ will thus be analytic in D, and our result is proved.

In proving that an analytic function gives rise to a conformal mapping we had to assume that $f'(z) \neq 0$. In order to study the character of the mapping at a point z_0 at which $f'(z_0)$ vanishes—a so-called *critical point*—we observe that $f(z)$ must have a Taylor expansion

$$f(z) = f(z_0) + a_k(z - z_0)^k + a_{k+1}(z - z_0)^{k+1} + \cdots, k \geq 2, \quad a_k \neq 0,$$

in the neighborhood of z_0. We have therefore

(6) $$f(z) - f(z_0) = (z - z_0)^k g(z),$$

where $g(z)$ is regular at $z = z_0$, and $g(z_0) \neq 0$. Hence,

$$\arg(w - w_0) = \arg[f(z) - f(z_0)] = k \arg(z - z_0) + \arg g(z).$$

If z tends to z_0, and if ϕ and θ have the same meaning as before, we thus have

$$\phi = k\theta + \arg g(z_0).$$

Since $\arg g(z_0)$ is independent of θ, the result analogous to (4) will now be

$$\phi_1 - \phi = k(\theta_1 - \theta),$$

i.e., *at a point z_0 at which $f'(z)$ has a zero of order $k - 1$, all angles will be magnified by the factor k.* It will be a useful exercise for the reader to illustrate this result by a study of the behavior of the function $w = z^k$ at its critical point $z = 0$.

From the fact that the mapping by an analytic function $w = f(z)$ is conformal we can conclude, among other things, that the horizontal and vertical lines $\text{Im}(z) = \text{const.}$ and $\text{Re}(z) = \text{const.}$ are transformed by the function into two families of curves which intersect each other at right angles. As an illustration, we compute these families of curves for the mapping $w = \cos z$. Since

$$u + iv = w = \cos z = \cos(x + iy) = \cos x \cos iy - \sin x \sin iy$$

$$= \cos x \cosh y - i \sin x \sinh y,$$

we have $u = \cos x \cosh y$, $v = -\sin x \sinh y$. The images of the horizontal lines $y = a$ will therefore be the ellipses

$$\frac{u^2}{\cosh^2 a} + \frac{v^2}{\sinh^2 a} = 1, \quad a \neq 0,$$

and the vertical lines $x = b$ are transformed into the hyperbolas

$$\frac{u^2}{\cos^2 b} - \frac{v^2}{\sin^2 b} = 1, \quad b \neq 0, \pm\frac{\pi}{2} \pm \pi, \cdots.$$

It will be a useful exercise for the reader to determine the degenerate forms of these conics which correspond to the excluded values of a and b. It is also instructive to observe in detail how the ellipses are traversed an infinity of times as x grows from $-\infty$ to ∞.

Since the half-axes of the ellipses are $\cosh a$ and $\sinh a$, the distance of the foci from the origin is $\sqrt{\cosh^2 a - \sinh^2 a} = 1$. All the ellipses have therefore their foci at the points $w = \pm 1$. Because of $\sin^2 b + \cos^2 b = 1$, the same is true of the hyperbolas, and we find that the mapping $w = \cos z$ transforms horizontal and vertical lines, respectively, into confocal ellipses and hyperbolas. The common foci of all these conics are at $w = \pm 1$. Since the mapping is conformal, any of these ellipses must intersect any of the hyperbolas at right angles.

EXERCISES

1. If $f(z)$ is an analytic function, show that the mapping $w = \overline{f(z)}$ preserves the magnitude of angles between smooth arcs, but inverts their orientation. Show that the mapping $w = f(\bar{z})$ has the same property.

2. If $f(z)$ is analytic in a domain D, use the result of the preceding exercise to show that the function $\overline{f(\bar{z})}$ is analytic in the domain $\overline{D}$, which is the mirror image of D with respect to the real axis.

3. If $w = f(z)$ ($z = x + iy$, $w = u + iv$) is an analytic function, show that the Jacobian of the transformation $x,y \to u,v$ is $|f'(z)|^2$.

4. Show that the function

$$w = z\sqrt{1 - a^2} + a\sqrt{1 - z^2}, \quad 0 \le a \le 1,$$

transforms any ellipse of foci ± 1 into itself.

5. Show that the function $w = \sqrt{1 - z^2}$ transforms the hyperbola $2x^2 - 2y^2 = 1$ into itself.

6. Show that the function $w = z^2$ transforms the circle $|z - a| = a$, $a > 0$, into the cardioid with the polar equation

$$\rho = 2a^2(1 + \cos \varphi), \quad w = \rho e^{i\varphi}.$$

7. Show that, under the mapping

$$w = \frac{1}{2}\left(z + \frac{1}{z}\right),$$

the circles $|z| = $ const. are transformed into ellipses and the rays $\arg(z) = $ const. into hyperbolas. Show that the foci of all these conics are at $w = \pm 1$.

8. If $\alpha = a + bi$ and $w = re^{i\theta}$, show that the function $w = e^{\alpha z}$ transforms the lines $\text{Im}(z) = c$ and $\text{Re}(z) = c$ into the logarithmic spirals

$$r = e^{-\frac{c}{b}(a^2 + b^2)} e^{\frac{a}{b}\theta}$$

and

$$r = e^{\frac{c}{a}(a^2 + b^2)} e^{-\frac{b}{a}\theta},$$

respectively.

9. Let $f(z)$ be regular at $z = z_0$, and denote by L the length of a short smooth arc terminating at z_0. If $f'(z_0) \neq 0$, and if L' is the length of the image of L under the mapping $w = f(z)$, show that

$$\lim_{L \to 0} \frac{L'}{L} = |f'(z_0)|.$$

2 MAPPING OF DOMAINS

Simple examples show that, unless the concept of a domain is suitably generalized, it is not necessarily true that the conformal image of a domain D is again a domain. For instance, if there are two distinct points in D at which the mapping function $w = f(z)$ takes the same value, the region onto which D is mapped may overlap itself in the manner indicated in Fig. 3. Also, at a critical point of $f(z)$ the image of a small neighborhood will be a multiply-covered region, and the image of the critical point itself will be an algebraic branch-point of the type discussed in Chapter II, Section 7.

FIG. 3

If the definition of a domain is generalized so as to permit self-overlappings and the occurrence of branch-points, it can be shown that the conformal map of a domain is again a domain. However, in the applications of conformal mapping to problems in physics and engineering it is in general sufficient to consider mappings of domains whose images are domains in the usual sense. The function $f(z)$ giving rise to such a mapping of the domain D cannot take there any value more than once. Such a function is said to be *univalent* in D. We shall show that, conversely, *an analytic function $w = f(z)$ which is regular and univalent in a domain D maps D onto a domain D' in the w-plane.*

Since a conformal mapping transforms a continuous arc into a continuous arc, it is clear that the set D' must be connected. All we have to show, therefore, is that D' is an open set, i.e., that all its points are interior points. If w_0 is a point of D', there exists a point z_0 of D such that $w_0 = f(z_0)$. Near z_0, $f(z)$ can be written in the form (6), where $g(z)$ is regular at z_0 and $g(z_0) \neq 0$. Since $g(z)$ is regular at z_0, we can draw a small circle $|z - z_0| = r$ such that $g(z)$ is regular, and does not vanish, for $|z - z_0| \leq r$. On $|z - z_0| = r$, the expression $|(z - z_0)^k g(z)|$ has a positive minimum, m. Let now w be a value such that $|w - f(z_0)| < m$, and consider the expression $f(z) - w$. By (6), we have

$$f(z) - w = (z - z_0)^k g(z) + f(z_0) - w.$$

Since on the circumference $|z - z_0| = r$ we have $|(z - z_0)^k g(z)| \geq m$, and since $|f(z_0) - w| < m$, we may conclude from Rouché's theorem (Chap. IV, Sec. 7) that the function $f(z) - w$ has as many zeros in $|z - z_0| < r$ as the function $(z - z_0)^k g(z)$. But the latter has a zero of order k at $z = z_0$ and does not vanish for $0 < |z - z_0| < r$. Hence, the total number of its zeros in $|z - z_0| < r$ is k, and it follows that the equation $f(z) = w$ has k solutions in this disk.

This proof shows two things. First, an analytic function cannot be univalent in the neighborhood of a critical point z_0. Indeed, if $k \geq 2$, all values w sufficiently near $f(z_0)$ will be taken at least twice in the neighborhood of z_0. Hence, *the derivative of a univalent function does not vanish.* The second fact shown by our proof is that every value in a sufficiently small neighborhood of $f(z_0)$ is actually taken by the function $f(z)$; if $f'(z_0) \neq 0$, these values are taken exactly once (this shows, incidentally, that in a sufficiently small neighborhood of a point z_0 at which $f'(z_0) \neq 0$, $f(z)$ is univalent). The point $f(z_0)$ is therefore an interior point of the image, and our result is proved.

We now assume that D is the interior of a simple closed contour C and that the function $f(z)$ is regular and univalent in $D + C$. The contour C will then be mapped by $w = f(z)$ onto a simple closed contour C', the boundary of the image domain D'. Conversely, if $f(z)$ is regular in $D + C$ and the mapping $w = f(z)$ transforms C into a simple closed contour C', $f(z)$ is necessarily univalent in D, and $w = f(z)$ maps the interior D of C onto the interior D' of C'. Before we give a formal statement of this result, we note that in general it is difficult to verify directly that a given analytic function is univalent in a domain, but it is often easy to find the closed contour C' into which the boundary C of D is transformed by the mapping $w = f(z)$. As the following statement shows, the knowledge of C' is sufficient to determine the character of the mapping.

Let $f(z)$ be analytic on a simple closed contour C and in its interior D. If $w = f(z)$ maps C onto a simple closed contour C' in the w-plane in such a way that C' is described by w once in the positive sense if z traverses C in the positive sense, then $w = f(z)$ maps D onto the domain D' bounded by C'.

We have to prove that, under the stated hypotheses, every value in D' is taken exactly once if z ranges over all the points of D. To do so, we observe that, according to Formula (50) of the preceding chapter, the number of times a value w_0 is taken by $f(z)$ is given by

$$N = \frac{1}{2\pi i} \int_C \frac{f'(z)\, dz}{f(z) - w_0},$$

provided $f(z) \neq w_0$ on C. With the substitution $w = f(z)$, $dw = f'(z)\, dz$, this may be written

$$N = \frac{1}{2\pi i} \int_{C'} \frac{dw}{w - w_0},$$

where, according to our assumptions, the contour C' is traversed in the positive sense. By the residue theorem, we have $N = 1$ if w_0 is a point in the interior of C' and $N = 0$ if w_0 is in the exterior of C'. Hence, every value in D' is taken exactly once, and values in the exterior of C' are not taken at all. Values on C' cannot be taken in D. Indeed, as just shown, the image of an interior point is an interior point. It would therefore follow that $f(z)$ takes all values in a small neighborhood of such a point. But such a neighborhood includes points in the exterior of C', and we have just shown that the image of D cannot contain any such points. We have thus proved that $f(z)$ is univalent in D and that $w = f(z)$ maps the domain D onto the domain D'.

We remark that the conditions under which this result was proved can be considerably relaxed. The result will remain true if $f(z)$ has singularities on C, provided the mapping of C remains continuous at these points. The contour C' can be permitted to contain arcs which are traversed twice, provided C' is the boundary of a simply-connected domain. For instance, C' may be the boundary of the domain D' obtained by cutting the disk $|w| < 1$ along the linear segment $\frac{1}{2} \leq w < 1$. In describing the entire boundary of this domain D', the linear segment clearly has to be traversed twice.

The fundamental result concerning the conformal mapping of domains onto domains is the *Riemann mapping theorem*. We shall confine ourselves here to a statement of this result, since its proof requires techniques which transcend the scope of this book.

If D and D' are two simply-connected domains, there always exists an analytic function $f(z)$ which is regular in D and maps D conformally onto D'.

It is easy to see that it is sufficient to state the theorem for the case in which one of the two domains is a circular disk. Indeed, if we know two functions which map D and D', respectively, onto the same disk, we obtain the mapping $D \to D'$ by first mapping D onto the disk, and then mapping the disk onto D'. In a "catalogue" of conformal mappings it is therefore sufficient to list the mappings of a number of given domains onto a disk, since this enables us to find the mapping of any of these domains onto any other. The use of the disk—and sometimes of a half-plane—as the "standard domain" has the advantage that the geometric simplicity of these domains often results in simple formulas. Besides, in the practical applications of conformal mapping, these standard mappings are often all that is required.

It will be shown in the following section that the analytic function (17) maps the unit disk onto itself. The constants c and K on the right-hand side of (17) are subject to the conditions $|c| < 1$, $|K| = 1$, and are otherwise arbitrary. They can be given definite values by imposing suitable conditions on the mapping (17). If we denote the function (17) by $F(z)$, we may do this by requiring that $F(\zeta) = 0$ and $F'(\zeta) > 0$, where ζ is an arbitrary point in $|z| < 1$. The first condition determines c (we evidently have $c = \zeta$), and the second gives a definite value to K.

If a conformal mapping $w = f(z)$ transforming a domain D into the unit disk is followed by a mapping of the type (17), the result is again a mapping of D onto the unit disk. This shows that there exists an infinity of such mappings. By a suitable choice of the constants c and K in (17), it is thus possible to find a mapping $w = f(z)$ for which $f(\zeta) = 0$ and $f'(\zeta) > 0$, where ζ is an arbitrary point of D. These conditions determine the mapping uniquely.

While the Riemann mapping theorem asserts the existence

of a function which maps a given domain onto a disk, it does not indicate how to obtain this function. The construction of the mapping function can be a matter of great difficulty. In Section 4, we shall discuss a method which makes it possible to construct the mapping function in the case in which the domain in question is a polygon.

We close this section with a remark concerning the *inverse* of a given analytic function $w = f(z)$. At points at which the mapping $z \to w$ is conformal, the same is obviously true of the inverse mapping $w \to z$. If $f(z)$ is univalent in a domain D, and $w = f(z)$ maps D onto a domain D' in the w-plane, it thus follows that the mapping $w \to z$ is conformal at all points of D'. In view of the results of the preceding section, this proves the existence in D' of an analytic function $z = F(w)$ inverse to $w = f(z)$. Since any analytic function is univalent in a sufficiently small neighborhood of a point z_0 at which $f'(z_0) \neq 0$, this implies the following result: *Let $f(z)$ be regular at z_0, and set $f(z_0) = w_0$. If $f'(z_0) \neq 0$, the equation $w = f(z)$ is solved by an analytic function $z = F(w)$ which is regular in a small neighborhood $|w - w_0| < \epsilon$.*

EXERCISES

1. By checking the mapping of the boundary of the domain, show that the function $w = e^z$ maps the rectangle with the vertices $\log r + i\theta$, $\log R + i\theta$, $\log R + i\phi$, $\log r + i\phi$ ($0 < r < R < \infty$, $\theta < \phi < \theta + 2\pi$) onto the domain bounded by parts of the circles $|w| = r$, $|w| = R$ and the half-lines $\arg w = \theta$, $\arg w = \phi$.

2. Show that the function $w = \cos z$ maps the rectangle with the vertices ic, $-ic$, $-ic + \pi$, $ic + \pi$ onto the domain bounded by the ellipse

$$\frac{u^2}{\cosh^2 c} + \frac{v^2}{\sinh^2 c} = 1$$

and the linear segments $-\cosh c < u \leq -1$, $1 \leq u < \cosh c$.

3. Show that the function $w = \sin z$ maps the half-strip $\operatorname{Im}(z) > 0$, $-\frac{\pi}{2} < \operatorname{Re}(z) < \frac{\pi}{2}$ onto the half-plane $\operatorname{Im}(w) > 0$. (Check the mapping of the boundary, and do not treat the points $z = \infty$ and $w = \infty$ as exceptional.)

4. Show that the function $w = e^z$ maps the infinite strip $0 < \text{Im}(z) < 2\pi$ onto the domain obtained by cutting the w-plane along the half-line $0 \leq w \leq \infty$.

5. If the function $w = f(z)$ maps a domain D onto a domain D', show that the area of D' is equal to

$$\iint_D |f'(z)|^2 \, dx \, dy.$$

3   THE LINEAR TRANSFORMATION

A simple, yet very important, conformal mapping is that given by the function

(7)
$$w = \frac{az + b}{cz + d}, \quad ad - bc \neq 0,$$

where a, b, c, d are complex constants. The mapping (7) is known variously as a linear transformation, a bilinear transformation, a fractional linear transformation, a linear substitution, and a Möbius transformation. Since (7) can be written in the form

(8)
$$w = \frac{a}{c} + \frac{bc - ad}{c(cz + d)},$$

the condition $ad - bc \neq 0$ prevents the function (7) from degenerating into a constant.

We first consider the particular case of (7) which corresponds to $c = 0$, $d = 1$, i.e., the transformation

(9)
$$w = az + b.$$

In order to see what effect this transformation has on a point in the z-plane, we assume first that $b = 0$ and introduce polar coordinates $z = re^{i\theta}$. If $a = |a|e^{i\alpha}$, we then have $w = r|a|e^{i(\theta+\alpha)}$, and this shows that $|w| = r|a|$ and $\arg w = \theta + \alpha$. In other words, all distances from the origin are multiplied by the same factor $|a|$, and the arguments of all numbers z are increased by the same amount α. This shows that the transformation $z \to az$ results in a magnification (or contraction, if $|a| < 1$) and rotation of any geometric figure in the z-plane. In particular, the image of a circle under this transformation will again be a circle. The addition of the constant b in (9) amounts only to a translation. If b is real, all points are translated horizontally by the same amount, and if b is complex we have an additional vertical translation. The mapping (9) will thus always transform circles into circles.

A more interesting special case of (7) is the transformation

$$(10) \qquad w = \frac{1}{z},$$

which corresponds to $a = d = 0$, $b = c$. If we set $z = re^{i\theta}$, (10) takes the form

$$(11) \qquad w = \frac{e^{-i\theta}}{r},$$

i.e., $|w| = r^{-1}$ and $\arg w = -\theta$. This shows that the mapping (11) transforms points in the interior of the unit circle into points in its exterior, and vice versa. The circumference of the unit circle is transformed into itself. However, since $\arg w = -\arg z$, the circumference $|w| = 1$ is described in the negative sense if $|z| = 1$ is described in the positive sense. This is not surprising once it is realized that the function (10) maps the interior of $|z| = 1$ onto the exterior of $|w| = 1$ and that, therefore, the exterior of $|w| = 1$ is the interior of the image domain. The negative direction on $|w| = 1$ is thus the positive direction with respect to the image.

The mapping (10) again transforms circles into circles. To prove this, we note that all circles in the xy-plane have equations of the form $x^2 + y^2 + Ax + By + C = 0$, where A, B, C are real constants. In polar coordinates, this becomes

$$r^2 + r(A \cos \theta + B \sin \theta) + C = 0.$$

If ρ, φ are polar coordinates in the w-plane, (11) shows that $\rho = 1/r$, $\varphi = -\theta$. The image of such a circle under the transformation (10) will therefore have the polar equation

$$(12) \qquad \frac{1}{\rho^2} + \frac{1}{\rho} (A \cos \varphi - B \sin \varphi) + C = 0.$$

If $C \neq 0$, we thus have

$$\rho^2 + \rho \left(\frac{A}{C} \cos \varphi - \frac{B}{C} \sin \varphi \right) + \frac{1}{C} = 0,$$

and this is again the equation of a circle in polar coordinates. If $C = 0$, (12) reduces to

$$A\rho \cos \varphi - B\rho \sin \varphi + 1 = 0,$$

or, if $w = u + iv$, to the equation $Au - Bv + 1 = 0$. The image of a circle $x^2 + y^2 + Ax + By = 0$ (i.e., a circle passing through the origin) is therefore a straight line. If we regard straight lines as special cases of circles (namely, circles passing through the point at infinity), it thus follows that the mapping (10) indeed transforms circles into circles.

Turning now to the general transformation (7), we observe that, because of (8), (7) can be broken up into the following three successive transformations:

$$z_1 = cz + d,$$

$$z_2 = \frac{1}{z_1}$$

$$w = \frac{a}{c} + \frac{bc - ad}{c} z_2.$$

The first and the third of these transformations are of the type (9), and the second coincides with (10). Since both (9) and (10) have been shown to transform circles into circles, this proves that *the general linear transformation* (7) *maps circles in the z-plane onto circles in the w-plane.* The point $z = -(d/c)$ is transformed by (7) into the point $w = \infty$; accordingly, circles passing through the point $z = -(d/c)$ will be transformed into straight lines.

The function (7) is univalent in the entire plane. Indeed, if w_1 and w_2 are the images of the points z_1 and z_2, respectively, we conclude from (8) that

(13) $$w_1 - w_2 = \frac{A(z_1 - z_2)}{(cz_1 + d)(cz_2 + d)}, \quad A = ad - bc.$$

This shows that $w_1 \neq w_2$ if $z_1 \neq z_2$, provided neither w_1 nor w_2 are infinite. Since, by (7), the point $w = \infty$ is the image of $z = -(d/c)$ and of no other point, the assertion follows.

If z_1, z_2, z_3, z_4 are four distinct finite points in the z-plane (and none of these points coincide with $z = -(d/c)$), (13) implies that

(14) $$\frac{(w_1 - w_4)(w_3 - w_2)}{(w_1 - w_2)(w_3 - w_4)} = \frac{(z_1 - z_4)(z_3 - z_2)}{(z_1 - z_2)(z_3 - z_4)}.$$

The expression

$$\frac{(z_1 - z_4)(z_3 - z_2)}{(z_1 - z_2)(z_3 - z_4)}$$

is called the *cross-ratio* of the four points z_1, z_2, z_3, z_4. Formula (14) shows that the cross-ratio of four points is equal to the cross-ratio of the images of these points under a linear transformation. This may also be expressed by saying that *the cross-ratio of four points is invariant under a linear transformation.* If one of the points w_k, say w_1, approaches the point at infinity, the left-hand side of (14) reduces to $(w_3 - w_2)(w_3 - w_4)^{-1}$. This expression is therefore to be regarded as the cross-ratio of the points ∞, w_2, w_3, w_4.

Formula (14) makes it possible to write down the linear transformation which carries three given points z_1, z_2, z_3 into three preassigned points w_1, w_2, w_3. Indeed, if z is any other point in the z-plane, and if w is its image under the transformation (7), it follows from (14) that we must have

$$(15) \qquad \frac{(w_1 - w)(w_3 - w_2)}{(w_1 - w_2)(w_3 - w)} = \frac{(z_1 - z)(z_3 - z_2)}{(z_1 - z_2)(z_3 - z)}.$$

If this equation is solved for w, the right-hand side is easily seen to be of the same form as the right-hand side of (7). The relation (15) is therefore equivalent to a linear transformation. It may also be noted that the three correspondences $z_k \rightarrow w_k$, $k = 1, 2, 3$, determine the transformation completely.

Since a linear transformation maps circles onto circles, and since a circle is determined by three of its points, we can thus find linear transformations which carry a given circle in the z-plane into a given circle in the w-plane. We can ask, moreover, that three points on the first circle be carried into three given points on the second circle. Once this is done, the transformation is completely determined. The inside of the circle C_z in the z-plane may be mapped either onto the inside of the circle C_w in the w-plane, or onto the exterior of C_w. In any given example, it is easy to decide which of these two cases occurs. If the point $z = -(d/c)$ lies inside C_z, the image of the inside must contain the point $w = \infty$, i.e., it is mapped onto the outside of C_w; otherwise, the interior of C_z corresponds to the interior of C_w. If C_w degenerates into a straight line, both the interior and the exterior of C_z are mapped onto half-planes bounded by this line.

We illustrate the use of Formula (15) by a few examples. To find all linear transformations which carry the real axis in the z-plane into the real axis in the w-plane, we have to consider all transformations (15) for which the numbers z_k, w_k, $k = 1, 2, 3$ are real. Solving (15) for w, we are led to transformations (7) for which the coefficients a, b, c, d are all real numbers. Conversely, if these numbers are real, (7) will evidently carry real numbers z into real numbers w. In view of what was said above, the image of the upper half-plane $\text{Im}(z) > 0$ may be either the upper half-plane $\text{Im}(w) > 0$ or the lower half-plane $\text{Im}(w) < 0$. In order to decide between these alternatives in a given case, we test the mapping of a point in $\text{Im}(z) > 0$, say the point $z = i$. By (7), we have

$$w = \frac{ai + b}{ci + d} = \frac{(ai + b)(-ci + d)}{c^2 + d^2},$$

and thus

$$\text{Im}(w) = \frac{ad - bc}{c^2 + d^2}.$$

Hence, $\text{Im}(z) > 0$ will be mapped onto $\text{Im}(w) > 0$ if $ad - bc > 0$, and onto $\text{Im}(w) < 0$ if $ad - bc < 0$.

We next consider the mapping of the disk $|z| < 1$ onto the disk $|w| < 1$. To obtain a particular mapping of this type, we set $z_1 = 1$, $z_2 = -1$, $z_3 = \alpha(|\alpha| = 1)$, $w_1 = 1$, $w_2 = -1$, $w_3 = \beta(|\beta| = 1)$ in Formula (15). A short computation (which the reader is recommended to carry out) shows that (15) is in this case equivalent to

$$(16) \qquad\qquad w = \frac{z - \gamma}{1 - \bar{\gamma}z},$$

where

$$\gamma = \frac{\beta - \alpha}{1 - \alpha\bar{\beta}}.$$

The number γ is real. Indeed, since $|\alpha| = |\beta| = 1$, we have $\alpha = (\bar{\alpha})^{-1}$, $\beta = (\bar{\beta})^{-1}$, and thus

$$\gamma = \frac{\beta - \alpha}{1 - \alpha\bar{\beta}} = \frac{(\bar{\beta})^{-1} - (\bar{\alpha})^{-1}}{1 - (\bar{\alpha}\bar{\beta})^{-1}} = \frac{\bar{\beta} - \bar{\alpha}}{1 - \bar{\alpha}\bar{\beta}} = \bar{\gamma}.$$

The function (16) maps $|z| < 1$ onto $|w| < 1$, and there must therefore exist a value z_0 in $|z| < 1$ for which w vanishes. Since the only zero of the right-hand side of (16) occurs at $z = \gamma$, we have $z_0 = \gamma$, and thus $|\gamma| < 1$.

To construct a more general mapping of this type, we observe that the transformation $z \to ze^{it}$ (t real) is a rotation about the origin. The function

$$w = \frac{e^{it}z - \gamma}{1 - e^{it}\bar{\gamma}z}$$

will therefore also map $|z| < 1$ onto $|w| < 1$, and the same will be true if the right-hand side of the last formula is multiplied by the factor e^{it_1}. This leads to

$$w = e^{it_1} \frac{e^{it}z - \gamma}{1 - e^{it}\gamma z} = e^{i(t+t_1)} \left(\frac{z - \gamma e^{-it}}{1 - \gamma e^{it}z} \right).$$

If we write $c = \gamma e^{-it}$ and note that γ is a real number such that $|\gamma| < 1$, we have $|c| < 1$ and $\gamma e^{it} = \bar{c}$. It therefore follows that the transformation takes the form

$$(17) \qquad\qquad w = K \left(\frac{z - c}{1 - \bar{c}z} \right),$$

where K and c are constants such that $|K| = 1$ and $|c| < 1$. It is easily confirmed that the function (17) gives the required mapping. If $|z| = 1$, we have $z = e^{i\theta}$ and therefore

$$|z - c| = |e^{i\theta} - c| = |e^{i\theta}| \, |1 - ce^{-i\theta}| = |1 - \bar{c}e^{i\theta}| = |1 - \bar{c}z|,$$

and thus

$$|w| = \left| \frac{z - c}{1 - \bar{c}z} \right| = 1.$$

The mapping (17) depends on the three real parameters $\operatorname{Re}(c)$, $\operatorname{Im}(c)$, and $\arg K$. These parameters may be chosen in such a way as to make three given points on $|z| = 1$ correspond to three given points on $|w| = 1$.

Since the function (7) maps circles onto circles (provided a straight line is regarded as a circle) this function will also map domains bounded by a number of circular arcs into domains of the same nature. The mapping being conformal, the angles between pairs of adjacent arcs must remain unchanged. For instance, the function

$$(18) \qquad\qquad w = \frac{az + b}{cz + d}, \quad a, b, c, d \text{ real}, \quad ad - bc > 0,$$

will map the quadrant indicated in Fig. 4a onto the half-circle of Fig. 4b. Indeed, the function (18) maps the upper half-plane $\operatorname{Im}(z) > 0$ onto the upper half-plane $\operatorname{Im}(w) > 0$. The upper half of the imaginary axis must be transformed into a circular arc. By (18) the points $z = 0$ and $z = \infty$ are transformed into $w = b/d$ and $w = a/c$, respectively. Since the line $\operatorname{Re}(z) = 0$ is perpendicular to the line $\operatorname{Im}(z) = 0$, the circular arc must intersect the line $\operatorname{Im}(w) = 0$ at right angles. Hence, this line must pass through the center of the circular arc, and the map is found to be the half-circle indicated.

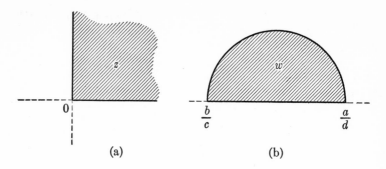

FIG. 4

Exercises

1. Show that the function

$$w = K\left(\frac{z - \alpha}{z - \bar{\alpha}}\right),$$

where $\mathrm{Im}(\alpha) > 0$ and $|K| = 1$, maps the upper half-plane $\mathrm{Im}(z) > 0$ onto the unit disk $|w| < 1$.

2. If α and K are constants such that $|\alpha| < 1$, $|K| = 1$, show that the function

$$w = \frac{1 - \alpha K + z(K - \bar{\alpha})}{1 + \alpha K - z(K + \bar{\alpha})}$$

maps the unit disk $|z| < 1$ onto the right half-plane $\mathrm{Re}(w) > 0$.

3. Show that the function

$$w = \frac{z}{1 - z}$$

maps $|z| < 1$ onto the half-plane $\mathrm{Re}(z) \geq -\tfrac{1}{2}$.

4. Show that the function $w = z^{-1}$ maps the intersection of the disks $|z - 1| < 1$ and $|z + i| < 1$ onto the quarter-plane $\mathrm{Re}(w) > \tfrac{1}{2}$, $\mathrm{Im}(w) > \tfrac{1}{2}$.

5. Let D be a domain whose boundary consists of three circular arcs. Show that there exists a linear transformation which maps D onto a triangle if, and only if, the three circles bounding D have a common point.

6. The inverse of the transformation (7) is again a linear transformation. Show that the coefficients of these two transformations are identical if, and only if, $a = -d$.

7. Show that the cross-ratio of four distinct points is real if, and only if, the four points lie on a circle. *Hint:* Transform the circle into the real axis.

8. If w and z are related by the transformation (17), show that

$$\frac{|dw|}{1 - |w|^2} = \frac{|dz|}{1 - |z|^2}.$$

9. Use the transformation (17) and the result of Exercise 5 of the preceding section to show that

$$\iint\limits_{|z| < 1} \frac{dx\, dy}{|1 - cz|^4} = \frac{\pi}{(1 - |c|^2)^2}, \quad |c| < 1.$$

10. The equation

$$z = \frac{az + b}{cz + d}$$

has, in general, two distinct solutions. If these solutions are denoted by α and β, show that (7) can be brought into the form

$$\frac{w - \alpha}{w - \beta} = k\left(\frac{z - \alpha}{z - \beta}\right),$$

where k is a complex constant. (The points α and β are known as the *fixed points* of the transformation (7). Why?)

11. Find a linear transformation with the fixed points ± 1 which maps $z = e^{it_1}$ onto $w = e^{it_2}$ $(0 < t_1 < t_2 < \pi)$. Verify that the transformation is of the form (17).

4 THE SCHWARZ-CHRISTOFFEL FORMULA

The Riemann mapping theorem guarantees the existence of an analytic function which maps a given simply-connected domain onto the unit circle, but it does not tell us how to find this function. Although it would be desirable to have a general formula by means of which the mapping function could be computed for any given domain, it is in the nature of things that this will be possible only if the domains are of certain simple types. As we shall show in this section, an explicit formula for the mapping function can be obtained in the case in which the domain in question is a polygon.

We shall derive two versions of this formula; the first of these will give the conformal mapping of the upper half-plane $\text{Im}(z) > 0$ onto a polygon D in the w-plane, and the second will give the mapping of the disk $|z| < 1$ onto this polygon. We begin with the formula for the half-plane. We assume D to be a polygon of n sides, and we denote its angles by $\pi\alpha_1, \pi\alpha_2, \cdots, \pi\alpha_n$. For the sake of convenient formulation we also introduce the exterior angles $\pi\mu_1, \cdots, \pi\mu_n$, defined by $\pi\alpha_k + \pi\mu_k = \pi$, i.e., $\alpha_k + \mu_k = 1$. It may be noted that μ_k is positive if the interior angle is smaller than π, and negative if it exceeds π. Since in a convex polygon all interior angles are smaller than π, the constants μ_k are all positive if D is convex. By a theorem of elementary geometry, the sum of all exterior angles of a polygon is 2π. This shows that the quantities μ_k are subject to the relation

$$(19) \qquad\qquad \sum_{k=1}^{n} \mu_k = 2.$$

Let now $w = f(z)$ be an analytic function mapping the upper half-plane $\text{Im}(z) > 0$ onto the polygon D, and denote by a_1, $a_2, \cdots, a_n$ ($a_k \neq \infty$) the points on the real axis (in the z-plane) which correspond, respectively, to the vertices of D with the interior angles $\pi\alpha_1, \pi\alpha_2, \cdots, \pi\alpha_n$. The function $w = f(z)$ will thus make each side of the polygon correspond to a linear segment connecting two adjacent points a_k (this includes a "segment" containing the point $z = \infty$). In the derivation of the formula for the mapping function we make use of the following property of mappings of this type.

Let A be a domain whose boundary includes a linear segment L, and let A' be a domain whose boundary includes a linear segment L'. If the function $w = f(z)$ maps A onto A' in such a way that the segment L is transformed into the segment L', then $f(z)$ is regular at the points of L.

In view of this result (whose proof can be found in Chap. VII, Sec. 3), the function mapping the half-plane $\text{Im}(z) > 0$ will be regular at all points of the real axis other than the points a_k.

Suppose now that a_1 and a_2 are such that $f(a_1)$ and $f(a_2)$ are two adjacent vertices of the polygon. If the real parameter t varies from 0 to 1, the point

$$f(a_1) + t[f(a_2) - f(a_1)]$$

describes the linear segment joining $f(a_1)$ and $f(a_2)$, i.e., the side of the polygon joining the two vertices. We thus have

$$f(z) = f(x) = f(a_1) + t(x)[f(a_2) - f(a_1)],$$

if x is in the interval bounded by a_1 and a_2. Since $f(z)$ is differentiable there, we have

$$f'(z) = f'(x) = t'(x)[f(a_2) - f(a_1)],$$
$$f''(z) = f''(x) = t''(x)[f(a_2) - f(a_1)],$$

and thus

$$\frac{f''(z)}{f'(z)} = \frac{t''(x)}{t'(x)}.$$

Since $t(x)$ is a real function of the real variable x, this shows that the expression $f''(z)/f'(z)$ is real at all points of the real axis other than the points a_k.

We now have to study the behavior of this expression at the points a_k. In view of the mapping properties of $w = f(z)$, the image of a small segment of the real axis containing the point a_k is composed of two linear segments which meet at $f(a_k)$ under the angle $\pi\alpha_k$. To simplify the algebra, we assume for a moment that $f(a_k) = 0$, i.e., that the vertex in question coincides with the origin. In this case the two segments meeting at $w = 0$ will have polar equations $w_1 = r_1 e^{i\theta}$ and $w_2 = r_2 e^{i(\theta + \pi\alpha_k)}$, where θ is a constant angle and r_1, r_2 take positive values. If β is a real number, we thus have

$$w_1^\beta = r_1^\beta e^{i\theta\beta}, \quad w_2^\beta = r_2^\beta e^{i(\theta + \pi\alpha_k)\beta}.$$

This shows that the transformation $w \to w^\beta$ maps the original pair of linear segments onto another pair of segments, and that the latter form the angle $\pi\alpha_k\beta$. If $\beta = \alpha_k^{-1}$, the angle is equal to π, and the two segments form a single linear segment passing through the origin. In other words, the function

$$h(z) = [f(z)]^{1/\alpha_k}$$

will map a section of the real axis containing the point a_k onto a linear segment.

In view of the result stated above, this function is therefore regular at a_k. The derivative of $h(z)$ cannot vanish at a_k, since the mapping is conformal at this point (the angle π is transformed into the angle π). Since $h(a_k) = 0$, we thus have

$$[f(z)]^{1/\alpha_k} = (z - a_k)g(z),$$

where $g(z)$ is regular at a_k and $g(a_k) \neq 0$. If $f(a_k)$ is not zero, the corresponding formula is evidently

$$[f(z) - f(a_k)]^{1/\alpha_k} = (z - a_k)g(z).$$

Hence,

$$f(z) = f(a_k) + (z - a_k)^{\alpha_k}[g(z)]^{\alpha_k},$$

and thus

$$f'(z) = (z - a_k)^{\alpha_k-1}\{\alpha_k[g(z)]^{\alpha_k} + \alpha_k(z - a_k)[g(z)]^{\alpha_k-1}g'(z)\},$$

i.e.,

$$f'(z) = (z - a)^{\alpha_k-1}p(z),$$

where, because of $g(a_k) \neq 0$, $p(z)$ is regular at a_k and $p(a_k) \neq 0$. Differentiating again, and observing that $1 - \alpha_k = \mu_k$, where $\pi\mu_k$ is the exterior angle, we obtain

$$\frac{f''(z)}{f'(z)} = -\frac{\mu_k}{z - a_k} + \frac{p'(z)}{p(z)}.$$

Since $p(a_k) \neq 0$, this shows that the function $f''(z)/f'(z)$ has a simple pole—with the residue $-\mu_k$—at $z = a_k$. Accordingly, the function

$$(20) \qquad H(z) \equiv \frac{f''(z)}{f'(z)} + \sum_{k=1}^{n} \frac{\mu_k}{z - a_k}$$

is regular at the points a_k. Since $f''(z)/f'(z)$ was shown to be regular at all other real points, $H(z)$ is thus regular at all points of the real axis.

We saw before that the function $f''(z)/f'(z)$ is real for real z. Since the μ_k and α_k are real numbers, (20) shows that the same is true of the function $H(z)$. This function is therefore regular, and takes real values, at all finite points of the real axis. To study its behavior at $z = \infty$, we observe that the mapping $z = \zeta^{-1}$ transforms the segment $-c < \zeta < c(c > 0)$ into the rays $-\infty < z < -c^{-1}$ and $c^{-1} < z < \infty$. The function $f(\zeta^{-1})$ will therefore transform a section of the real axis (including the origin) into a side of the polygon. By the result quoted above, $f(\zeta^{-1})$ is thus regular at $\zeta = 0$, and it therefore can be expanded into a power series $\Sigma c_\nu \zeta^\nu$. In terms of the variable z, this means that

$$f(z) = c_0 + \frac{c_1}{z} + \frac{c_2}{z^2} + \cdots,$$

where the series converges for large $|z|$. Hence,

$$f'(z) = -\frac{c_1}{z^2} - \frac{2c_2}{z^3} - \cdots$$

and

$$f''(z) = \frac{2c_1}{z^3} + \frac{6c_2}{z^4} + \cdots.$$

If c_m is the first non-vanishing coefficient, we thus have

$$\frac{f''(z)}{f'(z)} = -\frac{1}{z}\left(\frac{m(m+1)c_m + (m+1)(m+2)c_{m+1}z^{-1} + \cdots}{mc_m + (m+1)c_{m+1}z^{-1} + \cdots}\right),$$

and this makes it evident that $f''(z)/f'(z)$ is regular, and takes the value 0, at infinity. Formula (20) shows that the other terms making up the function $H(z)$ are also regular and equal to zero at $z = \infty$.

We have thus found that the function $H(z)$ is regular, and takes real values, at all points of the "extended" real axis, i.e., the real axis plus the point at infinity. In the upper half-plane, $H(z)$ is regular. Indeed, (20) shows that the only possible singularities of $H(z)$ in $\text{Im}(z) > 0$ are the zeros of $f'(z)$ and, as shown in Section 2, the derivative of a univalent function cannot vanish. We now recall that an analytic function which is regular in a domain and on its boundary and, in addition, takes real values on the boundary, must reduce to a constant (Chap. IV, Sec. 7). Since the extended real axis is the complete boundary of the upper half-plane, and since the function $H(z)$ has all the required properties, we conclude that $H(z)$ is a constant (the fact that the upper half-plane is not a finite domain makes no difference; by a linear transformation it can be mapped onto a disk, and the quoted result may then be applied to the disk). Since $H(\infty) = 0$, the value of the constant is zero. Hence $H(z) \equiv 0$, and it follows from (20) that

$$\frac{f''(z)}{f'(z)} = -\sum_{k=1}^{n}\frac{\mu_k}{z - a_k}.$$

Integrating, we have

$$\log f'(z) = -\sum_{k=1}^{n}\mu_k \log(z - a_k) + \log B,$$

i.e.,

$$f'(z) = B(z - a_1)^{-\mu_1}(z - a_2)^{-\mu_2} \cdots (z - a_n)^{-\mu_n},$$

where B is a constant.   Hence

$$(21) \qquad f(z) = A + B \int^z \frac{dz}{(z - a_1)^{\mu_1} \cdots (z - a_n)^{\mu_n}},$$

where A is another integration constant.

This is the *Schwarz-Christoffel formula*.   Any analytic function $w = f(z)$ which maps the upper half-plane onto a polygon with n sides and the exterior angles $\pi \mu_k$ must be of this form.   It is interesting to count the number of independent real parameters contained in (21).   Since the μ_k are subject to the condition (19), there are $n - 1$ independent numbers μ_k.   Next, there are $n - 3$ independent numbers a_k.   This becomes clear if it is remembered that there exists a three-parameter family of functions which map the upper half-plane onto itself.   Three of the numbers a_k may thus be arbitrarily chosen.   Finally, the complex numbers A,B are equivalent to four real numbers.   The total number of independent real parameters is therefore $(n - 1) + (n - 3) + 4 = 2n$. As was to be expected, this is identical with the number of real parameters determining a general polygon with n vertices.   Each vertex is given by two real numbers, and the total is thus $2n$.

In order to construct a mapping function with the help of Formula (21), we have to know the values of the constants a_k. These values depend of course on the shape of the given polygon, but in general the dependence is of a rather complicated nature. In the case $n = 3$ no problems arise since, as just pointed out, three of the constants a_k can be chosen arbitrarily.   For $n > 3$, the determination of the a_k can be very difficult, except in cases where the polygon has a high degree of symmetry.

Before we consider examples of such mappings, we adapt Formula (21) to the case in which one of the points a_k, say a_n, coincides with the point at infinity.   This is easily accomplished by means of the linear transformation $z = a_n - \zeta^{-1}$, which maps the upper half-plane onto itself and carries $\zeta = \infty$ into $z = a_n$. With this substitution, (21) becomes

$$f(\zeta) = A + B \int^\zeta \left(a_n - a_1 - \frac{1}{\zeta} \right)^{-\mu_1} \cdots$$

$$\left(a_n - a_{n-1} - \frac{1}{\zeta} \right)^{-\mu_{n-1}} \left(-\frac{1}{\zeta} \right)^{-\mu_n} \frac{d\zeta}{\zeta^2},$$

or, in view of (19) (and denoting the variable again by z),

$$(22) \qquad f(z) = A + B' \int^z \frac{dz}{(z - a_1')^{\mu_1} \cdots (z - a_{n-1}')^{\mu_{n-1}}},$$

where $a_1', \cdots, a_{n-1}'$ are real constants. The vertices of the polygon correspond now to the points $a_1', \cdots, a_{n-1}', \infty$. A comparison of (22) and (21) shows that the choice $a_n = \infty$ has the effect of the corresponding term being left out of the formula.

To illustrate the use of the Schwarz-Christoffel formula, we construct a function mapping the upper half-plane onto a triangle with the angles $\pi\alpha$, $\pi\beta$, $\pi\gamma$. To obtain a simpler formula, we let one of the vertices, say the vertex at the angle $\pi\gamma$, correspond to $z = \infty$, so that (22) applies. Setting $a_1' = 0$, $a_2' = 1$, and noting that the exterior angles are $\pi(1 - \alpha)$, $\pi(1 - \beta)$, we obtain

$$(23) \qquad f(z) = \int_0^z z^{\alpha-1}(1 - z)^{\beta-1}\, dz.$$

(A particular choice of A and B' in (22) will, of course, merely affect the position and size of the polygon.) To find the vertices of the triangle, we note that, by (23), $f(0) = 0$ and

$$f(1) = \int_0^1 x^{\alpha-1}(1 - x)^{\beta-1}\, dx.$$

This is a Beta-function, and its value is

$$f(1) = \frac{\Gamma(\alpha)\Gamma(\beta)}{\Gamma(\alpha + \beta)},$$

where $\Gamma(x)$ is the Gamma-function. Since $\alpha + \beta + \gamma = 1$ and $\Gamma(x)\Gamma(1 - x) = \pi[\sin \pi x]^{-1}$, this shows that the length of the side c (facing the angle $\pi\gamma$) is

$$c = \frac{1}{\pi} \sin \pi\gamma\, \Gamma(\alpha)\Gamma(\beta)\Gamma(\gamma).$$

Using the law of sines,

$$\frac{a}{\sin \pi\alpha} = \frac{b}{\sin \pi\beta} = \frac{c}{\sin \pi\gamma},$$

the other sides are found to be

$$a = \frac{1}{\pi} \sin \pi\alpha\, \Gamma(\alpha)\Gamma(\beta)\Gamma(\gamma), \quad b = \frac{1}{\pi} \sin \pi\beta\, \Gamma(\alpha)\Gamma(\beta)\Gamma(\gamma).$$

Our next example concerns the conformal mapping of the upper half-plane onto a rectangle. Since the upper half-plane can be mapped onto itself in such a way that four arbitrary real points are carried into the points ± 1, $\pm k^{-1}$, where $0 < k < 1$ (proof ?), and since all the exterior angles are equal to $\pi/2$, (21) shows that such a mapping is given by the function

$$f(z) = \int_0^z \frac{dz}{\sqrt{(1 - z^2)(1 - k^2 z^2)}}.$$

So far we have considered the conformal mapping of the upper half-plane onto a polygon. In order to obtain a formula for the analytic function mapping the unit circle onto this polygon, we combine (21) with the linear transformation

$$z = i\left(\frac{1 + \zeta}{1 - \zeta}\right), \quad \zeta = \frac{z - i}{z + i},$$

which maps $|\zeta| < 1$ onto $\mathrm{Im}(z) > 0$. We have

$$(z - a_k)^{\mu_k} = \left[i\left(\frac{1 + \zeta}{1 - \zeta}\right) - a_k\right]^{\mu_k}$$

$$= \left(\frac{a_k + i}{1 - \zeta}\right)^{\mu_k}\left[\zeta - \frac{a_k - i}{a_k + i}\right]^{\mu_k},$$

and

$$dz = \frac{2i\, d\zeta}{(1 - \zeta)^2}.$$

If we denote by b_k the point

$$b_k = \frac{a_k - i}{a_k + i}$$

on the unit circle which corresponds to the vertex of index k, and if we use the relation (19), a short computation shows that (21) is transformed into

$$(24) \qquad f(z) = A_1 + B_1 \int_0^z \frac{dz}{(z - b_1)^{\mu_1} \cdots (z - b_n)^{\mu_n}},$$

where A_1, B_1 are constants and the variable has again been denoted by z.

It is worth noting that the Formulas (21) and (24) are formally identical. The only difference between them is that the constants a_k in (21) are real, while the constants b_k in (24) are of absolute value 1.

The method of proof which led us to Formulas (21) and (24) can also be used to derive an expression for the function $f(z)$ which maps the unit disk onto the *outside* of the given polygon.

If $f(z)$ is normalized by the condition $f(0) = \infty$, the formula in question is

$$f(z) = A + B \int^z (z - b_1)^{\mu_1} \cdots (z - b_n)^{\mu_n} \frac{dz}{z^2},$$

where μ_k and b_k have the same meaning as in (24).

EXERCISES

1. Show that the function

$$w = \int_0^z \frac{dz}{\sqrt{z(1 - z^2)}}$$

maps the upper half-plane $\mathrm{Im}(z) > 0$ onto a square. Show that the sides of the square have the length

$$a = \frac{1}{2} \int_0^1 t^{-3/4}(1 - t)^{-1/2}\, dt = \frac{1}{2\sqrt{2\pi}}\, \Gamma^2\left(\frac{1}{4}\right).$$

2. Show that the function

$$w = \int_0^z \frac{dz}{(1 - z^2)^{3/4}}$$

maps $\mathrm{Im}(z) > 0$ onto a triangle with the angles $\dfrac{\pi}{2}, \dfrac{\pi}{4}, \dfrac{\pi}{4}.$ Show that the vertices of the triangle are at the points $\pm a,\ ai$, where a is the constant defined in the preceding exercise.

3. Show that

$$w = \int_0^z (1 - z^n)^{-2/n}\, dz$$

maps $|z| < 1$ onto the interior of a regular polygon of order n. Express the length of the side as a definite integral.

4. Show that the function

$$w = \int_0^z \frac{\sqrt{1 + z^4}}{1 - z^4}\, dz$$

maps $|z| < 1$ onto the domain indicated in Fig. 5. Show that the width of the strips is

$$\sqrt{2} \int_0^1 \frac{\sqrt{1 - t^4}}{1 + t^4}\, dt.$$

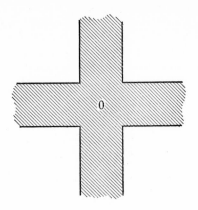

FIG. **5**

5. Show that the function

$$w = \int_0^z \frac{dz}{\sqrt{z(1 - z^2)(1 - k^2z^2)}}, \quad k > 1,$$

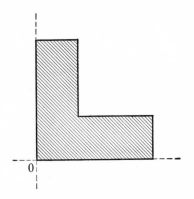

FIG. **6**

maps $\operatorname{Im}(z) > 0$ onto a domain of the type indicated in Fig. 6.

6. Show that the function

$$w = \int_0^z \frac{\sqrt{1 - z^2}}{1 - k^2z^2}\, dz, \quad k > 1,$$

maps $\operatorname{Im}(z) > 0$ onto a domain of the shape indicated in Fig. 7.

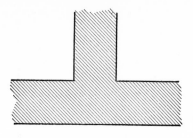

FIG. **7**

7. Show that the function

$$w = \int_1^z (1 - z^n)^{2/n} \frac{dz}{z^2}$$

maps $|z| < 1$ onto the exterior of a regular polygon of order n.

5 SOME ELEMENTARY MAPPINGS

In this section we use the Schwarz-Christoffel formula to construct a number of simple conformal mappings which are of importance in the applications. In most of these cases the domains will be unbounded, and they will therefore not be "polygons" in the usual sense. Since our proof of the Schwarz-Christoffel formula was carried out under the assumption that the polygon in question was bounded, we shall use the formula only as a heuristic means for obtaining the mapping function. Once the function is found, it is not difficult to confirm that it has indeed the required mapping properties.

As a first example, we consider the mapping of the upper half-plane $\operatorname{Im}(z) > 0$ onto the infinite half-strip $-\frac{\pi}{2} < \operatorname{Re}(w) < \frac{\pi}{2}$, $\operatorname{Im}(w) > 0$ (Fig. 8). The half-strip is bounded by straight lines and may thus be regarded as a "polygon." We note that, in addition to being unbounded, this polygon has another unusual feature: One of its angles is zero (the angle between the two parallels, which meet at $w = \infty$). We try to construct a map-

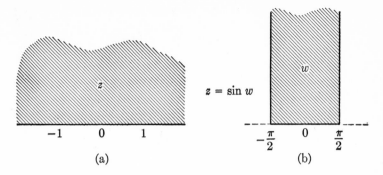

FIG. **8**

ping function which transforms the points $-1, 1, \infty$ into the points $-\frac{\pi}{2}, \frac{\pi}{2}, \infty$, respectively. Since the exterior angles at the finite vertices are both $\frac{\pi}{2}$, Formula (22) yields

$$w = A + B \int_0^z \frac{dz}{\sqrt{1 - z^2}}.$$

The constants A and B are determined by the conditions $w(1) = \frac{\pi}{2}$ and $w(-1) = -\frac{\pi}{2}$. Because

$$\int_0^1 \frac{dz}{\sqrt{1 - z^2}} = \frac{\pi}{2},$$

we have $A + \frac{\pi}{2} B = \frac{\pi}{2}$, $A - \frac{\pi}{2} B = -\frac{\pi}{2}$, i.e., $A = 0$, $B = 1$. Hence,

$$(25) \qquad\qquad w = \int_0^z \frac{dz}{\sqrt{1 - z^2}} = \text{arc sin } z.$$

We now confirm that this function indeed yields the desired mapping. As shown in Section 2, it is sufficient for this purpose to verify that the boundary of Fig. 8a is carried by the function (25) into the boundary of Fig. 8b, if both boundaries are positively oriented with respect to their interiors. Formula (25) shows that $w(0) = 0$ and that $w(z)$ grows to $\frac{\pi}{2}$ if z varies along the positive axis from 0 to 1. At the point $z = 1$, the integrand has a singularity, and the behavior of the integrand is best studied by "by-passing" this point along a small semicircle $z = 1 - \rho e^{i\theta}$, where θ decreases from 0 to $-\pi$. Since $\sqrt{1 - z} = \sqrt{\rho e^{i\theta}} = \sqrt{\rho} e^{i\theta/2}$, and since $e^{i\theta/2}$ varies from 1 to $-i$ if θ decreases from 0 to $-\pi$, we have $\sqrt{1 - z} = -i\sqrt{\rho} = -i\sqrt{z - 1}$ for $\theta = -\pi$. This shows that, for $z > 1$, $\sqrt{1 - z^2}$ becomes equal to $-i\sqrt{z^2 - 1}$. Hence,

$$w = \frac{\pi}{2} + i \int_1^z \frac{dz}{\sqrt{z^2 - 1}}, \quad z > 1,$$

and it becomes evident that w varies along the vertical line $\frac{\pi}{2} + it$,

$0 < t < \infty$, as z ranges over the line $1 < z < \infty$.

Repeating the same argument for negative values of z, we thus find that w traverses (in the positive direction) the boundary of Fig. 8b, if z varies along the positive axis from $-\infty$ to ∞. Since the latter is the boundary of the upper half-plane, this proves that the function (25) indeed effects the mapping indicated in Fig. 8.

We next consider the function mapping the unit circle $|z| < 1$

onto the infinite strip $-\frac{\pi}{4} < \mathrm{Re}(w) < \frac{\pi}{4}$ (Fig. 9). The strip may

be regarded as a polygon with two sides, both of whose angles are

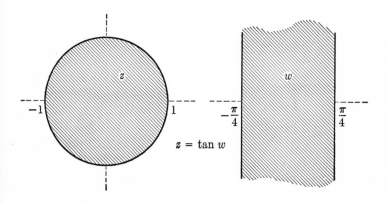

FIG. 9

zero. Accordingly, both exterior angles are equal to π. If the points $z = \pm i$ are to correspond to the "vertices" of the polygon, it will follow from (24) that the mapping function must be of the form

$$w = A + B \int_0^z \frac{dz}{1 + z^2}.$$

If we ask, moreover, that the images of $z = \pm 1$ should be $w = \pm\frac{\pi}{4}$, it is easy to see that $A = 0$, $B = 1$, and thus

(26) $$w = \int_0^z \frac{dz}{1 + z^2} = \text{arc tan } z.$$

To show that this is indeed the required mapping function, we find the value of w for a point $z = e^{i\theta}$ on the unit circumference. Computing the integral (26) along a path consisting of the segment $0 < z < 1$ and an arc of the unit circle, we obtain

$$w = \int_0^1 \frac{dx}{1 + x^2} + i \int_0^\theta \frac{e^{i\theta}d\theta}{1 + e^{2i\theta}}$$

$$= \frac{\pi}{4} + \frac{i}{2} \int_0^\theta \frac{d\theta}{\cos \theta},$$

and this makes it plain that the right half of the unit circumference is mapped onto the vertical line $z = \frac{\pi}{2} + it$, $-\infty < t < \infty$. A similar argument shows that the left half of $|z| = 1$ is mapped onto the line $-\frac{\pi}{2} + it$. The entire circumference $|z| = 1$ is thus transformed into the boundary of the strip, and this proves that the function (26) indeed gives the mapping of Fig. 9.

Our next example is the conformal mapping of the unit circle $|z| < 1$ onto the domain obtained by cutting the w-plane along the negative axis as indicated in Fig. 10b. This domain may be regarded as a "polygon," whose sides are the upper and the lower edges of the slit. At the finite end of the slit, the interior angle is 2π. The "exterior angle" is thus $\pi - 2\pi = -\pi$, and the exponent μ has the value -1. To satisfy (19), we have to associate the exponent 3 with the other end of the slit. Although all this looks rather questionable if interpreted geometrically, the Schwarz-Christoffel formula will nevertheless give the correct mapping function. If the points $z = -1$ and $z = 1$ are being made to

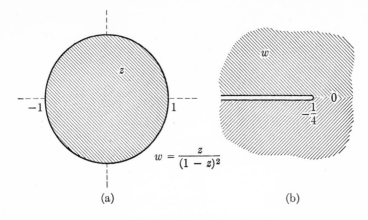

$$w = \frac{z}{(1 - z)^2}$$

(a)   (b)

FIG. 10

correspond, respectively, to $w = -\frac{1}{4}$ and $w = \infty$, a formal application of (24) (with $A = 0$, $B = -1$) yields

$$w = \int_0^z \frac{1 + z}{(1 - z)^3}\, dz,$$

i.e.,

(27)
$$w = \frac{z}{(1 - z)^2}.$$

A point $z = e^{i\theta}$ on the unit circumference is transformed by (27) into

$$w = \frac{e^{i\theta}}{(1 - e^{i\theta})^2} = \left(e^{-i\frac{\theta}{2}} - e^{i\frac{\theta}{2}}\right)^{-2} = -\frac{1}{4 \cos^2 \dfrac{\theta}{2}}.$$

If θ varies from 0 to π, w will therefore move along the negative axis from $-\frac{1}{4}$ to $-\infty$. If θ grows from π to 2π, w describes the same portion of the negative axis in the opposite direction. The positively oriented unit circumference is thus transformed into the positively oriented boundary of the cut plane of Fig. 10b, and it follows that (27) is the desired mapping function.

By combining (27) with the additional linear transformation

(28)
$$W = \frac{1}{2}\left(\frac{1}{w} + 2\right),$$

we obtain the mapping indicated in Fig. 11. Since (28) is a linear transformation which carries real values into real values, and

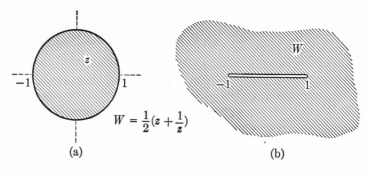

FIG. 11

since $w = -\frac{1}{4}$ and $w = \infty$ correspond, respectively, to $W = -1$ and $W = 1$, the slit of Fig. 10b is transformed into a rectilinear slit joining $W = -1$ and $W = 1$. In view of (27) and (28), this mapping is given by the function

(29) $$W = \frac{1}{2}\left(z + \frac{1}{z}\right).$$

It is worth noting that the right-hand side of (29) remains unchanged if z is replaced by z^{-1}. Since this corresponds to a transformation of the interior of the unit circle into its exterior, it follows that (29) also transforms the domain $|z| > 1$ onto the slit-domain of Fig. 11b.

As a final example of a degenerate polygon, we consider the slit-domain of Fig. 12b. Rather than construct the function mapping a circle onto this domain by means of the Schwarz-Christoffel formula, we verify directly that the function $w = z + e^z$ maps the

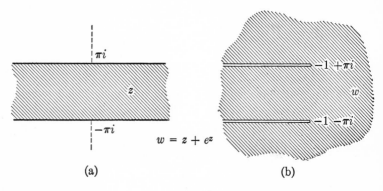

FIG. 12

infinite strip $-\pi < \operatorname{Im} z < \pi$ of Fig. 12a onto this slit-domain. On the upper boundary of the strip we have $z = \pi i + x$, and thus

$$w = \pi i + x + e^{\pi i + x} = \pi i + x - e^x.$$

On the lower boundary we have, similarly,

$$w = -\pi i + x + e^{-\pi i + x} = -\pi i + x - e^x.$$

This shows that the two boundary lines of the slit are mapped onto parts of the straight lines $\operatorname{Im}(w) = \pi$ and $\operatorname{Im}(w) = -\pi$, respectively. In both cases, we have $\operatorname{Re}(w) = x - e^x$, and it is easy to see that, as x grows from $-\infty$ to ∞, the value of $x - e^x$ grows from $-\infty$ to -1 and then decreases again to $-\infty$. Since, as the reader will confirm, the positively oriented boundary of the strip 12a is carried into the positively oriented boundary of the slit-domain 12b, it follows from the results of Section 2 that the function $w = z + e^z$ indeed gives the mapping of Fig. 12.

EXERCISES

1. Show that the function $w = \log z$ maps the half-plane $\operatorname{Re}(z) > 0$ onto the infinite strip $0 < \operatorname{Im}(w) < \pi$ (Fig. 13).

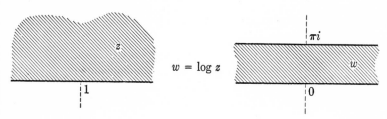

FIG. 13

2. Show that the function $w = \log (1 - z^2)$ gives the mapping indicated in Fig. 14.

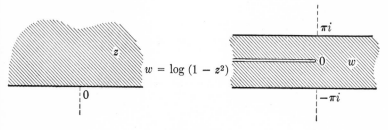

FIG. 14

3. Show that the function $w = \log \dfrac{1+z}{1-z}$ gives the mapping indicated in Fig. 15.

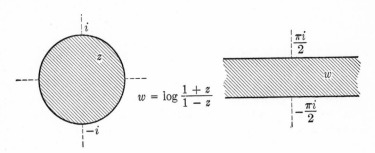

FIG. 15

4. Show that the function $w = \dfrac{1+z^{\alpha}}{1-z^{\alpha}}$, $0 < \alpha < 1$, maps the upper half-plane $\operatorname{Im}(z) > 0$ onto the circular segment of Fig. 16b.

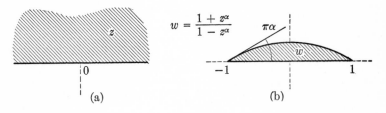

FIG. 16

Hint: Show first that $W = z^{\alpha}$ maps the half-plane onto the infinite sector $0 < \arg W < \pi\alpha$, and then apply the linear transformation $w = (1 + W)(1 - W)^{-1}$.

5. Show that the function $w = 2 \log z - z^2 - \pi i$ maps the half-plane $\operatorname{Im} z > 0$ onto the slit-domain of Fig. 12b. *Hint:* Combine the mappings of Fig. 12 and Fig. 13.

6. Show that the function $w = \tan^2 \sqrt{z}$ maps the "interior" of the parabola

$$64y^2 = \pi^2(\pi^2 - 16x)$$

onto the disk $|w| < 1$. *Hint:* Decompose this mapping into the transformations

$$z_1 = \sqrt{z}, \quad z_2 = e^{2iz_1}, \quad z_3 = \frac{z_2 - 1}{i(z_2 + 1)}, \quad w = z_3^2.$$

7. Show that the function

$$w = \log \frac{1 + z^2}{2z}$$

maps the half-circle $|z| < 1$, $\mathrm{Im}(z) > 0$ onto the infinite strip $0 < \mathrm{Im}(w) < \pi$.

VI

PHYSICAL

APPLICATIONS

1 BOUNDARY VALUE PROBLEMS

The successful treatment of many of the problems arising in applied mathematics and mathematical physics depends on the possibility of constructing functions $u = u(x, y, z)$ which are solutions of the Laplace equation

$$(1) \qquad \frac{\partial^2 u}{\partial x^2} + \frac{\partial^2 u}{\partial y^2} + \frac{\partial^2 u}{\partial z^2} = 0$$

(where x, y, z are rectangular coordinates), and which, moreover, satisfy certain additional conditions whose nature is determined by the particular problem under discussion. In many cases, the given physical data contain information as to the behavior of the function $u(x, y, z)$ on the boundary S of the three-dimensional region V in which the physical processes occur. In these cases, the original physical problem leads to a *boundary value problem* for the differential equation (1), i.e., to the problem of finding a function $u(x, y, z)$ which is a solution of (1) in the region V and which exhibits the required boundary behavior at the points of S.

If the physical situation is such that the value of the function $u(x, y, z)$ does not depend on the coordinate z, Equation (1) reduces to the two-dimensional Laplace equation

$$(2) \qquad \frac{\partial^2 u}{\partial x^2} + \frac{\partial^2 u}{\partial y^2} = 0.$$

Since any solution of (2) is the real part of an analytic function of a complex variable, this type of problem thus becomes accessible to the techniques of complex analysis.

If the function u is to depend only on the coordinates x and y, the same must be true of the boundary of the region V and of the prescribed boundary conditions. The intersections of V with planes parallel to the xy-plane must therefore all be identical, i.e., V must be a right cylinder of infinite length, perpendicular to the xy-plane. Since cylindrical bodies which occur in actual physical problems have, of course, finite length, it is clear that the use of the two-dimensional equation (2) cannot lead to entirely accurate results. Experience shows, however, that the errors introduced in this way are small provided the height of the cylinder is sufficiently large compared to its lateral dimensions, and provided the solution is not used at points too near to the top or the bottom of the cylinder.

We now assume that V is an infinite cylinder of the type described, and that the intersection of V with the xy-plane consists of a domain D and its boundary C. As an example of a boundary value problem we consider the problem of finding a solution $u = u(x, y)$ of (2) in D which assumes given values at the points of C. (We note here again that a function $u(x, y)$ is called a solution of (2) in D if the first and second derivatives of u with respect to x and y exist and are continuous, and if (2) is satisfied, at all points of D.) This problem—the *Dirichlet problem*—was discussed in Chapter IV, Section 9 for the particular case in which D is a circle. The fact that we were able to obtain an explicit solution of the Dirichlet problem in this case is due to the geometric simplicity of the circle; for a general domain, no such simple solution can be expected. We shall however show that in all those cases in which the domain D can be mapped conformally onto a circular disk by means of a known analytic function, the solution of the Dirichlet problem for the domain D can be reduced to the solution of a corresponding problem for the disk. Since the latter problem can be solved explicitly, we are thus in a position to solve the Dirichlet problem for all domains whose mapping functions onto a circular disk are known.

We first prove the following result:

Let $z = f(\zeta)$ be an analytic function of the complex variable ζ which maps a domain D' in the ζ-plane onto a domain D in the

z-plane. If $\zeta = \xi + i\eta$, $z = x + iy = x(\xi, \eta) + iy(\xi, \eta)$, and if $u(x, y)$ is a harmonic function in D, then

(3) $$U(\xi, \eta) \equiv u[x(\xi, \eta), y(\xi, \eta)]$$

is a harmonic function of ξ and η in D'.

In other words, if $u(x, y)$ is a solution of (2), then $U(\xi, \eta)$ is a solution of $U_{\xi\xi} + U_{\eta\eta} = 0$. To prove this result with a minimum of computation, we use the conjugate complex variables introduced in Chapter I, Section 4, and the fact that

(4) $$\Delta_z u \equiv u_{xx} + u_{yy} = 4u_{z\bar{z}}.$$

We have

$$u_\zeta = u_z \frac{\partial z}{\partial \zeta} + u_{\bar{z}} \frac{\partial \bar{z}}{\partial \zeta}.$$

Since $z = f(\zeta)$, where $f(\zeta)$ is an analytic function of ζ, it follows from the results of Chapter II, Section 3 that $\partial z/\partial \zeta = f'(\zeta)$ and $\partial \bar{z}/\partial \zeta = 0$. Hence,

$$u_\zeta = u_z f'(\zeta).$$

If we now differentiate this expression with respect to $\bar{\zeta}$ and observe that, in this differentiation, the analytic function $f'(\zeta)$ plays the role of a constant, we obtain

$$u_{\zeta\bar{\zeta}} = f'(\zeta) \left[u_{zz} \frac{\partial z}{\partial \bar{\zeta}} + u_{z\bar{z}} \frac{\partial \bar{z}}{\partial \bar{\zeta}} \right],$$

or, in view of $\partial z/\partial \bar{\zeta} = 0$, $\partial \bar{z}/\partial \bar{\zeta} = \overline{f'(\zeta)}$,

$$u_{\zeta\bar{\zeta}} = |f'(\zeta)|^2 u_{z\bar{z}}.$$

Because of (4), this is equivalent to

(5) $$\Delta_\zeta u = |f'(\zeta)|^2 \Delta_z u.$$

Since $u(x, y)$ is a solution of (2), (5) shows that the function (3) is a solution of $\Delta_\zeta U = 0$, and our result is proved.

If, in particular, D' is the unit disk $\xi^2 + \eta^2 < 1$ and if the mapping function $z = f(\zeta)$ is continuous for $\xi^2 + \eta^2 \leq 1$, then it follows from the definition (3) of $U(\xi, \eta)$ that the value of $U(\xi, \eta)$ at a point $\zeta_0 = \xi_0 + i\eta_0$ of the unit circumference is identical with the value of $u(x, y)$ at the point $z_0 = f(\zeta_0)$ on the boundary of D. Hence, the original boundary value problem for the domain D is transformed into a similar problem for the unit disk, which can be solved explicitly. If this solution is denoted by $U(\xi, \eta)$, the solution of the original problem will then be

$$u(x, y) = U[\xi(x, y), \eta(x, y)],$$

where $\xi(x, y) + i\eta(x, y) = \zeta(z)$ is the mapping inverse to $z = f(\zeta)$.

If a given Dirichlet problem has a solution which is continuous in the closure of the domain D, this solution is necessarily unique. Indeed, suppose that the functions $u(x, y)$ and $u_1(x, y)$ are both harmonic in D and that both have the same boundary values. The function $u_2(x, y) = u(x, y) - u_1(x, y)$ will then also be harmonic in D, and it will take the value zero at all points of the boundary. Since a harmonic function which is continuous in the closure of D takes both its maximum and its minimum on the boundary (Chap. IV, Sec. 8), both the maximum and the minimum of $u_2(x, y)$ in the closure of D must be zero. Hence, $u_2(x, y)$ vanishes identically, and we have $u(x, y) = u_1(x, y)$.

It can be shown that this uniqueness of the solution of the Dirichlet problem holds under much weaker assumptions. If the boundary values are permitted to have a finite number of discontinuities (as in the derivation of the Poisson integral in Chap. IV, Sec. 9), the solution $u(x, y)$ will still be unique, provided this function is bounded. If unbounded functions are admitted, it may very well happen that two different harmonic functions have the same boundary values. As an example, we consider the harmonic function

$$u(x, y) = \text{Re}\left[\frac{1 + z}{1 - z}\right]$$

in the disk $|z| < 1$. For $|z| = 1$, we have

$$u(x, y) = \text{Re}\left[\frac{1 + e^{i\theta}}{1 - e^{i\theta}}\right] = \text{Re}\left[-i\cot\frac{\theta}{2}\right] = 0,$$

and this shows that $u(x, y)$ has the boundary value 0 at all points of $|z| = 1$, except at the point $z = 1$ at which the boundary value ceases to be defined. Nevertheless, $u(x, y)$ does not coincide with the harmonic function 0. The reason for this anomaly is the easily confirmed fact that $u(x, y)$ is not bounded in $|z| < 1$.

Another important type of boundary value problem is the *Neumann problem* which, in the case of a circular disk, was discussed in Chapter IV, Section 9. To formulate this problem, we assume that the boundary C of D is smooth, and we denote by $\partial/\partial n$ the directional derivative at a boundary point in the direction determined by the outwards pointing normal of C at this point. In this notation, the Neumann problem asks for the construction of a harmonic function $u(x, y)$ in D if the values of $\partial u/\partial n$ on the boundary are given.

In three dimensions, the Dirichlet and Neumann problems are essentially different, and their solution requires different techniques. In the two-dimensional case, with which we are concerned here, every Neumann problem can be reduced to a related Dirichlet problem. Indeed, if $u(x, y)$ is a harmonic function and $v(x, y)$ is its conjugate, it follows from the Cauchy-Riemann equations (Chap. II, Sec. 2, Exercise 4) that

$$\frac{\partial u}{\partial n} = \frac{\partial v}{\partial s},$$

where $\partial/\partial s$ denotes the differentiation along the positively oriented boundary C. If s_0 is the value of the length-parameter corresponding to a given point of C, we thus have

$$v[x(s), y(s)] = v[x(s_0), y(s_0)] + \int_{s_0}^{s} \frac{\partial u}{\partial n} \, ds.$$

Hence, the boundary values of the harmonic conjugate $v(x, y)$ can be obtained from the given values of $\partial u/\partial n$ by a simple integration. The last formula also shows, incidentally, that the values of $\partial u/\partial n$ must be such that

$$\int_C \frac{\partial u}{\partial n} \, ds = 0$$

(where the integration is extended over the entire closed contour C), since otherwise the function $v(x, y)$ would not be single-valued on C.

The Neumann problem for $u(x, y)$ is thus equivalent to a Dirichlet problem for the conjugate harmonic function $v(x, y)$. Once the latter problem is solved, the harmonic function $u(x, y)$ can be found by one of the methods described in Chapter VII, Section 4.

The boundary value problems appearing in physical and engineering applications often refer to functions $u(x, y)$ which have specified singularities in one or more points of the domain D. For instance, one of the problems discussed in the following section requires the construction of a function $u(x, y)$ which takes the value zero on C, and is of the form

$$u(x, y) = -\log r + u_1(x, y),$$

where r is the distance of the point (x, y) from a given point

(x_0, y_0) of D, and the function $u_1(x, y)$ is harmonic throughout D. There is, however, no basic difference between this type of problem and the ordinary Dirichlet problem; evidently, the function $u_1(x, y)$ may just as well be defined as the harmonic function in D whose boundary values on C coincide with those of $\log r$.

In Section 3 we shall meet problems in which the desired harmonic functions $u(x, y)$ have given singularities, and are subject to the boundary condition $\partial u/\partial n = 0$. Since this condition is equivalent to $\partial v/\partial s = 0$, i.e., $v = $ const., the solution of such a problem may also be characterized by the condition that the harmonic conjugate $v(x, y)$ be constant along the boundary of the domain under consideration.

2   THE ELECTROSTATIC FIELD

It is shown in electromagnetic theory that, at points at which there is no electric charge, the force field generated by a given charge distribution is described by a vector function of the form

$$(6) \qquad\qquad \mathbf{E} = -\operatorname{grad} u,$$

where $u = u(x, y, z)$ is a solution of (1) (and grad u is the vector with the components $\partial u/\partial x$, $\partial u/\partial y$, $\partial u/\partial z$). The function $u(x, y, z)$ is known as the *electrostatic potential* of the field in question. The existence of a potential with these properties is a consequence of Coulomb's law. In the case of a field due to a single point charge of magnitude e, this is easily confirmed by a direct computation. In fact, if r denotes the distance of a point from the given point charge, the component of the vector

$$\operatorname{grad} \frac{e}{r}$$

along the line connecting the two points is $-e/r^2$. Since, by Coulomb's law, this is the force (acting on a unit charge of opposite sign) along the line in question, the field generated by a point charge is found to be of the form (6). Since the function e/r (where $r^2 = (x - x_0)^2 + (y - y_0)^2 + (z - z_0)^2$, and x_0, y_0, z_0 are the coordinates of the point charge) satisfies the Laplace equation (1), the assertion follows. For $r = 0$, i.e., at the point at which the charge is located, the potential ceases to be continuous.

At this point the potential is therefore *not* a solution of Equation (1).

To prove the existence of a potential in the case of a field due to finite number of distinct point charges, we denote the fields generated by them individually by $\mathbf{E}_1, \cdots, \mathbf{E}_n$. If $u_1, \cdots, u_n$ are the corresponding potentials, we have

$$\mathbf{E}_1 + \cdots + \mathbf{E}_n = -\operatorname{grad} u_1 - \cdots - \operatorname{grad} u_n$$
$$= -\operatorname{grad} (u_1 + \cdots + u_n).$$

Since the combined field generated by all point charges is obtained by vector addition of the individual fields, this shows that this field is again of the form (6), where $u = u_1 + \cdots + u_n$. The potential u associated with the given set of point charges is thus obtained by adding up the individual potentials. Each of these potentials is a solution of (1), and it follows therefore from the linearity of the Laplace equation that the same is true of the potential u.

The same argument can be extended to the case in which the electric charge is continuously distributed over volumes, surfaces, or curves. In the manner familiar from the integral calculus, the continuous distributions are approximated by suitable sets of point charges, and the result follows by a passage to the limit. We shall content ourselves here with this statement since a detailed proof, taking into account all the various possibilities of charge distributions, would lead us too far afield. The result is that, at points at which there is no charge, the field generated by an arbitrary charge distribution has a potential which is a solution of the differential equation (1).

In order to compute this potential, it is also necessary to take into account the presence of conductors and dielectrics in the field. Leaving aside the case of dielectrics altogether, we consider the case of a closed conducting surface which carries an electric charge. Since, on a conductor, charges are freely movable, an equilibrium position will be reached in which no forces act along the surface. According to (6), the component of the force in the direction s is $-\partial u/\partial s$, where $\partial/\partial s$ denotes the directional derivative. Hence, the absence of forces along the surface means that the potential must be constant on the conductor. The boundary condition to be applied to the solution $u(x, y, z)$ of (1) on a conducting surface is therefore $u = \operatorname{const}$. Accordingly, the solution of an electrostatic problem depends on the construction of a solution of (1) which takes constant values on the various conducting surfaces in the field, and shows the proper behavior near the given point charges (if there be any).

We now consider the case in which the conducting surfaces are infinitely long cylinders perpendicular to the xy-plane. Since on the entire surface of each cylinder the potential is constant, it is clear that the potential at a given point will depend on the projection of the point onto the xy-plane, but not on its distance z from this plane. As pointed out in Section 1, the potential will therefore be a solution of the two-dimensional Laplace equation (2). Hence, the solution of an electrostatic problem of this type will depend on the construction of a harmonic function $u(x, y)$ which takes constant values on each of the curves at which the infinite cylinders intersect the xy-plane.

As already mentioned, an "infinitely long" cylinder is to be interpreted, in practice, as a cylinder whose length is large compared to its greatest width. The field obtained under the assumption of infinite length will represent a very good approximation of the actual field at points not too near to the ends of the cylinder. However, in one respect the assumption of infinite length will cause a significant departure from physical reality. If such a cylinder carries a non-zero charge per unit length, the total charge is necessarily infinitely large! Fortunately, this unrealistic touch does not affect the structural properties of the field, such as, for instance, the shape of the *equipotential surfaces*, i.e., surfaces on which the potential has a constant value. (Since these surfaces are cylindrical, they are determined by their intersections with the xy-plane. If two-dimensional language is used, the latter are referred to as *equipotential curves*.)

The simplest cylindrical field is the one due to an infinite charged wire perpendicular to the xy-plane. To find the potential of this field, we introduce polar coordinates r, θ in the xy-plane. If $r = 0$ corresponds to the point at which the wire pierces the xy-plane, it is physically evident that the potential does not depend on the angle θ. Accordingly, we have to find a solution of (2) which is a function of r only. Since, in polar coordinates, Equation (2) takes the form

$$\frac{\partial}{\partial r}\left(r\,\frac{\partial u}{\partial r}\right) + \frac{1}{r}\frac{\partial^2 u}{\partial \theta^2} = 0,$$

the function $u = u(r)$ must be a solution of

$$\frac{d}{dr}\left(r\frac{du}{dr}\right) = 0.$$

Hence, $ru'(r) = -e$, where e is a constant, and we obtain $u = -e \log r + A$. The constant A has no physical significance; as (6) shows, the field depends on the partial derivatives of the potential u, and u is thus determined only up to an arbitrary additive constant. We may therefore set $A = 0$, and our solution becomes

(7) $$u = -e \log r.$$

Since this is the only solution of (2) with the required properties, it necessarily represents the desired potential. The constant e may be interpreted as the charge per unit length of the wire.

We next consider the case in which the infinite charged wire is enclosed in an infinite conducting cylinder whose intersection with the xy-plane is a closed contour C. The original field caused by the charged wire will now be modified so as to conform to the condition that the potential be constant on the surface of a conductor; according to a remark just made, this constant may be taken to be zero. If, for simplicity, the constant e in (7) is taken to be unity, the potential will be of the form

(8) $$u(x, y) = -\log r + u_1(x, y),$$

where the first term is due to the charged wire and the second term expresses the change in the potential caused by the presence of the cylinder. To solve the problem, we have to find a harmonic function $u_1(x, y)$ such that the function $u(x, y)$ takes the value zero on the contour C. The function $u(x, y)$ satisfying these conditions is known as the *Green's function* of the domain D whose boundary is the contour C. The Green's function plays an important role in many areas of pure and applied analysis.

The function (8) depends not only on x and y, but also on the coordinates ζ, η of the point in D from which the distance r is counted. If $z = x + iy$ and $\zeta = \xi + i\eta$, we therefore denote the Green's function by the symbol $g(z, \zeta)$. The use of complex notation is here merely a matter of convenience, and it does not imply that $g(z, \zeta)$ is an analytic function of the complex variables z or ζ. Since the distance r is equal to $|z - \zeta|$, (8) is thus replaced by

(9) $$g(z, \zeta) = -\log |z - \zeta| + h(z, \zeta),$$

where $h(z, \zeta)$ is a harmonic function of x,y in D and $g(z, \zeta) = 0$ on the boundary C.

We remark that there can exist only one function $g(z, \zeta)$ with these properties. Indeed, suppose there exists a function $g_1(z, \zeta) = -\log |z - \zeta| + h_1(z, \zeta)$ which likewise vanishes on C, and for which $h_1(z, \zeta)$ is harmonic in D. The function $g(z, \zeta) - g_1(z, \zeta)$ will then also vanish on C. Since, because of $g(z, \zeta) - g_1(z, \zeta) = h(z, \zeta) - h_1(z, \zeta)$, this function is harmonic throughout D, it follows from the maximum principle that this function vanishes identically in D. Hence, $g(z, \zeta) \equiv g_1(z, \zeta)$. This uniqueness of a function with the indicated properties shows that the Green's function indeed represents the required potential.

There exists a close connection between the Green's function $g(z, \zeta)$ of a domain D, and the analytic function $w = F(z)$ which maps D onto the disk $|w| < 1$. If ζ is the point of D for which $F(\zeta) = 0$, the relation between the functions is given by the formula

$$(10) \qquad\qquad g(z, \zeta) = -\log |F(z)|.$$

To prove (10), we observe that $F(z)$ must be of the form

$$(11) \qquad\qquad F(z) = (z - \zeta)F_1(z),$$

where $F_1(z) \neq 0$ in D; indeed, $F(z)$ is univalent in D, and it can take the value zero only once. Taking logarithms on both sides of (11), we obtain

$$(12) \qquad -\log F(z) = -\log (z - \zeta) - \log F_1(z),$$

and we note that, because of $F_1(z) \neq 0$, $\log F_1(z)$ is a regular analytic function in D. The function $\log (z - \zeta)$ has a singularity at $z = \zeta$, and it is infinitely many-valued in D. However, the real part of this function is $\log |z - \zeta|$, and this is single-valued in D. If we take real parts on both sides of (12), we obtain

$$(13) \qquad -\log |F(z)| = -\log |z - \zeta| - \log |F_1(z)|.$$

Since $\log |F_1(z)|$ is the real part of a regular analytic function, it is a harmonic function in D, and a comparison of (13) and (9) shows that the function $-\log |F(z)|$ has the required behavior at the point $z = \zeta$. To find the values of this function as z approaches the boundary C of D, we note that $w = F(z)$ maps D onto the disk $|w| < 1$ and that, accordingly, $|F(z)|$ tends to 1 as z approaches C. Hence, $-\log |F(z)|$ tends to zero as z approaches the boundary. Since, as shown before, there can exist only one function of the form (9) with this type of boundary behavior, this proves the identity (10).

In view of this connection between the Green's function and the analytic function mapping the domain onto the unit disk, our electrostatic problem can be solved in all cases in which this mapping function is known. As an example, we construct the electrostatic potential in the interior of the conducting circular cylinder $|z| = R$, caused by a charged wire which intersects the z-plane at $z = \zeta(|\zeta| < R)$. Since the function $w = F(z)$, mapping $|z| < R$ onto the disk $|w| < 1$ in such a way that $F(\zeta) = 0$, is of the form

$$(14) \qquad w = F(z) = \frac{R(z - \zeta)}{R^2 - \bar{\zeta}z}$$

(cf. Chap. V, Sec. 3), (10) shows that

$$(15) \qquad g(z, \zeta) = -\log \left| \frac{R(z - \zeta)}{R^2 - \bar{\zeta}z} \right|.$$

This result can be given a simple geometric interpretation. Since

$$\left| \frac{R(z - \zeta)}{R^2 - \bar{\zeta}z} \right| = \frac{R}{|\zeta|} \left| \frac{z - \zeta}{z - \dfrac{R^2}{\bar{\zeta}}} \right|,$$

(15) is equivalent to

$$(16) \qquad g(z, \zeta) = -\log |z - \zeta| + \log \left| z - \frac{R^2}{\bar{\zeta}} \right| - \log \frac{R}{|\zeta|}.$$

The term $\log (R|\zeta|^{-1})$ is without physical interest; as already pointed out, constants added to the potential do not affect the field. If we write

$$r = |z - \zeta|, \quad r_1 = \left| z - \frac{R^2}{\bar{\zeta}} \right|,$$

r and r_1 are, respectively, the distances of the point z from the points ζ and $R^2/\bar{\zeta}$. In terms of these distances, (16) can be written

$$g(z, \zeta) = -\log r + \log r_1 + K,$$

where K is a constant. A comparison with the potential (7) of a point charge reveals an interesting fact: The effect of enclosing the charged wire in the conducting cylinder $|z| = R$ is the same as that achieved by introducing a wire of equal but opposite charge which intersects the xy-plane at the point $R^2/\bar{\zeta}$.

The equipotential curves—i.e., the curves along which the function (16) has a constant value—are obtained from the condition $|w| = $ const., where $w = F(z)$ is the function (14). Since $|w| = $ const. is the equation of a circle in the w-plane, this shows that the linear substitution (14) transforms the equipotential curves into circles. According to the results of Chapter V, Section 3, these curves are therefore likewise circles.

We next consider an electrostatic problem of a slightly different type. We assume that the conducting cylindrical surface is cut into two parts by lines perpendicular to the xy-plane, and that these two parts are insulated from each other and kept at different potentials. Without loss of generality, the values of these potentials may be taken to be 1 and -1 (why?). The problem of finding the potential in the interior of the cylinder is equivalent to solving a boundary value problem for the domain D in the xy-plane. Indeed, if C_1 and C_2 are the arcs of C at which the two parts of the cylinder intersect the xy-plane, we have to find a harmonic function in D which takes the values 1 and -1 on C_1 and C_2, respectively.

As shown in the preceding section, the solution of a boundary value problem of this type can be reduced to the solution of the corresponding problem for the unit circle, provided the analytic function $w = f(z)$ mapping D onto $|w| < 1$ is known. This mapping will carry the arcs C_1 and C_2 into two complementary arcs C_1' and C_2' of the unit circumference, and it is thus sufficient to find a harmonic function in $|w| < 1$ which takes the values 1 and -1 on C_1' and C_2', respectively. Such a function can be easily constructed by means of the Poisson integral formula of Chapter IV, Section 9. In the case in which C_1' and C_2' are the semicircles $|w| = 1$, $\mathrm{Re}(w) > 0$ and $|w| = 1$, $\mathrm{Re}(w) < 0$, this function was computed explicitly in Chapter IV, Section 9, and it was found to be of the form (69) (with z substituted for w). We may thus conclude, in particular, that in the case in which the original problem refers to the two half-cylinders $|z| = 1$, $\mathrm{Re}(z) > 0$ and $|z| = 1$, $\mathrm{Re}(z) < 0$, the desired potential is of the form

(17) $u(x, y) = \dfrac{4}{\pi} \mathrm{Re}[\text{arc tan } z], \quad z = x + iy.$

We finally discuss the problem of finding the electric field *outside* of a charged conducting cylinder. Physical considerations make it plausible that, at a large (lateral) distance from the conductor, the field should be very little influenced by the particular shape of the cylinder, and should thus be essentially identical with the field generated by a wire of the same charge e per unit length. If we set $e = 1$, the behavior of the potential $u(z)$ for large values of $|z|$ $(z = x + iy)$ should therefore be asymptotically the same as that of the function $-\log |z|$. We accordingly write

$$(18) \qquad u(z) = -\log |z| + h(z),$$

where $h(z)$ is a harmonic function in the outside of the cylinder (this implies that $u(z)$ has a finite value at $z = \infty$). On the cylinder itself, $u(z)$ must have a constant value, which may be taken to be zero. If C is the intersection of the cylinder with the xy-plane, we thus have to find a harmonic function $h(z)$ in the outside of C which is such that the function $u(z)$ in (18) takes the value zero on C.

The solution of this problem is related to the conformal mapping of the exterior D' of D onto the exterior of the unit circle, i.e., onto the domain $|w| > 1$. Since both D' and the image domain contain the point at infinity (in their respective planes), we may require that the mapping function $w = F(z)$ be such that $F(\infty) = \infty$. In the neighborhood of $z = \infty$, $F(z)$ will then have an expansion of the form

$$F(z) = z \left(a_{-1} + \frac{a_0}{z} + \frac{a_1}{z^2} + \cdots \right), \quad a_{-1} \neq 0$$

(positive powers of degree higher than the first would destroy the univalence of the function near $z = \infty$). The function represented by the expansion in parentheses is regular, and different from zero, in the entire domain D'. Denoting this function by $F_1(z)$, we thus have

$$F(z) = zF_1(z), \quad F_1(z) \neq 0.$$

It follows that $\log F(z) = \log z + \log F_1(z)$ and finally, by taking real parts,

$$(19) \qquad -\log |F(z)| = -\log |z| - \log |F_1(z)|.$$

Since $F_1(z) \neq 0$, $-\log |F_1(z)|$ is a harmonic function at all points of D', and a comparison of (19) and (18) shows that the function (19) has the required behavior near $z = \infty$. On C, we have $\log |F(z)| = 0$. Indeed, the function $w = F(z)$ maps D' onto $|w| > 1$, and this implies that $|F(z)| = 1$ on the boundary. Accordingly, the function

$$(20) \qquad u(x, y) = -\log |F(z)|$$

is of the form (18) and it displays the proper boundary behavior. Since there can be only one function with these properties (this follows in the same way as the uniqueness of the Green's function), (20) represents the solution of our problem.

As an example, we consider the case in which the "cylinder" is an infinite plane strip which intersects the x-axis along the segment $-1 < x < 1$. To obtain the corresponding potential, we need the analytic function $w = F(z)$ which maps the exterior of this segment (i.e., the extended z-plane minus this segment) onto the domain $|w| > 1$. As shown in Chapter V, Section 5, the inverse mapping is given by the function

$$(21) \qquad\qquad z = \frac{1}{2}\left(w + \frac{1}{w}\right);$$

solving (21) for w, we thus obtain $F(z)$. The potential $u(x, y)$ is then found by means of (20).

The equipotential curves are determined from the equation $|w| = |F(z)| = r = $ const. In view of (21), the equations of these curves are of the form

$$x + iy = z = \frac{1}{2}\left(re^{i\theta} + \frac{1}{re^{i\theta}}\right), \quad 0 \leq \theta < 2\pi, \quad r > 1.$$

Hence,

$$x = \frac{1}{2}\left(r + \frac{1}{r}\right)\cos\theta, \quad y = \frac{1}{2}\left(r - \frac{1}{r}\right)\sin\theta,$$

and thus

$$\frac{4x^2}{\left(r + \dfrac{1}{r}\right)^2} + \frac{4y^2}{\left(r - \dfrac{1}{r}\right)^2} = 1.$$

The equipotential curves are therefore ellipses. The foci of all these ellipses are at the points $z = \pm 1$.

It should be noted that the knowledge of an equipotential curve S of a given problem makes it possible to solve an additional problem. Indeed, since the potential is constant on S, the field is identical with the field generated by a charged conducting surface which intersects the xy-plane along S. The example just treated can therefore also be used to find the potential associated with a charged conducting cylinder of elliptical cross-section.

Exercises

1. Show that the Green's function $g(z, \zeta)$ of the half-plane $\mathrm{Re}(z) > 0$ is

$$g(z, \zeta) = -\log|z - \zeta| + \log|z + \bar{\zeta}|,$$

where $\mathrm{Re}(\zeta) > 0$, and prove that the curves $g(z, \zeta) = \mathrm{const.}$ are circles.

2. Let $u(x, y)$ be the electrostatic potential generated by n charged wires perpendicular to the xy-plane, and denote by $e_1, \cdots, e_n$ their charges per unit length (e_k having a positive or negative value according as the charge is positive or negative). If $e_1 + \cdots + e_n = 0$, show that $u(x, y)$ tends to a finite limit as $x^2 + y^2 \to \infty$.

3. If the two conducting cylinders $|z| = R$ and $|z| = r$ $(0 < r < R < \infty)$ are kept at the potentials 1 and 0, respectively, show that the potential $u(x, y)$ in the space between the two cylinders is of the form

$$u(x, y) = \frac{\log |z| - \log r}{\log R - \log r}, \quad z = x + iy.$$

4. Using the result of Chapter II, Section 5, Exercise 2, show that the potential (17) can be expressed by the equivalent formula

$$u(x, y) = \frac{2}{\pi} \arctan \frac{2x}{1 - x^2 - y^2}.$$

5. Use the result of the preceding exercise to show that the equipotential curves associated with the potential (17) are circular arcs connecting the points $(0, 1)$ and $(0, -1)$.

6. Let D denote the crescent-shaped domain in the right half-plane which is bounded by arcs of the circles $|z| = 1$ and $|z - a| = \sqrt{1 + a^2}$, where a is a positive number. Use the results of the two preceding exercises to show that the harmonic function $u(x, y)$, in D which is 1 on the arc of $|z| = 1$ and 0 on the other arc, must be of the form

$$u(x, y) = (1 - c)^{-1} \left[\frac{2}{\pi} \arctan \frac{2x}{1 - x^2 - y^2} - c \right],$$

where

$$a = \cot \frac{\pi c}{2}.$$

7. An electric field is generated by the two charged half-planes $x < 0$, $y = 0$ and $x > 0$, $y = 0$ which are insulated from each other and kept at the fixed potentials 1 and 0, respectively. Show that, in the half-space $y > 0$, the potential of the field is

$$u(x, y) = \frac{1}{\pi} \arctan \frac{y}{x}.$$

8. If $0 < a < 1$, show that the Green's function $g(z, a)$ of the half-disk $|z| < 1$, $\text{Re}(z) > 0$ is

$$g(z, a) = \log\left|\frac{1 - az}{z - a}\right| - \log\left|\frac{1 + az}{x + a}\right|.$$

3   TWO-DIMENSIONAL FLUID FLOW

As another example of a physical situation which is governed by the Laplace equation—and is therefore accessible to the methods of complex analysis if the processes involved are essentially two-dimensional—we consider the flow of an incompressible fluid. A complete description of the motion of the fluid requires the knowledge of the velocity vector at all points of the fluid at any given time.   If the flow is *stationary*, the velocity at a given point does not depend on the time, and the velocity components are functions of the space variables x, y, z only.   If the physical conditions are such that the motion of the fluid is the same in all planes parallel to the xy-plane, the variable z will not appear explicitly, and the motion can be adequately described in terms of the x-component, $p(x, y)$, and the y-component, $q(x, y)$, of the velocity vector.   Conditions of this type will prevail, for instance, if the fluid flows past a long cylindrical object, such as an airplane wing.   In the discussion of such flows it is convenient to use two-dimensional language.   Thus, the flow will be assumed to occur in the xy-plane, and the objects obstructing the flow will also be regarded as lying in the xy-plane.

We now subject this two-dimensional flow to a few restrictions.   To formulate the first of these, we introduce the notion of the *circulation* of the fluid along a closed contour C.   This name is given to the integral

(22) $$\int_C V_s \, ds,$$

where V_s is the tangential component of the velocity of the fluid at the points of C, and ds is the length-element.   If the circulation along all closed curves is zero, the flow is said to be *irrotational*. All the flows considered here will be assumed to satisfy this condition.

In order to understand the meaning of this restriction, we

rewrite the integral (22) in a different form. The vector with the components dx, dy points in the direction of the tangent, and its length is ds. The expression $V_s ds$ is therefore the inner product of the vector (dx, dy) and the velocity vector (p, q). Hence, $V_s\, dx = pdx + qdy$, and (22) may be replaced by the line integral

$$(23) \qquad \int_C (pdx + qdy).$$

If this integral is to be zero for all closed contours C, there must exist a function $u = u(x, y)$ such that

$$(24) \qquad p = \frac{\partial u}{\partial x}, \quad q = \frac{\partial u}{\partial y}$$

(cf. Chap. III, Sec. 1). Conversely, if (24) holds, the integral over any closed curve is zero. The assumption of irrotationality is thus equivalent to the existence of a function $u(x, y)$ from which the velocity components can be obtained by means of (24).

It is worth noting that in order to obtain the conditions (24) it is not really necessary to require the vanishing of the integral (22) for *every* closed contour C. It is sufficient to require this for curves C which are circles of arbitrarily small radius R. By Green's theorem (Chap. III, Sec. 3), we have

$$\int_C (pdx + qdy) = \iint_D \left(\frac{\partial q}{\partial x} - \frac{\partial p}{\partial y} \right) dx\, dy,$$

where D is the disk enclosed by C. If the integral (23) vanishes, it follows that

$$\frac{1}{\pi R^2} \iint_D \left(\frac{\partial q}{\partial x} - \frac{\partial p}{\partial y} \right) dx\, dy = 0,$$

and thus, by keeping the center fixed and letting $R \to 0$,

$$\frac{\partial q}{\partial x} = \frac{\partial p}{\partial y}.$$

This condition—which must hold at every point of the fluid—is equivalent to the existence of a function $u(x, y)$ satisfying (24).

Accordingly, the irrotationality of the fluid is guaranteed by the assumption that

$$\frac{1}{2\pi R} \int_C V_s\, ds = 0,$$

where the integration is extended over arbitrarily small circles C.

Since $V_s = R\omega$, where ω is the angular velocity, this is equivalent to

$$\frac{1}{2\pi R} \int_C \omega \, ds = 0,$$

i.e., the average of the angular velocity over sufficiently small circles must be zero. This explains the term "irrotational." At a point at which the limit of this average for $R \to 0$ is not zero, some rather unusual behavior of the fluid may be expected.

We next assume that the fluid is *incompressible*, i.e., that a given area contains always the same amount of fluid. Although actual fluids are always compressible to a greater or lesser degree, the equations derived under the assumption of incompressibility lead to surprisingly accurate results even in the case of air, provided the velocities are not excessive. To express this condition in mathematical form, we observe that the quantity of fluid passing a length element ds per time unit is $V_n \, ds$, where V_n is the velocity component perpendicular to ds. If C is a closed contour and V_n is taken in the direction of the outwards pointing normal, the total quantity of fluid leaving the domain D bounded by C is therefore

(25) $$\int_C V_n \, ds.$$

If the fluid is incompressible, the amount of fluid in D is constant, and this integral must be zero for all closed contours C.

We now express the integrand in (25) in terms of the velocity components p and q. We have

$$V_n = V_x \cos \alpha + V_y \sin \alpha = p \cos \alpha + q \sin \alpha,$$

where α is the angle between the n-direction and the positive x-direction (Fig. 17). Since $dx = -\sin \alpha \, ds$, $dy = \cos \alpha \, ds$, this shows that the integral (25) can be replaced by

$$\int_C (p\,dy - q\,dx).$$

If this integral is to be zero for all closed contours C, we must have

$$\frac{\partial p}{\partial x} = \frac{\partial(-q)}{\partial y},$$

i.e.,

(26) $$\frac{\partial p}{\partial x} + \frac{\partial q}{\partial y} = 0.$$

This is the so-called *equation of continuity* of the fluid.

We saw before that the assumption of irrotationality of the fluid implies the existence of a function $u(x, y)$ from which the velocity components can be obtained by means of the relations (24). The function $u(x, y)$ is called the *velocity potential* of the

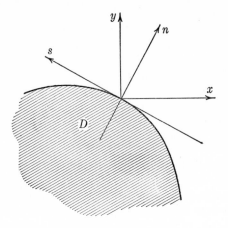

FIG. **17**

motion. If, in equation (26), p and q are replaced by the expressions (24), the equation of continuity is seen to be equivalent to the Laplace equation

$$(27) \qquad \frac{\partial^2 u}{\partial x^2} + \frac{\partial^2 u}{\partial y^2} = 0.$$

Our result is therefore that the velocity potential of an irrotational and incompressible fluid is a harmonic function. It should, however, be noted that (26) was derived under the tacit assumption that no fluid is created or annihilated at any point of the region under consideration. At points at which such processes occur, i.e., at *sources* or *sinks* of the fluid, the equation of continuity— and therefore also equation (27)—will not be satisfied.

An individual particle of the fluid will move along a curve whose direction coincides at every point with the direction of the velocity vector. Such a curve is called a *streamline*. The streamlines of a fluid with the velocity potential $u(x, y)$ are characterized by the equation

$$(28) \qquad v(x, y) = \text{const.},$$

where $v(x, y)$ is the harmonic conjugate of $u(x, y)$. Indeed, differentiating (28) we have $v_x \, dx + v_y \, dy = 0$ and thus, in view of the Cauchy-Riemann equations, $-u_y \, dx + u_x \, dy = 0$. Hence

$$\frac{dy}{dx} = \frac{u_y}{u_x},$$

and this shows that the direction of the curve (28) coincides at every point with that of the velocity vector (u_x, u_y).

Equation (28) may also be derived from the observation that, since the fluid moves along the streamline, the velocity component in a direction n perpendicular to the streamline must be zero. In view of (24) this velocity component is $\partial u/\partial n$. If s denotes the direction along the streamline, we have

$$\frac{\partial u}{\partial n} = \frac{\partial v}{\partial s}$$

(Chap. II, Sec. 2, Exercise 4), and thus $\partial v/\partial s = 0$. Integrating this, we obtain (28).

The function $v(x, y)$ is called the *stream function* of the flow. The analytic function

$$(29) \qquad\qquad F(z) = u(x, y) + iv(x, y)$$

is known as the *complex potential*. Since

$$F'(z) = u_x + iv_x = u_x - iu_y$$

(Chap. II, Sec. 2), we have

$$(30) \qquad\qquad p + iq = u_x + iu_y = \overline{F'(z)}.$$

This complex function—whose real and imaginary parts are equal to the velocity components in the x- and y-directions, respectively—is often referred to as the *complex velocity* of the fluid. The absolute value of the velocity vector—i.e., the actual velocity of the motion—is equal to $|F'(z)|$.

The simplest possible flow is that corresponding to the complex potential $F(z) = Az$, where A is a positive constant. Since $u = Ax$, $v = Ay$, the streamlines are the horizontal lines $Ay =$ const., and the velocity components are $p = A$, $q = 0$. This potential thus describes a uniform flow, with the speed A, in the positive x-direction. We now disturb this flow by immersing in the fluid an object bounded by a closed contour C. Since the fluid must now flow along C, it is clear—if, as we shall assume, the effects of viscosity can be neglected—that the contour C must coincide with part of a streamline. In view of (28) and (29), the complex potential $F(z)$ describing the flow must therefore satisfy the condition $\text{Im}[F(z)] = \text{const.}$ on C. At a large distance from C, the distortion of the streamlines caused by the object will hardly be noticeable, and $F(z)$ should therefore essentially coincide with Az for large values of $|z|$. Accordingly, $F(z)$ should have a Laurent expansion

$$(31) \qquad F(z) = Az + a_0 + \frac{a_1}{z} + \frac{a_2}{z^2} + \cdots$$

in the neighborhood of $z = \infty$. In order to obtain the desired flow, it is thus necessary to construct an analytic function $F(z)$ which has an expansion (31) for large $|z|$, is otherwise regular in the exterior of C, and has a constant imaginary part on C. (Since $F(z)$ contains an arbitrary additive constant the value of $\text{Im}[F(z)]$ may be taken to be zero.)

In order to be sure that $F(z)$ is indeed the desired complex potential, we have to show that there cannot exist two different analytic functions with these properties. Suppose, then, that both $F(z)$ and $F_1(z)$ have an expansion of the type (31) for large $|z|$, and that both $\text{Im}[F(z)]$ and $\text{Im}[F_1(z)]$ are zero on C. The function $h(z) = F(z) - F_1(z)$ will then be regular in the entire exterior of C (both expansions (31) start with the term Az), and $\text{Im}[h(z)] = 0$ on C. But an analytic function which is regular and bounded in a domain and real on the boundary, reduces to a real constant k (cf. Chap. IV, Sec. 7). Hence, $F_1(z) = F(z) + k$, and the uniqueness of the function $F(z)$ (except for the physically meaningless constant k) is proved.

As an illustration of the preceding theory, we consider the case in which the profile C is the circle $|z| = 1$. It is easy to see that the corresponding complex potential is

$$(32) \qquad F(z) = A\left(z + \frac{1}{z}\right).$$

This function is of the form (31), and we have

$$F(e^{i\theta}) = A(e^{i\theta} + e^{-\theta}) = 2A\cos\theta,$$

i.e., $F(z)$ is real for $|z| = 1$. Since there exists only one such function, (32) must be the potential in question. By (28) and (29), the streamlines of the flow are the curves

$$\text{Im}\left[z + \frac{1}{z}\right] = c,$$

where c is a constant. Since

$$z + \frac{1}{z} = z + \frac{\bar{z}}{|z|^2} = x + iy + \frac{x - iy}{x^2 + y^2},$$

this is equivalent to the equation

(33) $$y\left[1 - \frac{1}{x^2 + y^2}\right] = c.$$

Formula (33) shows that, at points far removed from the circle $|z| = 1$ (i.e., at points for which $x^2 + y^2$ is large), the streamlines differ but little from the horizontal lines $y = c$. The circle $x^2 + y^2 = 1$ is, of course, part of the streamline associated with the value $c = 0$ of the constant. It is worth noting that the entire streamline $c = 0$ contains also, in addition to this circle, the rays $-\infty < x < -1$ and $1 < x < \infty$ (Fig. 18).

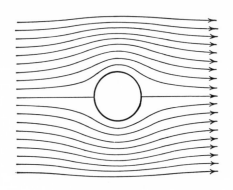

FIG. **18**

In the case of a general profile C, the construction of the complex potential can be carried out by means of the analytic function $w = f(z)$, which maps the exterior of C onto the disk $|w| > 1$ in such a way that $f(\infty) = \infty$ and $f'(\infty) > 0$. Since, near $z = \infty$, $f(z)$ has an expansion

(34) $$f(z) = Bz + b_0 + \frac{b_1}{z} + \cdots, \quad B > 0,$$

the function

(35) $$F(z) = f(z) + \frac{1}{f(z)}$$

will have there an expansion of the type (31). On C, we have $|f(z)| = 1$. Hence,

$$f(z) + \frac{1}{f(z)} = f(z) + \overline{f(z)} = 2 \operatorname{Re}[f(z)],$$

and this shows that the function $F(z)$ defined by (35) is real on C. In view of the uniqueness of a function with these properties, (35) is therefore the desired complex potential. The streamlines of the flow are determined from the equation

$$\operatorname{Im}\left[f(z) + \frac{1}{f(z)}\right] = c.$$

Since $f(z)\,\overline{f(z)} = |f(z)|^2$, this may also be written

$$(36) \qquad \operatorname{Im}[f(z)]\left\{1 - \frac{1}{|f(z)|^2}\right\} = c.$$

For large $|z|$, the streamlines (36) are very nearly horizontal. Indeed, (35) shows that $F(z)$ differs very little from $Bz + b_0$ for large z, and the curves (36) are therefore close to the horizontal lines $By + \operatorname{Im}(b_0) = c$.

The function (35) may also be characterized by the fact that the conformal mapping $W = F(z)$ transforms the exterior of C into the exterior of a finite segment of the real axis; this is seen by comparing (35) and the mapping of Fig. 11 (Chap. V, Sec. 5). In terms of the inverse mapping $z = F^{-1}(W)$ (i.e., the mapping of the exterior of the segment onto the exterior of C), the parametric equations of the streamlines can be written down explicitly. If $W = t + is$, the streamlines are characterized by the condition $s = c$. Hence, these lines have the equation $z = F^{-1}(t + ic)$ or, if the real and imaginary parts are separated,

$$(37) \qquad \begin{aligned} x &= \operatorname{Re}[F^{-1}(t + ic)], \\ y &= \operatorname{Im}[F^{-1}(t + ic)]. \end{aligned}$$

The real parameter t varies from $-\infty$ to $+\infty$.

As an illustration of this procedure, we treat the case in which C is a linear segment perpendicular to the direction of the flow (Fig. 19). To simplify the formulas, we assume that the segment joins the

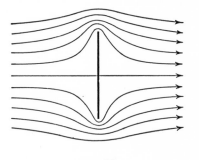

FIG. 19

points $z = i$ and $z = -i$. In order to find the function $W = F(z)$ mapping the exterior of this segment onto the exterior of the segment $-1 < W < 1$, we decompose the mapping $W = F(z)$ into two simpler mappings. Since the function

$$(38) \qquad W = \frac{1}{2}\left(\zeta + \frac{1}{\zeta}\right)$$

maps $|\zeta| > 1$ onto the exterior of the segment $-1 < W < 1$ and, as the reader will easily confirm, the function

$$(39) \qquad z = \frac{1}{2}\left(\zeta - \frac{1}{\zeta}\right)$$

maps the same disk onto the exterior of the segment joining $z = i$ and $z = -i$, the desired mapping is obtained by eliminating ζ from (38) and (39). Adding and subtracting these two equations, we have $W + z = \zeta$, $W - z = \zeta^{-1}$, and thus $W^2 - z^2 = 1$. Hence, the complex potential of the flow is

$$W = F(z) = \sqrt{z^2 + 1} = z\sqrt{1 + \frac{1}{z^2}}.$$

By expanding the last radical by powers of z^{-2} (and taking $\sqrt{1} = 1$), we also see that $F(z)$ shows the behavior indicated in (31) for large $|z|$.

The streamlines of the flow are obtained by setting $W = t + ic$. Hence,

$$(x + iy)^2 = z^2 = (t + ic)^2 - 1$$

and, by separating real and imaginary parts,

$$x^2 - y^2 = t^2 - c^2 - 1,$$

$$xy = ct.$$

These are the parametric equations of the streamlines. Eliminating the parameter, we obtain

$$(40) \qquad (x^2 + c^2)(y^2 - c^2) = c^2.$$

Some of these curves are indicated in Fig. 19. Equation (40) shows clearly that, at a large distance from the object disturbing the uniform flow, the streamlines flatten out and approach horizontal lines. Indeed, if x^2 is large, the curves

$$y^2 = c^2 + \frac{c^2}{x^2 + c^2}$$

approach the lines $y = \pm c$.

One of the most important applications of the theory discussed in this section concerns the flow of air past an airplane wing. To compute this flow, it is necessary to construct analytic functions which map the exterior of a given wing profile onto the exterior of a segment of the real axis. The simplest class of such functions is that corresponding to the so-called *Joukowsky profiles*. The construction of these functions is again based on the properties of the mapping

$$(41) \qquad z = \frac{1}{2}\left(\zeta + \frac{1}{\zeta}\right).$$

In our previous applications of this mapping, we used the fact that (41) transforms the exterior of the circle $|\zeta| = 1$ into the exterior of the segment $-1 < z < 1$. We shall now examine the type of domain which, under the mapping (41), corresponds to the exterior of a circle which passes through the point $\zeta = 1$ and contains the point $\zeta = -1$ in its interior.

In view of

$$\frac{dz}{d\zeta} = \frac{1}{2}\left(1 - \frac{1}{\zeta^2}\right),$$

the derivative of the function (41) vanishes at the points $\zeta = \pm 1$. Since the second derivative does not vanish there, it follows from the results of Chapter V, Section 1 that the mapping (41) doubles all angles whose vertices are at these points. In particular, the angle π is transformed into the angle 2π. As a result, the image of a smooth arc passing through one of these points will consist of two arcs which meet (with respect to the interior of the domain considered) under the angle 2π. We now consider the curve C into which a circle $|\zeta + a| = 1 + a$, $a > 0$, is transformed by the mapping (41). Since—except for the point $\zeta = 1$—this circle is contained in the domain $|\zeta| > 1$ in which (41) is univalent, C is a simple closed contour. At the image of $\zeta = 1$, the contour C changes its direction abruptly by the angle 2π, and C will therefore look as indicated in Fig. 20b. By taking different values of a, different shapes of the same general character can be obtained. All of these are symmetric with respect to the real axis.

To obtain profiles which do not have this symmetry, we replace the circle $|\zeta + a| = 1 + a$ in Fig. 20a by a circle $|\zeta - \alpha| = |1 - \alpha|$, where α is a non-real number such that $|1 + \alpha| < |1 - \alpha|$. This circle likewise passes through $\zeta = 1$ but, since α is not real. is not symmetric with respect to the real axis; the condition

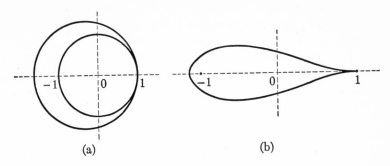

(a)   (b)

FIG. 20

$|1 + \alpha| = |-1 - \alpha| < |1 - \alpha|$ insures that the point $\zeta = -1$ is in the interior of the circle. An example of such a circle, and of the profile generated by it, is given in Fig. 21.

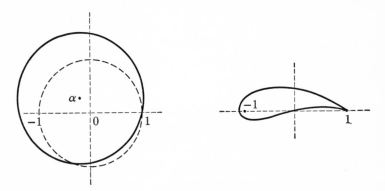

FIG. 21

Turning now to the construction of the function $W = F(z)$ which maps the exterior of a Joukowsky profile onto the exterior of a linear segment, we observe that the function

$$\zeta_1 = K\left(\frac{\zeta - \alpha}{1 - \alpha}\right), \quad |K| = 1$$

maps the exterior of the circle $|\zeta - \alpha| = |1 - \alpha|$ onto the exterior of the unit circle. Hence, the function

$$(42) \qquad W = \frac{1}{2}\left[K\left(\frac{\zeta - \alpha}{1 - \alpha}\right) + \frac{1}{K}\left(\frac{1 - \alpha}{\zeta - \alpha}\right) \right], \quad |K| = 1$$

will map the exterior of $|\zeta - \alpha| = |1 - \alpha|$ onto the exterior of the segment $-1 < W < 1$. Since (41) maps the exterior of the same circle onto the outside of the Joukowsky profile, it follows that the mapping $W = F(z)$ is obtained by eliminating ζ from (41) and (42). By setting $\zeta = \infty$ in these formulas, it is seen that $F(\infty) = \infty$, as required. The constant K in (42) depends on the original direction of the flow. If this flow is parallel to the x-axis, K has to be chosen in such a way that $F'(\infty) > 0$.

To find the streamlines of the flow, we set $W = t + ic$ in (42) and express x and y ($z = x + iy$) as functions of the real parameter t. For the sake of simplicity, we confine ourselves to the symmetric profiles of Fig. 20b (corresponding to negative values of α); in the case of a general profile, the algebra becomes quite involved. For $K = 1$, it follows from (42) that

$$W - 1 = \frac{(\zeta - 1)^2}{2(\zeta - \alpha)(1 - \alpha)}.$$

Since, by (41),

$$z - 1 = \frac{(\zeta - 1)^2}{2\zeta},$$

we thus have

(43) $$\frac{(1 - \alpha)(W - 1)}{z - 1} = \frac{\zeta}{\zeta - \alpha} = 1 + \frac{\alpha}{1 - \alpha}\left(\frac{1 - \alpha}{\zeta - \alpha}\right).$$

Solving (42) for $(1 - \alpha)(\zeta - \alpha)^{-1}$, we have

$$\frac{1 - \alpha}{\zeta - \alpha} = W - \sqrt{W^2 - 1},$$

where $\sqrt{W^2 - 1} \sim W$ for large $|W|$. Substituting this in (43), we arrive at the formula

(44) $$z = 1 + \frac{(1 - \alpha)^2(W - 1)}{1 - \alpha + \alpha(W - \sqrt{W^2 - 1})}, \quad \alpha < 0,$$

for the inverse of the mapping function $W = F(z)$. Since $W - \sqrt{W^2 - 1} \to 0$ for $W \to \infty$, it follows from (44) that

$$\left(\frac{dz}{dW}\right)_{z = \infty} = 1 - \alpha > 0,$$

and this shows that the original flow is indeed parallel to the x-axis (and proceeds from left to right). To obtain the parametric equation of the streamlines, we set $W = t + ic$ and decompose (44) into its real and imaginary parts. Accordingly, these equations are of the form

$$x = 1 + \text{Re}[Q(t)],$$

$$y = \text{Im}[Q(t)],$$

where

$$Q(t) = \frac{(1 - \alpha)^2(t + ic - 1)}{1 - \alpha + \alpha(t + ic - \sqrt{(t + ic)^2 - 1})},$$

and the real parameter t varies from $-\infty$ to $+\infty$.

We finally make a few remarks concerning the behavior of the complex potential in the vicinity of sources and sinks of the fluid. We first assume that a point-source is located at $z = a$, and that there are no obstructions to the flow of the fluid in the rest of the plane. Since there are no preferred directions, it follows from physical considerations that the velocity potential $u(x, y)$ will depend only on the distance r from the source. As shown in the preceding section, the only harmonic function with this property is the function $u(x, y) = A \log r + B$, where A and B are constants. Neglecting the physically meaningless additive constant B, we thus find that the velocity potential of an unobstructed point source $z = a$ must be $u(x, y) = A \log |z - a|$. The complex potential is, therefore,

(45) $$F(z) = A \log (z - a),$$

where A is a real constant. The stream function $v(x, y)$ is $A \arg (z - a)$, and the streamlines $A \arg (z - a) = \text{const.}$ are, of course, rays emanating from the point $z = a$.

Because of the incompressibility of the fluid, the amount of fluid originating at the source during a given time interval must be equal to the amount of fluid passing during the same time through any closed contour C surrounding the source. The latter amount is (per time unit) expressed by the quantity (25). If we take C to be a circle of radius R about $z = a$, and observe that the radial velocity component is $\partial/\partial r (A \log r)$, i.e., Ar^{-1}, the quantity (25) is found to be

$$\frac{A}{r} \int_0^{2\pi} r \, d\theta = 2\pi A.$$

Except for the factor 2π, the constant A is thus to be interpreted as the amount of fluid generated in a unit of time. This is also referred to as the *intensity* of the source. If A is negative, fluid is vanishing at the point $z = a$, and this point is therefore called a *sink* of the fluid. It should also be noted that, in the case of a single point-source in the plane, the point $z = \infty$ must be regarded as a sink; all the fluid flows to this point, and no fluid returns from there. More generally speaking, it is clear that a streamline can originate only at a source, and can terminate only at a sink.

An obstacle placed in the flow will modify the original streamline pattern, since part of one streamline must now coincide with the boundary of the obstacle. For instance, if the flow due to a point-source is disturbed by an object with the boundary C, the complex potential $F(z)$ describing the flow will still show the behavior indicated in (45) near $z = a$ and $z = \infty$, but it must now be such that the stream function $\text{Im}[F(z)]$ is constant on C. If C is the circle $|z| = R$ ($R < |a|$), it is easy to see that this complex potential must be of the form

$$(46) \qquad F(z) = A \log (z - a) + A \log \left(\frac{R^2}{z} - \bar{a} \right).$$

Indeed, the only singularities of the second term on the right-hand side are at the points $z = 0$ and $z = R^2(\bar{a})^{-1}$, both of which are in $|z| < R$, and the singular behavior of (46) in the region occupied by the fluid is therefore the same as that of (45). On C, we have $R^2 = z\bar{z}$, and it follows that

$$A \log (z - a) + A \log \left(\frac{R^2}{z} - \bar{a} \right)$$

$$= A \log (z - a) + A \log (\bar{z} - \bar{a}) = 2A \, \text{Re}[\log (z - a)].$$

The function (46) is thus real on the circumference C. Since, except for an additive constant, there can exist only one function with these properties, (46) is the required potential. The streamlines of the flow are the curves $\text{Im}[F(z)] = \text{const.}$, i.e., the curves

$$(47) \qquad \arg (z - a) + \arg \left(\frac{R^2}{z} - \bar{a} \right) = c.$$

If $|z|$ is large, they approach the streamlines $\arg (z - a) = \text{const.}$ of the undisturbed flow.

If a source and a sink of equal intensity are placed at the points $z = a$ and $z = b$, respectively, and if the flow is unobstructed, the corresponding complex potential is, evidently,

$$(48) \qquad F(z) = A \log (z - a) - A \log (z - b).$$

The streamlines are the curves

$$A \arg \left(\frac{z - a}{z - b} \right) = c.$$

As the reader will confirm, these are circular arcs connecting $z = a$ and $z = b$ (Fig. 22).

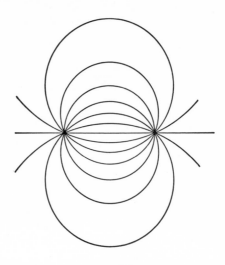

FIG. 22

The source and the sink may be located at the same point. In this case, we speak of a *double source*, or a *dipole*. To obtain the complex potential of a dipole, we let $b \to a$ in (48) and, at the same time, we let A increase in such a way as to obtain a finite limit for $F(z)$. If b tends to a along the linear segment $b = a + re^{i\alpha}$ ($r > 0$, α real), and if we set $A = B/r$, where B is a positive constant, a short computation shows that (48) has the limit

$$F(z) = \frac{K}{z - a}, \quad K = Be^{i\alpha}.$$

B is the intensity of the dipole, and α indicates its direction. The streamlines are the curves

$$\mathrm{Im}\left[\frac{K}{z - a}\right] = c,$$

and it is easily confirmed that these are circles which pass through $z = a$ and are tangent to the line of inclination α through $z = a$ (Fig. 23). It is worth noting that the uniform flow corresponding to the potential $F(z) = Az$ ($A > 0$) may be regarded as the flow due to a horizontal dipole at $z = \infty$.

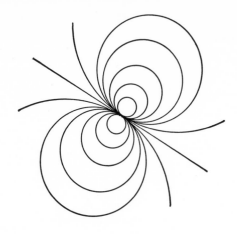

FIG. 23

EXERCISES

1. In the flow of Fig. 19, show that the velocity of the fluid on the boundary of the obstacle is

$$V = \frac{|y|}{\sqrt{1 - y^2}}.$$

2. In the flow of Fig. 18 (Formula (32)), show that the points at which the fluid has the velocity V ($V \neq A$) lie on the lemniscate

$$r^2 = \frac{2A^2}{A^2 - V^2} \cos 2\theta.$$

3. If $F(z)$ denotes the analytic function

$$f(z) = e^{-i\alpha}z\left[\cos \alpha + i \sin \alpha \sqrt{1 - \frac{e^{2i\alpha}}{z^2}}\right],$$

show that $F(\infty) = \infty$, $F'(\infty) = 1$, and verify that $F(z)$ takes real values on the linear segment $z = se^{i\alpha}$, $-1 \leq s \leq 1$. Conclude that $F(z)$ is the complex potential of a uniform horizontal flow around this segment (Fig. 24).

4. In the flow of the preceding exercise, show that the velocity of the fluid at the point $z = \cos \lambda e^{i\alpha}$ ($-\pi < \lambda < \pi$) of the boundary is

$$V = \frac{|\sin (\alpha - \lambda)|}{|\sin \lambda|}.$$

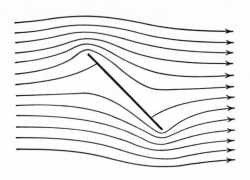

FIG. 24

5. If a is real, show that the polar equation of the streamlines (47) is

$$a(R^2 - r^2) \sin \theta = c[(R^2 + a^2)r - a(r^2 + R^2) \cos \theta].$$

6. Show that a flow which is generated by a point source of intensity 1 at $z = a$ $(a > 0)$, and is confined to the half-plane $\text{Re}(z) > 0$, has the complex potential

$$F(z) = \log (z - a) + \log (z + a).$$

7. Show that, with one exception (which?), the streamlines of the flow of the preceding exercise are arcs of the hyperbolas

$$c(x^2 - y^2) - xy = ca^2, \quad x > 0.$$

Verify that all streamlines begin at the point $z = a$.

8. A flow is generated by a double source with the complex potential $A(z - a)^{-1}$. If the only obstacle in the way of the flow is the circle $|z| = R$ $(R < |a|)$, show that the complex potential of the flow is of the form

$$F(z) = \frac{A}{z - a} + \frac{\overline{A}z}{R^2 - \bar{a}z}.$$

9. If the flow of Fig. 22 (Formula (48)) is disturbed by the insertion of the circle $|z| = R$ $(R < |a|, R < |b|)$, show that the complex potential becomes

$$F(z) = A \log (z - a) + A \log \left(\frac{R^2}{z} - \bar{a}\right)$$
$$- A \log (z - b) - A \log \left(\frac{R^2}{z} - \bar{b}\right).$$

10. A double source with the complex potential z^{-1} is located at the origin. If the flow generated by this source is confined to the channel $-\pi < \mathrm{Im}(z) < \pi$, show that its complex potential is

$$F(z) = \frac{1}{2}\frac{e^z + 1}{e^z - 1}.$$

Verify that the velocity of the flow tends to zero for $x \to \pm\infty$ (in agreement of the fact that neither sources nor sinks are located at the "ends" of the channel).

11. If the double source of the preceding exercise acts in conjunction with a uniform horizontal flow of velocity A in the channel, show that the complex potential takes the form

$$F(z) = Az + \frac{1}{2}\frac{e^z + 1}{e^z - 1}.$$

12. Let $W = F(z)$ denote the complex potential of a flow through an open channel bounded by the half-lines $-\infty < x < -1,\ y = \pi$ and $-\infty < x < -1,\ y = -\pi$, if it is assumed that originally—i.e., at a large distance from the orifice—the flow was horizontal and had the speed 1 (Fig. 25). Using

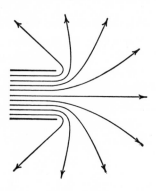

FIG. **25**

the conformal mapping of Fig. 12 (Chap. V, Sec. 5), show that $W = F(z)$ is implicitly given by the equation

$$z = W + e^W.$$

13. Show that the streamlines of the flow of the preceding exercise have the parametric representation

$$x = t + e^t \cos c$$
$$y = c + e^t \sin c,$$

where t varies from $-\infty$ to $+\infty$.

14. If A is a real constant, show that the complex potential

$$F(z) = iA \log z$$

corresponds to a rotation (with the angular velocity $-A$) of the entire fluid around the origin.

15. Consider a fluid motion composed of a uniform horizontal translation of velocity 1 and a rotation about the origin with the angular velocity A. If the motion is disturbed by the insertion of the circle $|z| = 1$, show that the complex potential of the resulting flow is

$$F(z) = z + \frac{1}{z} - iA \log z.$$

VII

ADDITIONAL

TOPICS

1 ANALYTIC CONTINUATION

It often happens that an explicit expression defining an analytic function is valid only for a limited range of the variable. For instance, the power series

$$1 + z + z^2 + z^3 + \cdots$$

defines the function $(1 - z)^{-1}$ only in the disk $|z| < 1$. For other values of z, the series diverges and thus becomes meaningless, although the function itself is well defined for all values of z other than $z = 1$. The reason for this phenomenon is, of course, the singularity of the function at the point $z = 1$ which, as it were, "stops" the convergence of the series. As another example, we consider the function $f(z)$ defined by the integral

$$f(z) = \int_0^\infty e^{-zt}\, dt,$$

where the integration is extended over the interval $(0, \infty)$. In view of

$$|e^{-zt}| = |e^{-(x+iy)t}| = e^{-xt},$$

the integral converges absolutely for $x = \mathrm{Re}(z) > 0$, and an elementary computation shows that $f(z) = z^{-1}$. The relation

$$\frac{1}{z} = \int_0^\infty e^{-zt}\, dt$$

is thus valid for $\text{Re}(z) > 0$. For $\text{Re}(z) \leq 0$, the integral fails to converge, although the function z^{-1} is well defined throughout this region except at the origin.

In both of these examples the limited validity of the expressions in question presents no problems, since we possess alternative definitions which permit us to compute these functions wherever they are defined. In general, however, this is not the case. A function will be defined by means of some representation—such as a power series—which is valid only in some limited region, and no direct information is available as to the behavior of the function outside this region. In order to obtain such information, it is necessary to employ methods which make it possible to "continue" the function from its original region of definition to other parts of the plane. A procedure which accomplishes this is referred to as *analytic continuation* of the function.

The method of analytic continuation to be described here is based on the fact that, in the neighborhood of a regular point, an analytic function possesses a Taylor expansion whose circle of convergence is determined by the position of the nearest singular point of the function. For the sake of simplicity we assume that the function $f(z)$ under consideration is originally defined by means of a power series of the form

$$(1) \qquad f(z) = a_0 + a_1 z + a_2 z^2 + \cdots ,$$

which converges in a finite disk $|z| < R$ (if the radius of convergence is infinite, we can compute the values of $f(z)$ for every finite z, and no problem of analytic continuation arises). If a is a value such that $0 < |a| < R$, $f(z)$ is regular for $z = a$ and we may expand $f(z)$ into a power series of the form

$$(2) \qquad f(z) = b_0 + b_1(z - a) + b_2(z - a)^2 + \cdots .$$

According to Taylor's theorem, this series will converge in the largest disk of center a in which $f(z)$ is regular. Hence, (2) will certainly converge in the interior of the circle about a which is tangent to the circle $|z| = R$ and contained in its interior. The radius of convergence R_a of the series (2) is therefore at least equal to $R - |a|$.

We must now distinguish between two possibilities, according as $R_a = R - |a|$ or $R_a > R - |a|$. In the first case we can say that the point of contact of the two circles must be a singular point of the function $f(z)$. Indeed, according to the results of Chapter

IV, Section 2, there must be at least one singular point of $f(z)$ on the circumference $|z - a| = R - |a|$. Since all points of $|z - a| = R - |a|$ other than the point of contact are within $|z| < R$—and are therefore regular points of the function— the point of contact is necessarily singular.

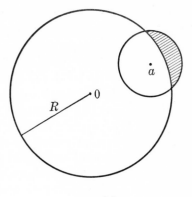

We now turn to the consideration of the second case. Since $R_a > R - |a|$, the disk $|z - a| < R_a$ will not be entirely contained in $|z| < R$ (see Fig. 26). In the region common to both disks, the series (1) and (2) necessarily yield the same values (because of Taylor's

FIG. **26**

theorem), and the two series thus represent one and the same function $f(z)$. But the series (2) also converges in the sickle-shaped part of the disk $|z - a| < R_a$ which is not contained in $|z| < R$, and it therefore represents there the same function $f(z)$. Accordingly, the expansion (2) yields the analytic continuation of the original function $f(z)$ into this sickle-shaped region.

The reader will recall that in the study of the function $\log z$ we found it useful to observe the behavior of $\log z$ as z traversed a given curve C. In the terminology of the present section, we may say that we studied the analytic continuation of the function $\log z$ along the curve C. The reason we had to do this was that, because of the many-valuedness of the function, the value of $\log z$ at which we arrived depended not only on the point z but also on the particular curve C along which we reached this point. A similar precaution must be observed in studying the analytic continuation of the function $f(z)$ defined by (1). Since we cannot tell in advance whether or not this function is single-valued throughout its region of existence, we shall replace the general idea of analytic continuation by the more precise concept of *analytic continuation along a curve C*. If C is a continuous curve which begins in $|z| < R$ and ends at a point z outside this disk, this continuation is carried out by repeated application of the process described above. The idea is to cover the curve C by a chain of disks—each of them being the region of convergence of a Taylor series of $f(z)$—in such a way that each adjacent pair of disks overlaps in the manner indicated in Fig. 26. If the centers of these disks are denoted by $\alpha_1, \alpha_2, \cdots, \alpha_k$ is thus a point in the interior of the region of convergence of the Taylor expansion about α_{k-1}. In order to make sure that these disks actually cover the curve C, we use only points α_k which lie on C.

There are now two possibilities: either we can reach the point z by a finite number of such steps, or we cannot. In the first case, our procedure yields the desired analytic continuation of the function $f(z)$ along the curve C. In the second case, we must have met a point on C beyond which the function cannot be continued. Such a point is necessarily a singular point of the function. Indeed, if our procedure leads to an infinite number of disks with centers α_k on C, any sequence of such disks must converge to a point z_0 of C (their radii must evidently converge to zero). On the boundary of each of the disks there must be at least one singular point of the function, and the point z_0 is therefore the limit point of a sequence of singular points. Since regularity at z_0 would imply regularity in a neighborhood of z_0, this shows that the point z_0 on C is a singular point of the function. Our result is therefore that, along any arbitrary continuous curve C which starts in the disk $|z| < R$, the function $f(z)$ can be continued analytically until a singularity of the function is encountered.

There is an interesting special case which deserves mention here. It may happen that *all* points of the circumference $|z| = R$ are singular points of the function $f(z)$. In this case it is impossible to continue the function analytically to points outside $|z| = R$, and this circumference is said to be the *natural boundary* of the function.

From our results regarding analytic continuation we can draw the following important conclusion: If two analytic functions coincide in a disk, the two functions are identical, i.e., the analytic continuations of the two functions along any curve lead to identical results. To show that two analytic functions are identical, it is thus sufficient to show that they coincide in a disk. As the following statement shows, the conditions required for ensuring the identity of two functions can be reduced even further.

Let $z_1, z_2, \cdots$ be a sequence of points converging to a point z_0, and let $f(z)$ and $g(z)$ be two analytic functions regular at z_0. If $f(z_k) = g(z_k)$ for $k = 1, 2, \cdots$, then $f(z)$ and $g(z)$ are identical.

To prove this statement, we set $f(z) - g(z) = h(z)$ and we

observe that, in view of our assumptions, $h(z)$ is regular at z_0. There will thus exist a Taylor expansion

$$h(z) = a_0 + a_1(z - z_0) + a_2(z - z_0)^2 + \cdots$$

converging in a neighborhood $|z - z_0| < r$. Since $h(z_k) = 0$ for $k = 1, 2, \cdots$, it follows from $\lim z_k = z_0$, and the continuity of $h(z)$ at z_0, that $a_0 = h(z_0) = 0$. Our aim is to show that all the other coefficients of this expansion are likewise equal to zero. If this were not true, there would exist an index m such that $a_m \neq 0$ and $a_0 = a_1 = \cdots = a_{m-1} = 0$, and $h(z)$ could be written in the form $h(z) = (z - z_0)^m h_1(z)$, where

$$h_1(z) = a_m + a_{m+1}(z - z_0) + \cdots, \quad a_m \neq 0.$$

Since $h(z_k) = 0$ implies $h_1(z_k) = 0$, and since $h_1(z)$ is continuous at z_0, this leads to $a_m = h_1(z_0) = 0$, contrary to our assumption. This shows that $h(z) \equiv 0$ for $|z| < r$. Hence, $f(z)$ and $g(z)$ coincide in this disk and, in view of the remark made above, the two functions are identical.

The assumptions under which this statement was proved are certainly fulfilled if the functions $f(z)$ and $g(z)$ coincide along a small arc on which both are regular. Two such functions are therefore identical. In particular, the identity of two analytic functions is established if it can be shown that they take the same values on a segment of the real axis. This fact can be used to extend known real identities to complex values. For instance, if z and w are real numbers, it is known from trigonometry that

(3) $\sin(z + w) = \sin z \cos w + \cos z \sin w.$

We further know that there exist analytic functions—denoted by the same symbols—which for real values of z coincide with the real trigonometric functions $\sin z$ and $\cos z$. If w is a real constant, the two sides of (3) are therefore analytic functions of z. Since they coincide for real values of z, it follows that they must be identical, and (3) must hold for all values of z for which the functions involved are defined (i.e., in this case, for all complex values z). Equation (3) has thus been proved for real w and complex z. If we now keep z constant and let w vary, the same argument extends the validity of (3) from real values of w to general complex values, and this shows that (3) holds for arbitrary complex values of z and w.

Similar considerations can be applied to all real identities known from elementary analysis. Once it is verified that all the functions involved are analytic, these identities can be immediately extended to complex values.

2 EXAMPLES: THE GAMMA AND ZETA FUNCTIONS

The method of analytic continuation described in the preceding section can be applied to all analytic functions, but it does not necessarily provide the easiest way of obtaining the continuation of a given function beyond its original domain of definition. By utilizing the special properties of the given function it is often possible to achieve the same purpose at a considerable saving of computational labor. We shall consider here a number of examples of this type.

Our first example concerns the *Gamma function*, which occurs in many branches of pure and applied analysis. For values of z such that $\mathrm{Re}(z) > 0$, this function is defined by

$$(4) \qquad \Gamma(z) = \int_0^\infty t^{z-1} e^{-t}\, dt,$$

where the integration is carried out along the positive axis in the t-plane. Since

$$\left| t^{z-1} \right| = \left| e^{(z-1)\log t} \right| = e^{(x-1)\log t} = t^{x-1},$$

where $z = x + iy$, it is easily confirmed that the integral (4) converges absolutely for $x > 0$. Moreover, the limit for $h \to 0$ of the expression $h^{-1}[\Gamma(z + h) - \Gamma(z)]$ exists and is equal to

$$\int_0^\infty t^{z-1} \log t e^{-t}\, dt,$$

provided $\mathrm{Re}(z) > 0$ (the proof of this fact is left to the reader as an exercise). It follows therefore that $\Gamma(z)$ is an analytic function of z in the half-plane $\mathrm{Re}(z) > 0$.

For $\mathrm{Re}(z) > 0$, the Gamma function satisfies the functional equation

$$(5) \qquad z\Gamma(z) = \Gamma(z + 1).$$

Indeed, substituting $z + 1$ for z in (4), and integrating by parts, we obtain

$$\Gamma(z + 1) = [-t^z e^{-t}]_0^\infty + z \int_0^\infty t^{z-1} e^{-t} \, dt.$$

Since $\mathrm{Re}(z) > 0$, the integrated part vanishes, and (5) follows by another application of (4).

With the help of the relation (5) it is easy to continue the function $\Gamma(z)$ beyond the original domain of definition $\mathrm{Re}(z) > 0$. Since (5) holds for $\mathrm{Re}(z) > 0$, it follows from the results of the preceding section that this relation remains valid for all analytic continuations of the functions involved. The right-hand side of (5) can be continued to all points z such that $\mathrm{Re}(z + 1) > 0$, i.e., to the entire half-plane $\mathrm{Re}(z) > -1$. Hence, the same must be true of the left-hand side of (5), and the relation (5) must hold throughout the half-plane $\mathrm{Re}(z) > -1$. The values of $\Gamma(z)$ in the strip $-1 < \mathrm{Re}(z) \leq 0$ (which was not included in the original domain of definition of the function) can thus be obtained from the formula

$$\Gamma(z) = \frac{\Gamma(z + 1)}{z}.$$

As this formula shows, $\Gamma(z)$ is a regular analytic function at all points of the strip, except at the point $z = 0$ at which it has a simple pole.

By a slight modification of the preceding argument, the function $\Gamma(z)$ can be continued analytically to all points of the half-plane $\mathrm{Re}(z) > -n$, where n is an arbitrary positive integer. In view of (5), we have $z(z + 1)\Gamma(z) = (z + 1)\Gamma(z + 1) = \Gamma(z + 2)$. Similarly, $z(z + 1)(z + 2)\Gamma(z) = (z + 2)\Gamma(z + 2) = \Gamma(z + 3)$. Continuing in this fashion, we finally obtain

$$z(z + 1)(z + 1) \cdots (z + n - 1)\Gamma(z) = \Gamma(z + n).$$

Since $\Gamma(z + n)$ is a regular analytic function for $\mathrm{Re}(z) > -n$, the same is true of the left-hand side of this identity. The values of $\Gamma(z)$ in the strip $-n < \mathrm{Re}(z) \leq 0$ are thus obtained from the formula

$$\Gamma(z) = \frac{\Gamma(z + n)}{z(z + 1)(z + 2) \cdots (z + n - 1)},$$

and this shows that $\Gamma(z)$ is regular throughout this region except for simple poles at the points $z = 0, -1, -2, \cdots - (n - 1)$. Because of the arbitrariness of the positive integer n, this implies that the function $\Gamma(z)$ can be continued analytically to all finite points of the plane, with the exception of the points $z = 0, -1, -2, -3, \cdots$ at which the function has simple poles.

The analytic continuation of the Gamma function to the half-plane $\mathrm{Re}(z) < 0$ can also be accomplished by means of a method similar to the one used to evaluate the integral (41) of Chapter IV, Section 6. We consider the contour integral

$$(6) \qquad \int_C t^{z-1} e^{-t}\, dt,$$

where C is an integration path beginning and ending at $+\infty$, and surrounding the origin in the negative direction (Fig. 27a). Unless

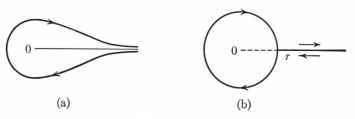

(a)   (b)

FIG. **27**

z is a positive integer, the point $t = 0$ is a singularity of the integrand. Since there are no other finite singularities, it follows from Cauchy's theorem that the integral (6) will not change its value if the contour C is continuously deformed, provided the origin is not crossed during this deformation (compare the discussion in Chap. III, Sec. 4). We may therefore replace C by an integration path which consists of the part of the positive axis between $+\infty$ and a positive number r, the circumference $|t| = r$, and again the positive axis from r to $+\infty$ (Fig. 27b). If the symbol t^{z-1} denotes the value of this function on the "upper edge" of the positive axis, then, as shown in detail in the evaluation of the integral (41) of Chapter IV, the two integrals along the positive axis combine to

$$(1 - e^{2\pi i z}) \int_r^\infty t^{z-1} e^{-t}\, dt.$$

The integral over the circumference $|t| = r$ will tend to zero for $r \to 0$, provided $|t^z| \to 0$ for $|t| \to 0$. For $\mathrm{Re}(z) > 0$, this condition is satisfied, and the integral (6) is therefore equal to

$$(1 - e^{2\pi i z}) \int_0^\infty t^{z-1} e^{-t}\, dt.$$

Comparing this with (4), we have the result

$$(7) \qquad \Gamma(z) = \frac{1}{1 - e^{2\pi i z}} \int_C t^{z-1} e^{-t}\, dt,$$

where C is an integration path of the type indicated in Fig. 27a.

Formula (7) was derived under the assumption $\mathrm{Re}(z) > 0$, which was necessary to ensure the existence of the integral (4). The integral appearing in (7) is, however, an analytic function of z *for all finite values of z*. Indeed, the integration path C does not pass through the singularity at the origin, and an elementary argument—which is left as an exercise to the reader—shows that the derivative of the integral with respect to z exists for all finite z. The right-hand side of (7) is therefore a regular analytic function for all values of z, with the possible exception of the points at which $1 - e^{2\pi iz} = 0$, i.e., the points $z = 0, \pm1, \pm2, \cdots$. Since for $\mathrm{Re}(z) > 0$ this function coincides with $\Gamma(z)$, it represents for $\mathrm{Re}(z) \leq 0$ the analytic continuation of $\Gamma(z)$. As (4) shows, the function $\Gamma(z)$ is regular at $z = 1, 2, \cdots$ (it may also be noted that, for these values, the integrand in (7) is regular at the origin, and the integral thus vanishes by Cauchy's theorem). The only remaining singularities thus are simple poles at the points $z = 0, -1, -2, \cdots$.

We mention here without proof that the function $\Gamma(z)$ also satisfies the functional relation

$$(8) \qquad \Gamma(z)\Gamma(1 - z) = \frac{\pi}{\sin \pi z},$$

which establishes a connection between the Gamma function and the trigonometric functions. This relation provides yet another possibility of continuing the Gamma function from its original domain of definition to the entire z-plane.

Our next example concerns the *Zeta function*

$$(9) \qquad \zeta(z) = \sum_{n=1}^{\infty} \frac{1}{n^z},$$

which plays a prominent part in the analytic theory of numbers. The series (9) converges uniformly in any closed subdomain of the half-plane $\mathrm{Re}(z) > 1$ and thus represents there an analytic function (cf. Chap. II, Sec. 8, Exercise 4).

In order to obtain the analytic continuation of $\zeta(z)$ to points outside this half-plane, we transform the series (9) into a definite integral over the interval $0 \leq t < \infty$. Since

$$(10) \qquad \int_0^{\infty} t^{z-1} e^{-nt} \, dt = \frac{1}{n^z} \int_0^{\infty} t^{z-1} e^{-t} \, dt = \frac{\Gamma(z)}{n^z},$$

we have

(11)

$$\Gamma(z) \sum_{n=1}^{m} \frac{1}{n^z} = \int_0^\infty t^{z-1} \left(\sum_{n=1}^{m} e^{-nt} \right) dt = \int_0^\infty t^{z-1} e^{-t} \left(\frac{1 - e^{-mt}}{1 - e^{-t}} \right) dt.$$

For $m \to \infty$, the integral

$$I = \int_0^\infty \frac{t^{z-1} e^{-mt}}{1 - e^{-t}} e^{-t} \, dt$$

tends to zero. Indeed, because of

$$\frac{e^{-t}}{1 - e^{-t}} = \frac{1}{e^t - 1} \le \frac{1}{t}$$

and $|t^{z-1}| = t^{x-1}$, we have

$$|I| \le \int_0^\infty t^{x-2} e^{-mt} \, dt = \frac{1}{m^{x-1}} \int_0^\infty t^{x-2} e^{-t} \, dt$$

$$= \frac{\Gamma(x - 1)}{m^{x-1}}.$$

Since $x = \mathrm{Re}(z) > 1$, this tends to zero for $m \to \infty$. Letting $m \to \infty$ in (11), we thus obtain

$$\zeta(z) = \frac{1}{\Gamma(z)} \int_0^\infty \frac{t^{z-1} \, dt}{e^t - 1}.$$

The point $t = 0$ is the only singular point of the integrand, and we may therefore replace the integral over the real axis by a contour integral over an integration path of the type indicated in Fig. 27a. As pointed out before, this introduces the factor $[1 - e^{2\pi i z}]^{-1}$. In analogy to (7), we thus obtain the identity

(12)
$$\zeta(z) = \frac{1}{(1 - e^{2\pi i z})\Gamma(z)} \int_C \frac{t^{z-1} \, dt}{e^t - 1}.$$

This can be brought into a simpler form with the help of (8). We have

$$1 - e^{2\pi i z} = e^{\pi i z} \left(e^{-\pi i z} - e^{\pi i z} \right) = -2i \, e^{\pi i z} \sin \pi z,$$

and thus

$$(1 - e^{2\pi i z})\Gamma(z) = -2i \, e^{\pi i z} \sin \pi z \Gamma(z) = \frac{-2\pi i \, e^{\pi i z}}{\Gamma(1 - z)}.$$

Formula (12) is therefore equivalent to

(13)
$$\zeta(z) = \frac{-e^{-\pi i z} \Gamma(1 - z)}{2\pi i} \int_C \frac{t^{z-1} \, dt}{e^t - 1}.$$

Although this identity was derived under the assumption that $\text{Re}(z) > 1$, it is now easy to see that the right-hand side of (13) is a regular analytic function of z in the entire z-plane, with the possible exception of the points at which $\Gamma(1 - z)$ becomes singular. Indeed, the only singular point of the integrand is situated at $t = 0$, and the integration path C does not pass through this point. As pointed out in the similar case of the integral (7), it follows therefore that the integral on the right-hand side of (13) is a regular analytic function for all finite values of z. In view of the results of the preceding section, we may thus conclude that Formula (13) provides the analytic continuation of the function $\zeta(z)$ to the entire plane.

As already mentioned, the only possible singularities of $\zeta(z)$ are the points at which $\Gamma(1 - z)$ becomes singular, i.e., the points $z = 1, 2, 3, \cdots$. Since $\zeta(z)$ is regular for $\text{Re}(z) > 1$, this leaves the point $z = 1$ (it may also be noted that the integral in (13) vanishes by Cauchy's theorem if $z - 1$ is a positive integer). The function $\zeta(z)$ is thus regular for all finite values of z, with the possible exception of a simple pole at $z = 1$. To show that this pole actually exists, we compute its residue. For $z = 1$, the contour integral takes the form

$$I = \int_C \frac{dt}{e^t - 1},$$

where C may be taken to be the integration path of Fig. 27b. Since the integrand is single-valued, the integrals along the two edges of $r < t < \infty$ cancel out. Hence,

$$I = \int_{|t|=r} \frac{dt}{e^t - 1},$$

where, in accordance with Fig. 27b, the integration is to be carried out in the negative direction. The only singularity of the integrand in $|t| < r$ is a simple pole at the origin with the residue 1. By the residue theorem, we thus have $I = -2\pi i$.

In the representation (12), the pole of $\zeta(z)$ at $z = 1$ is caused by the zero of $1 - e^{2\pi i z}$ at this point. Since the derivative of this expression at $z = 1$ is $-2\pi i$, the residue of

$$\frac{1}{1 - e^{2\pi i z}}$$

at $z = 1$ is $(-2\pi i)^{-1}$. In view of $\Gamma(1) = 1$ and the fact that, for $z = 1$, the value of the integral in (12) is $-2\pi i$, the residue of $\zeta(z)$ at

$z = 1$ is thus found to be equal to 1.   Hence, the only finite singularity of the function $\zeta(z)$ is a simple pole of residue 1 at the point $z = 1$.

EXERCISES

1. If n is a positive integer, show that $\Gamma(n) = (n - 1)!$.

2. If n is a positive integer, show that the residue of the simple pole of $\Gamma(z)$ at $z = -n$ is $(-1)^n(n!)^{-1}$.

3. Show that, except for the coefficient a_1, all odd coefficients of the Taylor expansion

$$p(t) = \frac{t}{e^t - 1} = \sum_{\nu=0}^{\infty} a_\nu z^\nu$$

are zero.   *Hint:* Consider $p(t) - p(-t)$.

4. Use the formula (13) and the result of the preceding exercise to show that $\zeta(-2n) = 0$ if n is a positive integer.   *Hint:* Use the fact that, for integral n, the integration path C in (13) may be replaced by a circle about the origin.

5. The Bernoulli numbers B_n are defined by the expansion

$$\frac{t}{e^t - 1} = 1 - \frac{t}{2} - \sum_{n=1}^{\infty} (-1)^n \frac{B_n t^{2n}}{(2n)!}.$$

Use Formula (13) to show that $\zeta(0) = -\frac{1}{2}$ and

$$\zeta(1 - 2n) = (-1)^n \frac{B_n}{2n},$$

if n is a positive integer.

6. The power series

$$f(z) = \sum_{n=1}^{\infty} \frac{z^n}{n^s}, \quad s > 0$$

converges in the disk $|z| < 1$ and represents there an analytic function.   Using the identity (10) (with s substituted for z), show that $f(z)$ has the representation

$$f(z) = \frac{z}{\Gamma(s)} \int_0^\infty \frac{t^{s-1}\, dt}{e^t - z}.$$

Show further that this expression provides the analytic continuation of the function $f(z)$ to the domain obtained by cutting the z-plane along the section $1 \le t \le \infty$ of the positive axis.

3   THE SYMMETRY PRINCIPLE

In the present section we describe a method of analytic continuation which, whenever it is applicable, can be carried out almost without computation. This method is based on the elementary geometric concept of the *symmetry* of two points z and z^* with respect to a straight line T. The two points are said to be *symmetric with respect to* T if they have the same distance from T, lie on different sides of this line, and if the linear segment connecting z and z^* is perpendicular to T (Fig. 28). The following statement, which describes the method

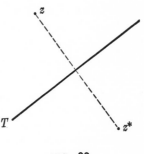

FIG. **28**

in question, is known as the *symmetry principle* or also, since the point z^* may be regarded as the mirror image of the point z with respect to T, as the *reflection principle*.

Let A be a domain whose boundary includes a linear segment L, and let A' be a domain whose boundary includes a linear segment L'. If the analytic function $w = f(z)$ maps A onto A' in such a way that the segment L is transformed into the segment L', then $f(z)$ can be continued analytically across L.

If z^* is the point symmetric to z with respect to L, and w^* is the point symmetric to $w = f(z)$ with respect to L', this analytic continuation is given by the formula

$$(14) \qquad\qquad f(z^*) = w^*.$$

We may also say, briefly, that in symmetric points the function takes symmetric values (Fig. 29).

The symmetry principle consists of two parts. The first part asserts that, under the given assumptions, the function $f(z)$ can be continued across L, i.e., $f(z)$ is regular at the points of L. The reader will recall that this result was used in the derivation of the

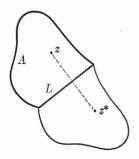
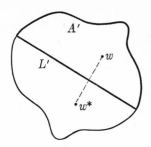

FIG. **29**

Schwarz-Christoffel formula (Chap. V, Sec. 4). The second part
of the symmetry principle states that this continuation can be
computed by means of the simple relation (14). In the proof
of the principle, we shall make the simplifying assumption that
both L and L' coincide with segments of the real axis (in the z-plane
and w-plane, respectively); the fact that any straight line can be
transformed into the real axis by a linear substitution of the form
$z \to az + b$ shows that no generality is lost by this assumption.
Since two points which are symmetric with respect to the real axis
correspond to two complex numbers which are conjugate to each
other (Fig. 30), Formula (14) may in this case be replaced by

$$(15) \qquad\qquad f(\bar{z}) = \overline{f(z)}.$$

Once it is known that $f(z)$ is regular at the points of L, it is
not difficult to show that (15) yields the analytic continuation of
$f(z)$ across L. Indeed, the mapping $z \to \bar{z}$ preserves all angles but

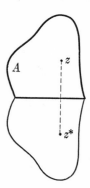
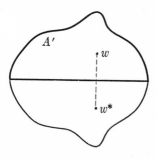

FIG. **30**

inverts their sense (Chap. V, Sec. 1), and the same is true of the mapping $f(z) \rightarrow \overline{f(z)}$. Two such inversions will thus restore the original sense of the angles involved, and also preserve their magnitudes. Accordingly, the function $\overline{f(\bar{z})}$ generates a conformal mapping—and is therefore a regular analytic function—at the points conjugate to the points of regularity of $f(z)$. Since a point on the real axis is conjugate to itself, $\overline{f(\bar{z})}$ is thus a regular analytic function at the points of L. If z is on L, $f(z)$ is real, and $f(z)$ is therefore identical with its conjugate. Hence, $f(z) = \overline{f(z)} = \overline{f(\bar{z})}$, i.e.,

(16) $$f(z) = \overline{f(\bar{z})}$$

at all points of the linear segment L. On this segment, both of these functions are regular, and we may therefore conclude from the results of Section 1 that they are identical. Thus, (16) is identically satisfied for all values z to which $f(z)$ can be continued. Since $\overline{f(\bar{z})}$ is defined if $\bar{z}$ is in A, it follows that $f(z)$ can be continued to the domain $\overline{A}$ which is the mirror image of A with respect to the real axis, and that the values of $f(z)$ in $\overline{A}$ are found by means of (16). This proves Formula (15).

The symmetry principle will therefore be established if we can show that an analytic function $f(z)$ which takes real values on a segment L of the real axis (and is regular in a domain A partly bounded by L) is necessarily regular on L. Since $v(x, y) = \text{Im}[f(z)]$ is a harmonic function in A, and $v = 0$ on L, it is sufficient to show that a harmonic function with these properties is regular on L. Indeed, if a harmonic function is regular at a point, it follows from the Cauchy-Riemann equations that the same is true of its conjugate function. The regularity of an analytic function is thus a consequence of the regularity of either its real or its imaginary part.

To prove the regularity of the harmonic function $v(x, y)$ at the points of L, we choose an arbitrary interior point of L, and we draw about this point a circle C whose upper half is entirely contained in the interior of A. We now construct a harmonic function $w(x, y)$ which is regular in the interior of C and satisfies the following boundary conditions: If (x, y) is a point on the upper half of C, we set $w(x, y) = v(x, y)$; if (x, y) is on the lower half of C, then $w(x, y) = -v(x, -y)$. Since $v(x, y)$ is zero on L, the two definitions give identical values at the points of intersection of C with the real axis, and it is clear that the prescribed boundary values vary continuously along the circumference C. According to the results of Chapter IV, Section 9, there exists therefore a uniquely determined harmonic function $w(x, y)$ in the interior D of C which takes these boundary values.

It is easy to see that this harmonic function satisfies the functional equation

$$(17) \qquad\qquad -w(x, -y) = w(x, y)$$

in $D + C$. Indeed, if $w(x, y)$ is a solution of the Laplace equation $\phi_{xx} + \phi_{yy} = 0$ in D, the same is true of the function $-w(x, -y)$, and it is immediately confirmed that both functions have the same boundary values on C. Since these boundary values determine a harmonic function uniquely, the two functions must be identical, and (17) follows.

If we set $y = 0$ in (17), we obtain $-w(x, 0) = w(x, 0)$, i.e., $w(x, 0) = 0$. The function $w(x, y)$ thus takes the value zero at the points at which the real axis intersects $D + C$. Since $v(x, y)$ likewise vanishes at these points, and since—by its definition—$w(x, y)$ coincides with $v(x, y)$ on the upper half of the circumference C, the functions $v(x, y)$ and $w(x, y)$ thus have the same values on the boundary of the upper half of D. Both functions being harmonic in this domain, we may therefore conclude that $v(x, y) = w(x, y)$ in the intersection of D and the upper half-plane $y \geq 0$. As shown in Section 1, two analytic functions are identical if their values coincide at the points of a domain. Taking the real parts of the functions involved, we see that the same statement holds for harmonic functions. Hence, $v(x, y) \equiv w(x, y)$ wherever $w(x, y)$ is harmonic, and this implies that $v(x,y)$ is regular throughout D. It follows, in particular, that $v(x, y)$ is regular at the center of D. Since this center was an arbitrary point of the segment L, this completes the proof of the symmetry principle.

The symmetry principle can be generalized to the case in which L and L' are not linear segments but circular arcs. This is not surprising if it is remembered that a suitable linear transformation of the type considered in Chapter V, Section 3 will transform a given circular arc into a linear segment. The concept of a pair of symmetric points with respect to a line is here replaced by the corresponding concept of a pair of *inverse points* with respect to a circle. Two points P and Q are said to be inverse to each other with respect to a given circle of center S and radius R if S lies on the same straight line as P and Q but not between them, and if

(18) $$\overline{PS} \cdot \overline{QS} = R^2$$

(Fig. 31).   The linear substitution which transforms a circle into
a straight line transforms a pair of inverse points with respect to
the circle into a pair of symmetric points with respect to the line.
To prove this fact, we assume that the inverse points lie on the

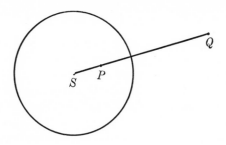

FIG. **31**

positive axis and that the circle C passes through the origin (this
configuration can always be obtained by means of a translation
and a rotation, both of which do not affect the relation (18)).
Since C intersects the real axis at $z = 0$ and $z = 2R$, the transformation

(19) $$w = \frac{1}{z}$$

maps C onto a vertical straight line intersecting the real axis at the
point $w = (2R)^{-1}$.   If $z = a$ and $z = b$ are the two inverse points
$(R < a < 2R < b)$, it follows from (18) that $(a - R)(b - R) = R^2$.
A short computation shows that this is equivalent to

$$\frac{1}{a} - \frac{1}{2R} = \frac{1}{2R} - \frac{1}{b}.$$

Since $w = a^{-1}$ and $w = b^{-1}$ are the images of $z = a$ and $z = b$,
respectively, under the transformation (19), this shows that these
points have the same distance from the vertical line into which C
is transformed by (19).   Hence, they are symmetric with respect
to this line.

This connection between inverse points and symmetric points
leads to a simple geometric construction of the point inverse to a
given point with respect to a given circle.   An elementary geometric argument shows that a circle passing through two points

which are symmetric with respect to a straight line L must intersect L at right angles and that, conversely, a circle passing through one of the symmetric points and intersecting L at right angles must also pass through the other point. As just shown, a linear substitution transforming a circle C into a line L transforms inverse points associated with C into symmetric points with respect to L. According to the results of Chapter V, Section 3, any substitution of the form

$$(20) \qquad\qquad w = \frac{az + b}{cz + d}$$

transforms circles into circles (if straight lines are regarded as special cases of circles). Since (20) is a conformal transformation, it preserves the angles between two smooth curves. In particular, (20) will thus transform two circles which intersect at right angles—two circles which are *orthogonal* to each other—into two circles which are likewise orthogonal to each other. The elementary geometric result just quoted has thus the following immediate generalization: A circle which passes through two points inverse to each other with respect to a circle C, is orthogonal to C; conversely, a circle orthogonal to C which passes through a given point must also pass through the point inverse to it with respect to C. To find the inverse point z^* to a given point z, we thus construct a circle passing through z which intersects C at right angles; the point of intersection of this circle with the line passing through z and the center will then be the point z^*. Since, under any transformation (20), a pair of orthogonal circles is carried into another pair of orthogonal circles, it also follows that, if a circle C_z is transformed into a circle C_w, a pair of points inverse with respect to C_z is transformed into a pair of points inverse with respect to C_w. If C_w is a straight line, the word "inverse" has to be replaced by "symmetric." As a result, the symmetry principle formulated at the beginning of this section can be extended in the following manner.

If the word "symmetric" is replaced by "inverse," the symmetry principle remains valid in the case in which L and L' are circular arcs.

We add here a few words regarding the analytic character of an inversion—i.e., a transformation carrying points z into their inverses z^*—with respect to a given circle C. If C is a straight line, the inversion becomes a simple reflection, transforming any geometric figure into its mirror image. A reflection will thus trans-

form circles into circles, and it will preserve the magnitude of the
angle between two smooth arcs. It will, however, reverse the
sense of the angle. Since a substitution of the type (20) transforms a reflection into an inversion, and since (20) is conformal and
carries circles into circles, it is seen that an inversion likewise
transforms circles into circles, and that it preserves the magnitude
of angles but not their sense. Hence, if an inversion is combined
with the sense-reversing transformation $z \rightarrow \bar{z}$, we obtain a conformal mapping transforming circles into circles. Since such a
mapping is necessarily of the form (20), it follows that an inversion
with respect to a fixed circle is equivalent to a transformation
of the form

$$z^* = \frac{a\bar{z} + b}{c\bar{z} + d}.$$

This generalizes the relation $z^* = \bar{z}$ which obtains in the case in
which the inversion reduces to a reflection with respect to the
real axis.

Wherever it is applicable, the symmetry principle provides
a simple and powerful tool for constructing the analytic continuation of functions to regions outside their original domains of
definition. It should also be noted that the use of the principle
is not restricted to the pointwise computation of the values of the
function by means of Formula (14). Since this formula is valid
for all points of the original domain A (whose image under the
conformal mapping $w = f(z)$ was the domain A'), it follows that
the values taken by the function in the "reflection" of A will cover
the reflection of A'. For instance, if $w = f(z)$ maps the shaded
semicircle of Fig. 32a onto the shaded rectangle of Fig. 32b in such
a way that the real segment $-1 < z < 1$ is transformed into the

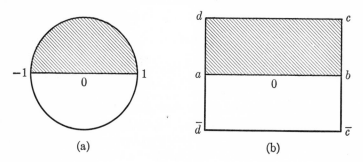

(a)   (b)

FIG. 32

real segment $a < w < b$, the symmetry principle shows that the same function also maps the unshaded semicircle onto the unshaded rectangle. Hence, it also maps the entire disk $|z| < 1$ onto the interior of the rectangle with the corners $\bar{c}, \bar{d}, d, c$.

As another example, we consider the function $w = f(z)$ mapping the semicircle $|z| < 1$, $\mathrm{Re}(z) > 0$ onto the infinite strip $0 < \mathrm{Re}(w) < \frac{\pi}{4}$ in such a way that $f(0) = 0$, and that the points $z = \pm i$ correspond to the two "ends" of the strip (Fig. 33). A

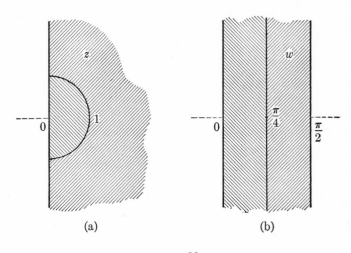

(a)   (b)

FIG. 33

reflection of the semicircle with respect to the vertical diameter corresponds to a reflection of the strip with respect to the line $\mathrm{Re}(w) = 0$. The reflection principle shows therefore that the function $w = f(z)$ maps the disk $|z| < 1$ onto the infinite strip $-\frac{\pi}{4} < \mathrm{Re}(w) < \frac{\pi}{4}$. This mapping was discussed in Chapter V (Fig. 9) and was found to correspond to the function $w = \tan z$. We now apply the reflection principle to the curved portion of the boundary of the semicircle. According to the definition of the inverse point, the inversion of the shaded semicircle in Fig. 33a with respect to the arc in question results in the infinite domain indicated by different shading. Since the reflection of the original half-strip with respect to the line $\mathrm{Re}(w) = \frac{\pi}{4}$ produces the half-strip $\frac{\pi}{4} < \text{Re}(z) < \frac{\pi}{2}$, this proves that the function $w = \tan z$ maps

the half-plane $\text{Re}(z) > 0$ onto the half-strip $0 < \text{Re}(w) < \frac{\pi}{2}$. As

this example illustrates, the reflection principle can often be used to obtain new conformal mappings by means of simple geometric considerations.

EXERCISES

1. Using the mapping indicated in Fig. 8 (Chap. V), show that the function $z = \sin w$ maps the infinite strip $-\frac{\pi}{2} < \text{Re}(w) < \frac{\pi}{2}$ onto the domain obtained from the z-plane by cutting it along the rays $-\infty \leq z \leq -1$ and $1 \leq z \leq \infty$.

2. Show that the function of the preceding exercise maps the half-strip $\text{Im}(w) > 0$, $-\frac{\pi}{2} < \text{Re}(w) < \frac{3\pi}{2}$ onto the domain obtained from the z-plane by cutting it along the ray $-\infty < z < 1$.

3. Using the mapping of Fig. 9 (Chap. V), show that the function $z = \tan w$ maps the infinite strip $-\frac{\pi}{4} < \text{Re}(w) < \frac{3\pi}{4}$ onto the domain obtained by removing the circular arc $z = e^{i\theta}$, $\frac{\pi}{2} \leq \theta \leq \frac{3\pi}{2}$ from the z-plane.

4. From the fact that the function $w = \log z$ gives the conformal mapping indicated in Fig. 13 (Chap. V), deduce that the same function maps the z-plane minus the ray $-\infty < z < 0$ onto the infinite strip $-\pi < \text{Im}(w) < \pi$.

5. Let $w = f(z)$ denote the analytic function mapping the quarter-plane of Fig. 34a onto the sector of Fig. 34b, and satisfying the conditions $f(0) = 0, f(1) = 1, f(\infty) = e^{\pi i \alpha}$. Show that $w = f(z)$ maps the entire half-plane $\text{Im}(z) > 0$ onto the infinite sector $0 < \arg w < \pi\alpha$, and verify that

$$f(z) = \left(\frac{z}{2 - z}\right)^{\alpha}.$$

6. Show that the function of the preceding exercise maps the domain obtained by removing the ray $-\infty < z < 0$ from the

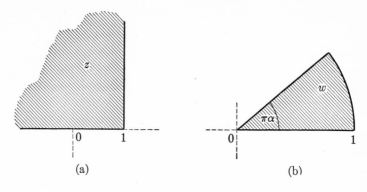

FIG. 34

half-plane $\text{Re}(z) < 1$ onto the circular sector $-\pi\alpha < \arg w < \pi\alpha$, $|w| < 1$.

4 THE HARMONIC CONJUGATE

We saw earlier (Chap. II, Sec. 3) that the real harmonic functions $u(x, y)$ and $v(x, y)$ which make up an analytic function $f(z) = u(x, y) + iv(x, y)$ are related by the Cauchy-Riemann equations

$$(21) \qquad u_x = v_y, \quad u_y = -v_x.$$

We also saw that, given a harmonic function $u(x, y)$, it is always possible to find a harmonic function $v(x, y)$—the harmonic conjugate of $u(x, y)$—so that the relations (21) are satisfied. In the present section we shall study the relation between a harmonic function and its conjugate in some additional detail.

The conjugate $v(x, y)$ of a given harmonic function $u(x, y)$ can be found by integrating the differential equations (21). If C is a given integration path connecting the point (x, y) with an arbitrarily chosen fixed point (x_0, y_0), we have

$$v(x, y) = v(x_0, y_0) + \int_C (v_x\, dx + v_y\, dy)$$

and thus, by (21)

$$(22) \qquad v(x, y) = v(x_0, y_0) + \int_C (-u_y\, dx + u_x\, dy).$$

For instance, if $u(x, y) = \mathrm{Re}(z^2) = x^2 - y^2$, we have

$$-u_y \, dx + u_x \, dy = 2y dx + 2x dy = 2d(xy),$$

and (22) yields therefore $v(x, y) = 2xy + k$, where k is a constant. In cases which are not quite so simple, the evaluation of (22) may require transforming the line integral into an ordinary integral over a particular curve C joining (x, y) and (x_0, y_0).

The construction of the harmonic conjugate is equivalent to a complex integration. To see this, we use the fact that (Chap. II, Sec. 2, Formula (2))

$$f'(z) = u_x + iv_x.$$

By (21), we have therefore

(23) $$f'(z) = u_x - iu_y,$$

and this shows that the derivative $f'(z)$ of the function $f(z) = u(x, y) + iv(x, y)$ can be computed from $u(x, y)$ by differentiation processes. Integrating $f'(z)$, we find $f(z)$, and thus $v(x, y)$. We note, incidentally, that (23) may also be obtained by applying the differential operator $\partial/\partial z$ to the identity

$$f(z) + \overline{f(z)} = 2u(x, y).$$

The result is

(24) $$f'(z) = 2\frac{\partial u}{\partial z},$$

and this is equivalent to (23).

As shown in Chapter III, an analytic function which is regular in a simply-connected domain D possesses a single-valued indefinite integral which is likewise a regular analytic function in D. If the function $u(x, y)$ is harmonic in such a domain D, we thus have, by (24),

(25) $$u(x, y) + iv(x, y) = f(z) = f(z_0) + 2\int_{z_0}^{z} \frac{\partial u}{\partial z} \, dz,$$

where the integration is carried out along any contour in D which connects z_0 and z. The harmonic function $v(x, y)$ is then equal to the imaginary part of the right-hand side of (25). It may be noted that, since $v(x, y)$ is obtained by means of an integration process, this function is determined only up to an arbitrary constant.

If the domain D is not simply-connected, the integration process (25) will in general lead to a many-valued function $f(z)$. Since the given harmonic function $u(x, y)$ was assumed to be single-valued in D, this implies that, in such cases, the harmonic conjugate $v(x, y)$ will be many-valued. This many-valuedness is caused by the fact that, in the case of a domain which is not simply-connected, not all integration paths connecting z_0 and z are "equivalent" to each other, and it may be possible to find two such paths which do not lead to the same value of the integral (25). As an example, we consider the construction of the conjugate of the harmonic function $u(x, y) = \log r$, $r^2 = x^2 + y^2$, in the domain $0 < |z| < R$, $R > 1$. Since $u(x, y)$ is not harmonic at the origin, this point must be excluded, and the domain is not simply-connected. By (23), we have

$$f'(z) = \frac{x}{r^2} - \frac{iy}{r^2} = \frac{\bar{z}}{r^2} = \frac{\bar{z}}{z\bar{z}} = \frac{1}{z},$$

and (25) shows therefore that

(26) $u(x, y) + iv(x, y) = f(z) = \int_1^z \frac{dz}{z},$

if the integration constant is determined by the condition $v(1, 0) = 0$. To compute this integral, we introduce polar coordinates $z = re^{i\theta}$, $-\pi < \theta \leq \pi$, and choose an integration path consisting of the interval $[1, r]$—or $[r, 1]$, as the case may be—and of an arc of the circle C_r about the origin of radius r. This leads to

$$u(x, y) + iv(x, y) = \int_1^r \frac{d\rho}{\rho} + i \int_0^\theta d\varphi,$$

where ρ and φ are real variables. If the integration over φ is carried out along the shortest arc of C_r connecting the points 1 and z, the result is $v(x, y) = \theta$. However, if the integration path describes C_r a sufficient number of times before terminating at the point z, we arrive at the value $v(x, y) = \theta + 2\pi n$, where n is an arbitrary integer. The harmonic conjugate of the function $u(x, y) = \log r$ is thus found to be the infinitely many-valued function $v(x, y) = \theta + 2\pi n$, $n = 0, \pm 1, \pm 2, \cdots$.

The appearance of the "period" 2π is due to the fact that the integral

$$\int \frac{dz}{z}$$

over the closed curve C_r is equal to $2\pi i$, and not to zero. In the computation of the harmonic conjugate of a given function $u(x, y)$ by means of the formula (25), such periods will always appear whenever there exist closed integration paths C in D for which

$$\int_C \frac{\partial u}{\partial z}\, dz = P \neq 0.$$

Indeed, if z is a point of C and C_1 is a contour connecting z_0 and z, we may find the value of $f(z)$ by computing the integral (25) either along C_1 or along $C_1 + C$; both of these contours connect z_0 and z. If $f(z)$ denotes the first of these values, the second will then be $f(z) + P$. By letting the integration path contain the closed contour C a sufficient number of times, it is thus possible to give to the right-hand side of (25) the value $f(z) + nP$, where n is an arbitrary integer.

The construction of the harmonic conjugate by means of either (22) or (25) involves an integration. This is to be expected, since the problem to be solved amounts to the integration of the differential system (21). Nevertheless, there exists a method for obtaining the harmonic conjugate which requires no integration. This method is based on the use of the conjugate complex variables z and $\bar{z}$ discussed in Chapter I.

Our aim is to construct an analytic function $f(z)$ whose real part is a given harmonic function $u(x, y)$. We thus have to determine $f(z)$ from the relation

$$2u(x, y) = f(z) + \overline{f(z)}.$$

In view of

$$x = \frac{z + \bar{z}}{2}, \quad y = \frac{z - \bar{z}}{2i},$$

this may also be written

$$2u\left(\frac{z + \bar{z}}{2}, \frac{z - \bar{z}}{2i}\right) = f(z) + \overline{f(z)}.$$

As pointed out in the preceding section, the function $f^*(z) = \overline{f(\bar{z})}$ is an analytic function of z. The last formula may therefore be replaced by

(27) $$2u\left(\frac{z + \bar{z}}{2}, \frac{z - \bar{z}}{2i}\right) = f(z) + f^*(\bar{z}),$$

where f^* is an analytic function of its argument.

We now treat the variables z and $\bar{z}$ as though they were independent of each other, and we regard (27) as an identity valid for arbitrary values of z and $\bar{z}$ (i.e., values which are not necessarily conjugate to each other). Setting $\bar{z} = 0$ in (27), we obtain

(28) $$2u\left(\frac{z}{2}, \frac{z}{2i}\right) = f(z) + f^*(0).$$

Since the harmonic conjugate $v(x, y)$ is determined only up to an arbitrary real constant, we can dispose of this constant by requiring that $v(0, 0) = 0$. We then have $f^*(0) = \overline{f(0)} = f(0)$, and it follows from (28)—for $z = 0$—that

$$2u(0, 0) = f(0) + f^*(0) = 2f^*(0).$$

With this value of $f^*(0)$, (28) leads to the formula

(29) $$f(z) = 2u\left(\frac{z}{2}, \frac{z}{2i}\right) - u(0, 0).$$

We illustrate the use of (29) by two examples. If $u(x, y)$ is the harmonic function $x^3 - 3xy^2$, (29) yields

$$f(z) = 2\left[\left(\frac{z}{2}\right)^3 - 3\left(\frac{z}{2}\right)\left(\frac{z}{2i}\right)^2\right] = z^3.$$

If $u(x, y) = \sin x \cosh y$, (29) shows that

$$f(z) = 2 \sin \frac{z}{2} \cosh \frac{z}{2i}.$$

In view of

$$\cosh \frac{z}{2i} = \cosh\left(\frac{-iz}{2}\right) = \cos \frac{z}{2},$$

this leads to

$$f(z) = 2 \sin \frac{z}{2} \cos \frac{z}{2} = \sin z.$$

Since $\text{Re}[\sin z] = \text{Re}[\sin (x + iy)] = \sin x \cosh y$, this is the correct result.

If $z = 0$ is a singular point of the analytic function $f(z)$ (and, therefore, also of the harmonic function $u(x, y)$), it is not permissible to set $z = 0$ in (27). In this case, we choose a value c such that $f(z)$ is regular at $z = c$, and we set $\bar{z} = \bar{c}$ in (27). In the identity

$$2u\left(\frac{z + \bar{c}}{2}, \frac{z - \bar{c}}{2i}\right) = f(z) + f^*(\bar{c})$$

obtained in this way, we set $z = c$. Thus,

$$2u\left(\frac{c + \bar{c}}{2}, \frac{c - \bar{c}}{2i}\right) = f(c) + f^*(\bar{c}) = \overline{f^*(\bar{c})} + f^*(\bar{c}).$$

Requiring that $f^*(\bar{c})$ be real, we have

$$2u(a, b) = 2f^*(c),$$

where $c = a + bi$, and therefore

(30) $f(z) = 2u\left(\dfrac{z + \bar{c}}{2}, \dfrac{z - \bar{c}}{2i}\right) - u(a, b), \quad c = a + bi.$

As an application, we reconstruct the analytic function $\log z$ from its real part $u(x, y) = \log r = \frac{1}{2}\log(x^2 + y^2)$. With the choice $c = 1$, (30) yields

$$f(z) = \log\left[\left(\frac{z + 1}{2}\right)^2 + \left(\frac{z - 1}{2i}\right)^2\right],$$

and thus $f(z) = \log z$. With an arbitrary non-zero value of c, we obtain

$$f(z) = \log\left[\left(\frac{z + \bar{c}}{2}\right)^2 + \left(\frac{z - \bar{c}}{2i}\right)^2\right] - \log|c|$$

$$= \log(\bar{c}z) - \log|c| = \log z + \log\frac{\bar{c}}{|c|}.$$

The constant $\log(\bar{c}/|c|)$ is pure imaginary and, in accordance with the derivation of Formula (30), it is such that $f(c)$ is real.

The derivation of Formulas (29) and (30) was, of course, purely formal. To turn this procedure into a proof, it would be necessary to justify the treatment of z and $\bar{z}$ as two genuinely independent variables. It is, however, easier to give a direct verification of these formulas. Since in both cases the argument is essentially the same, we shall confine ourselves to the verification of Formula (29). We accordingly assume that $f(z)$ is regular in a neighborhood $|z| < R$ of the origin. By Taylor's theorem, $f(z)$ has an expansion

(31) $f(z) = \sum_{n=0}^{\infty} a_n z^n,$

which converges for $|z| < R$. If $u(x, y)$ denotes the real part of $f(z)$, we have $2u(x, y) = f(z) + \overline{f(z)}$ and therefore

(32) $2u(x, y) = \sum_{n=0}^{\infty} a_n(x + iy)^n + \sum_{n=0}^{\infty} \overline{a_n}(x - iy)^n.$

The two series on the right-hand side converge for $|x + iy| < R$ and $|x - iy| < R$, respectively. This convergence does not depend on the fact that x and y are real variables. If x and y are permitted to take complex values of modulus smaller than $R/2$, we have $|x + iy| \leq |x| + |y| < R$ and $|x - iy| < |x| + |y| < R$. For such values of x and y, the series on the right-hand side of (32) will thus be absolutely convergent. For a fixed x such that $|x| < R/2$, these series are power series in y which converge for $|y| < R/2$, and they therefore represent an analytic function of the complex variable y in this disk. The same is true if the values of x and y are interchanged. Hence, the right-hand side of (32) is an analytic function of the two complex variables x and y, if these variables range over the disks $|x| < R/2$ and $|y| < R/2$. For real values of x and y, this function coincides with $2u(x, y)$.

We now choose a complex number ζ for which $|\zeta| < R$ and set

$$x = \frac{\zeta}{2}, \quad y = \frac{\zeta}{2i}.$$

Since both $|x|$ and $|y|$ are smaller than $R/2$, these values may be substituted in (32). In view of

$$x + iy = \zeta, \quad x - iy = 0,$$

we obtain

$$2u\left(\frac{\zeta}{2}, \frac{\zeta}{2i}\right) = \sum_{n=0}^{\infty} a_n \zeta^n + \overline{a_0},$$

or, because of (31),

(33) $$2u\left(\frac{\zeta}{2}, \frac{\zeta}{2i}\right) = f(\zeta) + \overline{a_0}.$$

If the harmonic conjugate $v(x, y)$ is normalized by the condition $v(0, 0) = 0$, we have $\overline{a_0} = a_0 = u(0, 0)$. Substituting this in (33), we obtain (29).

This proof of the relation (29) was carried out under the assumption that the variable is restricted to the disk $|z| < R/2$. As shown in Section 1, this is sufficient to establish the validity of the identity (29) for all values z to which $f(z)$ can be continued analytically.

Index